HEINEMANN

BEGI

CW00530684

JOHN MILNE

The Long Tunnel

HEINEMANN

BEGINNER LEVEL

Series Editor: John Milne

The Heinemann Guided Readers provide a choice of enjoyable read-ing material for learners of English. The Series is published at five levels – Starter, Beginner, Elementary, Intermediate and Upper. At **Beginner Level**, the control of content and language has the follow-ing main features:

Information Control
The stories are written in a fluent and pleasing style with straight-forward plots and a restricted number of main characters. The cultural background is made explicit through both words and illus-trations. Information which is vital to the story is clearly presented and repeated where necessary.

Structure Control
Special care is taken with sentence length. Most sentences contain only one clause, though compound sentences are used occasionally with the clauses joined by the conjunctions 'and', 'but', and 'or'. The use of these compound sentences gives the text balance and rhythm. The use of Past Simple and Past Continuous Tenses is permitted since these are the basic tenses used in narration and students must become familiar with these as they continue to extend and develop their reading ability.

Vocabulary Control
At **Beginner Level** there is a controlled vocabulary of approximately 600 basic words, so that students with a basic knowledge of English will be able to read with understanding and enjoyment. Help is also given in the form of vivid illustrations which are closely related to the text.

For further information on the full selection of Readers at all five levels in the series, please refer to the Heinemann Guided Readers catalogue.

1

Holiday Plans

At universities in England, May is the month of examinations.

Paul was lying on the grass in front of the examination hall. His friends, Sheila and Charles, were sitting near him.

The three of them were first year students at university. They were sitting their first year exams. Paul and Charles were nineteen and Sheila was a year younger.

The next exam began in half an hour's time. But the three students were not talking about the next examination. They were talking about their holidays.

'Where are you going this summer?' Sheila asked Paul.

'To Wales,' Paul replied. 'I'm going to stay in a cottage in the country.'

'You have a cottage in Wales?' asked Charles.

'It's not my cottage,' replied Paul. 'It belongs to my uncle. He usually goes there for his holidays every summer. But this year he's going to Greece. And I'm going to stay in his cottage for two months – July and August.'

'Where are you going for your holidays?' Paul asked.

'We don't know,' replied Sheila. 'We haven't decided yet.'

'Why don't you both come to Wales?' said Paul. 'You can stay with me for a week or two.'

'What do you think, Charles?' asked Sheila.

The college bell rang loudly. It was time for the next examination.

'We'll talk about it after this exam,' Charles replied. 'Let's go now.'

The students got up from the grass. They picked up their notebooks and hurried towards the examination hall.

Three hours later, the examination was over. Paul, Sheila and Charles were sitting in a café.

'What's your uncle's cottage like?' Sheila asked Paul.

Paul took a photograph out of his wallet.

'It looks lovely,' said Sheila.

'It is lovely,' agreed Paul. 'But it's very lonely. There are no houses near the cottage. And there's no electricity and no telephone.'

'Let's go and stay with Paul,' Sheila said to Charles.

'OK,' agreed Charles. 'We can stay there for a week.'

The three students made arrangements for their holiday in Wales.

'Come on the fifth of August,' said Paul. 'That's a Monday. The train from London arrives at Llanvoy Station at half past one.'

'Where's Llanvoy?' asked Sheila.

'It's a small railway station near the cottage,' answered Paul. 'Fast trains from London stop there.'

6

'How do we get from the station to the cottage?' asked Charles.

'Look, I'll draw a map,' said Paul. 'The railway line goes through a long tunnel before Llanvoy Station. The cottage is on the hill above this tunnel.'

Charles gave Paul his diary. Paul drew a map and wrote down the name and address of the cottage.

'There you are,' said Paul. 'But don't worry. I'll meet you at Llanvoy Station. I'll see you there on Monday the fifth of August at half past one.'

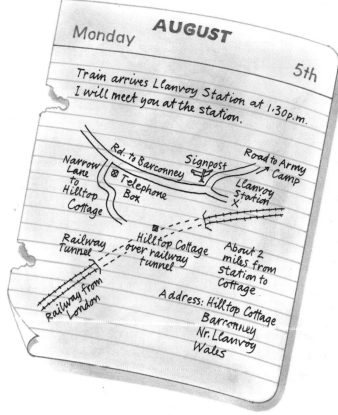

Monday   **AUGUST**   5th

Train arrives Llanvoy Station at 1.30 p.m.
I will meet you at the station.

Rd. to Barconney   Signpost   Road to Army Camp
Narrow
Lane
to
Hilltop
Cottage   ⊠ Telephone
                    Box   Llanvoy
                                           Station
                                           X

Railway   Hilltop Cottage   About 2
Tunnel   over railway   miles from
             tunnel   station to
                                  cottage
Railway from London

Address: Hilltop Cottage
         Barconney
         Nr. Llanvoy
         Wales

It is the fifth of August. Sheila and Charles arrive at Llanvoy station in Wales.

2

A Stranger at the Door

Sheila and Charles went into the small café. There was a young girl behind the counter. Sheila went up to her.

'Has a young man been in here this morning?' asked Sheila.

'A soldier?' asked the young girl.

'No, not a soldier – a student,' replied Sheila.

'We see a lot of soldiers here,' said the girl. 'But no students.'

Charles asked for two coffees. He sat down with Sheila at a table near the window.

'Paul's forgotten about our visit,' he said. 'We'll have a coffee. Then we'll walk to Hilltop Cottage.'

They sat at the table and looked out of the window. Some soldiers were loading bags into the lorry. Other soldiers were standing on guard.

The girl brought the coffees.

'What's in those bags?' Charles asked her.

'Banknotes,' replied the girl. 'The money comes from London by train. Then the soldiers take it to a large army camp near here.'

'What do they do with the money?' Sheila asked.

'I don't know,' said the girl. And she walked away.

'They are probably old banknotes,' said Charles. 'After some years, the government destroys old banknotes and new money is printed. The money in those bags will not be used any more.'

Charles and Sheila waited in the café. Paul did not come. It was now after two o'clock.

They left the café and walked to a crossroads. Charles looked at Paul's map. Sheila pointed to a signpost.

'That's the road to Barconney,' she said.

They pulled their rucksacks onto their shoulders and walked along the road. It was a very hot day. The sun was shining brightly and they walked slowly.

After an hour, they came to a telephone box. On the left, there was a narrow lane into the woods.

'The telephone box is on Paul's map,' said Charles. 'This is the way to the cottage.'

They walked up the narrow lane. Tall trees grew on each side. The branches were thick with leaves.

'It's dark in here,' said Charles. 'There's no sun.'

'It's nice and cool after the hot road,' replied Sheila. 'Anyway, Paul's cottage is higher up. It'll be brighter up there.'

They walked farther up the steep, dark lane.

'I don't like this place,' said Charles. 'It's too dark. What a place for a holiday.'

'Oh, come on,' said Sheila.

Sheila and Charles arrived at the cottage. There were high trees all round it.

'There's something wrong,' said Charles. 'Look at the curtains. They are all closed. There's no one here.'

'Don't be silly,' said Sheila.

She went up to the cottage and knocked loudly on the door. They waited for some time.

Sheila pushed at the cottage door. It did not open. It was locked.

'Paul?' shouted Charles. 'Paul? Are you there?'

There was no reply.

Sheila knocked again on the door. They stood and listened.

'There's someone inside,' said Sheila. 'I heard a noise. Listen!'

They both stood in silence. Someone unlocked the door.

'It's Paul,' said Charles. 'Why is he taking so long?'

The door slowly opened. A tall man with a beard stood in the doorway. He was about forty years old. Sheila and Charles did not know him. He was a stranger.

'Who are you?' asked the stranger. 'What do you want?'

3

Paul is Here

Sheila looked up at the tall man.

'Is Paul in?' she asked.

'Paul?' said the stranger. 'There's no one here with that name. You've made a mistake.'

The stranger slowly closed the door.

'But this cottage belongs to Paul's uncle,' said Sheila. 'We saw it in a photograph.'

'It was another cottage in your photograph,' said the man. 'It wasn't this one. This cottage is mine. I live here.'

The man was becoming angry.

'You've made a mistake,' he shouted. 'I don't like visitors here. Go away.'

The door closed with a loud bang.

Sheila turned away from the door. She saw a piece of paper under a bush. She stopped and quickly picked up the paper.

'We've made a mistake,' said Charles. 'Paul isn't here. We've come to the wrong cottage. Let's go back to the road.'

They walked back down the lane. After a few minutes, Sheila stopped. The cottage was now behind the trees. Sheila opened the piece of paper and looked at it in surprise.

'We haven't made a mistake,' she said to Charles. 'Look at this!'

Charles took the paper and looked at it. 'It's an examination paper,' he said. 'It's our exam paper. We sat this exam in May.'

19

4

What's Happening?

Sheila and Charles waited in the old building. Slowly it became dark. They walked quietly back to the cottage and hid behind a bush. A lorry was parked near the cottage door.

They waited quietly in the darkness. Suddenly a man hurried up the lane. He knocked at a window of the cottage. The door opened quickly.

'Everything is OK, Frank,' said the man outside. 'Bill has telephoned from London. He's put sleeping pills in the guard's coffee.'

'Good,' said Frank. 'We can start now. Get the bags out of the lorry and into the cottage.'

'What's happening?' Charles asked Sheila. 'Bill's put sleeping pills in the guard's coffee – what does that mean? And what's in those bags?'

'I don't know,' said Sheila. 'Listen – they're talking again.'

'What about that young man?' one of the men asked Frank.

'We'll leave him in the upstairs bedroom,' Frank replied. 'He's tied up tightly. He'll be found tomorrow. By then, we'll be far from here.'

'Paul's in the cottage,' Sheila whispered to Charles. 'And he's a prisoner.'

Four men carried all the bags into the cottage. They closed the door behind them and locked it.

'Paul's in one of the upstairs bedrooms,' said Sheila. 'We must help him.'

'How are you going to get into the cottage?' asked Charles. 'They've locked the door.'

'I'll climb up onto the top of the porch,' said Sheila. 'Then I'll get in through a window.'

Sheila and Charles waited for half an hour. Then they walked up quietly to the front door. There were no lights in the cottage.

'Help me up, Charles,' said Sheila.

Sheila stood on top of the porch. She reached up and pulled at the window. It opened slowly and made a loud noise. Sheila waited for a few moments. Nothing happened.

She opened the window wide. The curtains inside were closed. She opened them carefully and climbed into the bedroom.

In the dark room, Paul was lying on a bed. He was tied up tightly and there was a gag over his mouth.

Sheila quickly took off the gag.

'Sh!' she said. 'Don't make a noise. There are some men downstairs.'

'It's all right,' said Paul. 'They won't hear us. They're not in the cottage. They're out at the back.'

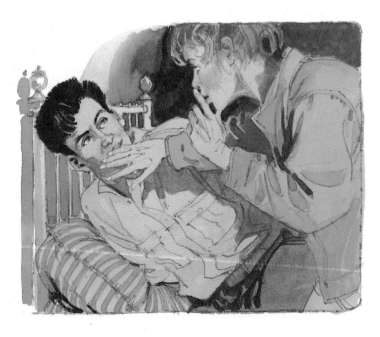

Sheila slowly untied the ropes round Paul.

'What's happening?' she asked him. 'Who are those men? What are they doing?'

'They're going to rob a train tonight.'

'Rob a train?' asked Sheila in surprise.

'They've found an old shaft behind the cottage,' said Paul. 'The shaft goes down into the railway tunnel. They're going to change the signal in the tunnel. The signal light will be red and the train will stop.'

'Now I understand,' said Sheila. 'Someone has put sleeping pills in the guard's coffee.'

'That's part of their plan,' said Paul. 'The train will stop in the tunnel and the guard will be asleep. The men will steal the bags of money from the train and escape up the shaft.'

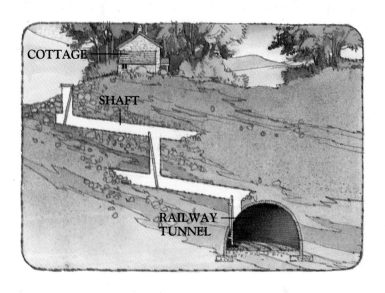

'But these men have taken bags into the cottage,' said Sheila. 'What are they for?'

'The bags are full of paper,' said Paul. 'They look like the bags of money. The soldiers won't find the paper until tomorrow morning. Then these men will be far away from here.'

'We can run down to the telephone box,' said Sheila. 'We can telephone the police from there.'

'There isn't enough time,' said Paul. 'We have to stop these men. We can put heavy stones over the shaft. Then the men can't get out.'

'And Charles can run down and telephone the police,' said Sheila.

Now all the knots were untied and Paul was free. They climbed out of the window. Charles was waiting for them in the darkness.

5

The Robbery

The train from London was in the long tunnel.

'The signal is red,' said the driver to his mate. 'That's unusual.'

The train slowed down. It stopped on a long bend in the tunnel.

The driver's mate looked back. The end of the train was out of sight.

'What about the money in the guard's van?' the mate asked the driver.

'Don't worry,' replied the driver. 'Pete's a good guard.'

The driver watched the signal. It was red. The train waited in the long tunnel.

Frank and his men were in the tunnel. They were waiting at the bottom of the shaft. The train slowed down and stopped. The guard's van was in front of them.

Frank quickly climbed up. He opened the lock on the door of the guard's van. He looked inside.

'It's all right,' he said to the others. 'The guard has drunk the coffee. He's sleeping.'

Frank threw down the bags of money.

'Throw up the bags of paper,' he told his men. 'And move quickly. We haven't much time.'

A few minutes later, Frank and his men were at the bottom of the shaft. They were carrying the bags of money.

'Get up to the cottage,' Frank said. 'I'll follow you in a moment.'

The signal changed from red to green. The train moved towards Llanvoy Station.

'Good,' thought Frank. 'The plan has worked.'

At the top of the shaft, Sheila and Paul were working fast in the darkness. There was a heavy iron cover at the entrance to the shaft. They pulled the cover over the entrance and put some heavy stones on top of it.

The first of Frank's men reached the top of the shaft. His head hit the iron cover. He reached up with one hand and pushed. The cover did not move.

'There's something wrong,' he shouted. 'I can't get out.'

Below him in the shaft, the other men waited. They were trapped.

6

The End

The police moved quickly. A police car came to the telephone box. Charles jumped in and they drove fast towards the cottage.

The police arrested two men at the top of the shaft.

An hour later, Sheila, Paul and Charles were in the police station at Barconney.

'Thanks to you, we've got the men and the money,' said the police sergeant. 'We arrested the other two men at Llanvoy Station.'

'But there were five men,' said Paul. 'Have you arrested the leader? He's called Frank.'

Sheila, Charles and Paul spent the night in the home of the police sergeant. The next morning the sergeant left early.

'I must go to the police station,' he told them. 'I'll phone you later in the morning.'

At breakfast, Sheila turned on the radio.

'Here is a police message. The police are looking for Frank Steel . . . aged forty . . . this man was last seen on the railway line to Llanvoy Station in the early hours of this morning. He is a dangerous. . .'

Sheila turned off the radio.

'It's a strange beginnning to a holiday,' she said.

Later, the phone rang. Paul answered it. It was the sergeant.

'Good news,' said the sergeant. 'A police car has picked up Frank Steel.'

Paul put down the phone.

'The police have arrested Frank Steel,' he said to the other two.

'That's great,' said Sheila. 'Now we can go back to the cottage and begin our holiday.'

Heinemann English Language Teaching
A division of Heinemann Publishers (Oxford) Ltd
Halley Court, Jordan Hill, Oxford OX2 8EJ

OXFORD   MADRID   ATHENS   PARIS   FLORENCE   PRAGUE
SÃO PAULO   CHICAGO   MELBOURNE   AUCKLAND
SINGAPORE   TOKYO   GABORONE
JOHANNESBURG   PORTSMOUTH (NH)   IBADAN

ISBN 0 435 27174 1

A recorded version of this story is available on cassette.
ISBN 0 435 27277 2

Illustrated by David Barnett
Typography by Adrian Hodgkins
Cover by Graham Bence and Threefold Design
Typeset in 12/16 pt Goudy
by Joshua Associates Ltd, Oxford
Printed and bound in Malta by Interprint Limited

94   95   96   97   10   9   8   7   6   5   4

A Casualty of War

A Casualty of War

The Arcadia Book of Gay Short Stories

Edited by Peter Burton

Bath & North East Somerset	
1 9 0027036 1	
Askews	07-Jul-2009
AF	£7.99

ARCADIA BOOKS

Arcadia Books Ltd
15-16 Nassau Street
London W1W 7AB

www.arcadiabooks.co.uk

First published in the United Kingdom by Arcadia Books 2008
This B format edition published 2009
Copyright for this collection and introduction © Peter Burton 2008
Copyright for individual stories rests with the author.

A catalogue record for this book is available from the British Library.

ISBN 978-1-906413-31-6

Typeset in Bembo by Basement Press, London
Printed in Finland by WS Bookwell

Arcadia Books supports English PEN, the fellowship of writers who work together to promote
literature and its understanding. English PEN upholds writers' freedoms in Britain and around
the world, challenging political and cultural limits on free expression. To find out more, visit
www.englishpen.org or contact
English PEN, 6-8 Amwell Street, London EC1R 1UQ

Arcadia Books distributors are as follows:

in the UK and elsewhere in Europe:
Turnaround Publishers Services
Unit 3, Olympia Trading Estate
Coburg Road
London N22 6TZ

in the US and Canada:
Independent Publishers Group
814 N. Franklin Street
Chicago, IL 60610

in Australia:
Tower Books
PO Box 213
Brookvale, NSW 2100

in New Zealand:
Addenda
PO Box 78224
Grey Lynn
Auckland

in South Africa:
Quartet Sales and Marketing
PO Box 1218
Northcliffe
Johannesburg 2115

Arcadia Books is the *Sunday Times* Small Publisher of the Year

Contents

Introduction

Any editor compiling an anthology starts with a premise and a wish list.

The premise for *A Casualty of War: The Arcadia Book of Gay Short Stories* was very simple; other than the stipulation that a major component of the story be in some way concerned with gay there was no essential premise.

Because Scott Brown's 'A Casualty of War' (written whilst he was working in Baghdad) was already to hand, it provided a title for the whole collection and my commissioning letter asked for short stories for an anthology which would be titled after Brown's story.

Although that initial communication made it quite clear that there was no specific theme to the collection, the title provoked several of the writers who had been asked to contribute to submit stories that were in some way war-related. Those stories which didn't in any way deal with war and its consequences could be categorised as being about other and smaller kinds of conflict.

Thus there are stories here which are rooted in the two World Wars (Stephen Gray's 'Brothers in Arms' and Michael Wilcox's 'Dead Man's Hand' are examples) and stories in which other conflicts – Northern Ireland, Sudan – provide a background. Yet elsewhere the tensions are more personal, though no less destructive.

Conflict, this collection of stories reminds us, isn't restricted to the action of armies; it is all around us, all the time.

The wish list for *A Casualty of War: The Arcadia Book of Gay Short Stories* consisted of a large number of writers to be contacted with a view to their writing a story for inclusion. It was obvious at the outset that the list

3

contained far more writers than the book could include, but it was equally obvious that not all of those approached would want to contribute. After all, wish lists are as much about the impossible as they are about the possible.

Some of those approached responded promptly but in the negative. Several writers (all American) didn't bother to reply one way or another and, more surprisingly, a handful of people responded with great enthusiasm – but were not heard from again.

However, by the time of the final deadline, I had the twenty stories which follow. Sixteen of those stories were especially written for this book, one ('Awkward Relations' by the late John Haylock) had been on file for some time and three had been previously published but seen by a restricted readership.

Michael Davidson's 'Atti Innominabili' seemed well worth reprinting, not least because on original publication almost forty years ago it can have reached an audience of little more than two thousand people. Steven Saylor's 'Gentler, Kinder' was first published in *The San Francisco Bay Guardian* in 1989. 'It's one of the very few Steven Saylor gay-themed stories,' he explained, 'but was very important to me in my early career. I submitted it to a short story contest … and won; one of the judges was the great Anglo-American gay poet Thomas Gunn (now deceased), who was a literary idol of mine, and meeting him under such circumstances was a tremendous thrill, a real landmark for the budding young author. I felt quite a member of the San Francisco gay literati after that!' Richard Zimler's 'A Dry Past' is a revised version of a story which first appeared in *Puerto del Sol*, a magazine published in Portugal (where Zimler makes his home).

There will be those who will wonder at the need for a specifically gay anthology, feeling that now that gay has entered the mainstream of publishing (Patrick Gale on *Richard & Judy*, Armistead Maupin an international bestseller, Alan Hollinghurst snaffling major awards) there should be no need for such specialist volumes. But the market for short stories seems to be ever diminishing and the market for gay short stories is now all but non-existent. It is important that gay writers (established as well as tyro) should be able to practise the art of the short story with at least the hope they can find a home for their wares.

One of the writers in this collection is making his fiction debut, a further two (struggling with novels) have so far only been published in anthologies. So it remains vital that gay writers can find a place for their stories with work of a similar hue from writers who are like-minded.

'Atti Innominabili' by Michael Davidson is published with the permission of Colin Spencer and the Literary Estate of Michael Davidson; 'Awkward Relations' by John Haylock is published with the permission of Sebastian Beaumont and the Literary Estate of John Haylock. Thanks are due to Gary Pulsifer and Daniela de Groote at Arcadia Books who looked after me at the Independent Publishers Guild dinner at which this project was first mooted and to Tasty Torsten Højer (*3Sixty*) and Cliff James (*one80news*) who enabled me to return to that to which I've devoted most of my adult life, gay journalism. Especial thanks, too, to David Hicks and the Book Trade Benevolent Society for their much appreciated continuing support.

Peter Burton
Brighton, 2008

When the Time Comes;
or, the Case of the Man Who Didn't Know

Neil Bartlett

For David Halperin

It happened in a moment.

That is to say, one moment he was in the middle of an action so familiar he was barely conscious of performing it, and the next, he was standing still – stock still – staring in the mirror, and apparently quite incapable
of deciding what to do next with his hands.

It wasn't as if he hadn't done this a thousand times, he told himself. Get
up; get dressed; get started – what could be more normal.

More obvious.

More not-requiring-of-any-special-thought.

But this morning, *this* morning… his hand hesitated in mid-air. This
morning, there was something about the sight of the crowded (crowded?
– let's be frank; it was bulging) about the sight of the crowded rail of shirts
in the open right-hand side of the wardrobe that he found, well… confus-
ing. Daunting.

If you've ever had one of these moments, then you'll know what happens
next. The hesitation, so momentary, so innocuous at first, becomes, as it
stretches, momentous. It becomes about all sorts of other things, things far
beyond the confines of deciding which shirt to wear – and, well, that's
exactly what happened to him. He tried reminding himself that he did
sometimes find, ever since he'd started taking these new pills, that the first
hour of the day was sometimes a little more, well, *cloudy* shall we say, a little
more confused and a little less *conscious* than perhaps it ought to have been
– but this attempt to explain the situation away rationally did nothing to

quell his growing sense of panic. As he stared at the rail of shirts, and the seconds passed, he found that it was becoming not so much a question of *which* shirt to pick, but more a question of whether or not he was going to give way to the sudden, large and potentially alarming thought – well, more of a sensation, really, a feeling; a feeling of falling off one thing and down, deep down, into another – a question of whether or not he was going to give way to the overwhelming feeling that he had, this morning, no apparent means, so far as he could see, no apparent means of *making any one shirt seem a more likely or rational choice than any of the others*. So far as he could see. On this particular morning.

For some reason.

Now before we continue, dear reader, let me reassure you that no, you don't need to know any more about this man than what I'm telling you. It won't help. It is enough that you visualise him standing – frowning, and naked from the waist up – in front of a large but perfectly ordinary-looking Edwardian mahogany-veneered wardrobe, one of those ones in which the two doors are separated by a full-length bevel-edged mirror, and leave it at that. His dilemma is one that we all face at certain points in our lives, and the inclusion here of any extraneous and unduly weighty biographical detail – his name or age, for instance, or how his parents had met in the early 1960s during the provincial tour of a particularly undis-tinguished musical comedy, or that he had once described himself (only half-jokingly) as 'just an ordinary working wife' – would hardly serve to clarify it. Trust me; paying careful attention to his gestures, to his exact sequence of movements and their attendant thoughts as this crisis assails him will be by far the most instructive way of dealing with him – of accounting for him, if you like, since any new character introduced to the reader in the course of a volume of fiction must I believe always be first and foremost treated by the reader as a problem to be dealt with, an enigma to be explained, a mystery to be accounted for. I mean, one's first glance at any middle-aged man, especially one one encounters half-naked, is quite normally tinged with suspicion, is it not?

Anyway.

Making a distinct and determined effort to suppress the swelling sense of nausea which he felt at the sight of so much assembled fabric (Excuse me? How many shirts were hanging on the rail altogether? Well, let's say forty, shall we: certainly enough to be going on with), all of it hanging there disconcertingly inert, like so much shed skin, with no apparent trace or memory of the limbs and torsos it had once covered, of the more or less muscular neck or necks which all of those now-empty collars must once have been buttoned round, he closed his eyes: then, feeling more confident about making gestures now that he could not see himself making them in the mirror, he reached out and groped for the door. He found it, and closed the right-hand side of the wardrobe. Thinking that a slight change in his normal routine might be in order, he decided that a consideration of which *shoes* he should choose to wear this morning might ease his dilemma – might return him to his normal, reassuringly-vacant-if-not-actually-positively-*happy* first-thing-in-the-morning frame of mind – and so he took a deep breath, opened his eyes again, and turned his attention to the left-hand side of the wardrobe, since this was where these items were housed. In order to do so, of course, he had to look from right to left. And this, of course, involved locking eyes with his own reflection in the full-length mirror.

We've all done it.

We've all caught sight of ourselves and seen a stranger – but normally it happens while we're walking out in the street, with the plate glass of a shop window serving as the mirror, and there the impression can be relied upon to be as fleeting as it is horrible. Less frequently, it can happen in some place of public resort such as a bar or foyer, and there, though the effect is no less alarming, it is in a quite different genre – to catch oneself wondering who that apparently unattached and oddly attractive stranger in the corner is, only to find oneself moments later recognising one's own hair or cut of jacket, can be quite a flattering experience. And, once again, it is brief. But to find oneself (as this man now does) staring with undisguised alarm into one's own wardrobe mirror, first thing in the morning, and with barely ten inches separating skin and eyes from silvered glass from skin and eyes... well, in that case, the instant is rather bound to become a long one.

How is it possible to not recognise oneself?

How is it possible not to have any idea what clothes one should wear?

His nerve failed him; he abandoned the idea of opening the left-hand side of the wardrobe, and went back, perplexed, to the rail of hanging shirts.

Having said that I need not and would not provide you with any extraneous biographical details, I find I must now relent for a moment, and admit that this man's problem was to some degree exacerbated by the fact that all the shirts on the rail were not, strictly speaking, his. That is to say, he lived with someone. Although he had probably worn at least thirty out of the fifty-eight shirts (I lied, you see; I did know how many there were) he had probably purchased considerably less than half of that number himself. Of the two people in his house, it tended to be the other one who bought most of the clothes. Now, if you like (if it makes you feel any easier), you can use this piece of information to reassure yourself that this dilemma – this man – is *not you*. In fact, come to think of it, knowing you, you've probably already used it to explain away (that is, dismiss) as much of this situation as you possibly can without any prompting from me… Ah yes, I hear you saying to yourself, that's it; he's *not single* – and hasn't been, from the look of and sheer number of shirts in that wardrobe, for some time. In fact (I hear you continue) this whole situation is probably nothing more than one of those entirely typical 'at a certain time of life' crises that one hears and reads about so much these days. And since the crisis seems to be occurring first thing in the morning, then more than likely its source lies in trouble of some kind at work, because what else does one think about as one is getting dressed in the morning? – trouble, moreover, of a specifically *mid-career* kind. (That would explain the pills, too, wouldn't it? – they certainly need explaining.) I wouldn't be at all surprised if you've already begun to give him, in your mind's eye, the just-about-to-spread waistline and incipient nasal hair that unmistakeably marks a man of his generation out as approaching that particular and dangerous time of life when every *not-single* person begins to wonder if the personality they once felt so sure of, like the trim figure that seemed so boldly, so effortlessly well-defined back in the more vigorous days of their youth, has not somehow over the intervening years been inexorably diluted, or eroded, or macerated (or some other suitably geographical or chemical-sounding verb) by their long immersion in the company of or proximity to *another*.

Suit yourself.

Tell yourself you're not remotely like him if that makes your life easier. Tell yourself you're the spitting image, for all I care. That's your problem, not mine.

All I need you to do is to look back into his mirror.

Needing a definite and achievable task to ease himself through this moment of self-doubt, he decided to use his still-uselessly-hovering right hand to count the shirts. To assess the scale of the problem, as it were. To tame it somewhat.

However, this proved not to be so easy a task as he'd thought it would be; there was so much fabric, his eyes slid off it. They refused to sort it into any comprehensible list or sequence of separate incidents or textures – and the shirts were so many, and the rail in consequence so crowded, that it was actually quite hard, when he had to resort to counting them off by hand, to shift the wire of each hanger along the rail as his fingers ticked it off. *Fifty-six*, he muttered to himself, when he was nearly there, cursing the thin wire of the hangers as they bruised his finger-tips, *fifty-seven; Jesus Christ; fifty-eight*. He'd had no idea. Some of them, he hadn't even recognised. Were there shirts in the house that he didn't even know they owned?

This thought – oddly – gave him some relief. Was that it, he wondered; was it the simple fact that he had *too many shirts to even know how many he owned* that was causing him to hesitate so queasily like this? (He glanced down at his watch – Christ, nearly seven minutes already he'd been standing there like this, he'd better get a move on.) Was this sense of – what was he to call it, exactly? – because it was nothing so physically definite as nausea, as it turned out; now that he'd started to get a grip on things it wasn't as if he felt he was actually going to throw up or anything, which had felt like a distinct possibility at one point – ah yes, his mother's word, *unsettledness* – that would do nicely – was this sense of *unsettledness* that had gradually risen up out of the pit of his stomach and up into his abdomen, neck and across his bewildered face throughout the last seven – no, he checked – the last *eleven* – minutes best accounted for as being the by-product of some ill-defined but nonetheless undeniable sense of Shame? Shame, that is, that he found himself so glutted; so burdened, so cluttered, so mired and bogged down with *possessions*; shame that all that he had to show – no, he stopped himself there; be fair, he thought, be fair – shame that *all he felt at this particular moment* that he had to show for the not-inconsiderable number of years he had patiently lived and worked his way through was this ridiculous mountain of *stuff* that he and the other one lived amidst, this mountain – no, really, a mountain; a heap, a junkyard, graveyard or possibly fucking *iceberg* of uncounted, unwanted, unlovely and unaccounted-for possessions, an iceberg of which this bulging, crowded, fabric-softened, ironed, checked, useless, striped, half-

13

forgotten, embroidered, unconvincing, ill-fitting and potentially utterly defeating rail of fabric was merely the headache-inducing *tip*?

He drew a breath, and told himself to get a grip, and pick a shirt. After all, spending the day bare-chested was not an option. Only in dreams do we stride to work with the air touching those parts of us that we normally only offer to the inspection of our lovers; in life, we hide almost everything away. And even if we are not heading to work, but to some kind of play or other, we will always be turning our flesh-circumscribed self into a very particular version of that self, one that will, we think, be appropriate to the occasion. To the person or persons we plan or hope to meet. No one, I think, ever really goes out without thinking what to wear. That would be truly unmanly.

He decided to make it a game. It would be simple – a sort of one-man 'Blind Man's Bluff'. All he had to do was close his eyes, breathe out, extend his hand a little further, and grab. Of course, while his eyes were closed, and his hand hovered again for a moment, he couldn't help but visualise a few possible results of his game. The pink cotton with the button-down collar, which really didn't do his skin any favours. The very expensive sky-blue, which when he wore it made even his close friends, the ones who really should have known better, tell him how well he was looking these days. Those terrible embroidered red roses – why oh why do we keep these things, he wondered – or perhaps the most beautiful and inappropriate of them all, the one shirt on the rail that he was quite sure he had never worn, the plain white cotton evening shirt with the impossible-to-press-properly pleats, those impeccable, vertical, snowy knife-fold pleats that moulded themselves so subtly across his chest, the one that he (no, not he himself, the other one; *him*) the dress-shirt that he had looked so devastatingly handsome in on that one particular and oh-so-memorable black-tie night of their courtship, the one he'd worn with three gold studs and his grandfather's plain gold cufflinks, the ones he always needed help putting in – so handsome that they'd got carried away, right there in front of the wardrobe mirror, and had had to dress all over again, and then take a taxi, they were so late, and –

He did it.

Immediately, as soon as his fingers closed over the sleeve, he knew he'd made the wrong choice. Completely inappropriate. The fabric was too soft, too worn, too floppy – oh, he knew it, it was that old red–and–blue check flannel workman's shirt of which the collar was so frayed, it really wouldn't stand another outing. No, he told himself, that was really taking the whole distressed thing too far – the shirt-tails were practically see-through, you could put your finger through them. Now it was in his hand, he really should take the opportunity and throw it away, as he had meant to do so many times before. After all, as he hardly needed reminding, he was no longer twenty, which was surely the age he'd been when he'd bought the damn thing (and it had been second-hand, even then); there is such a thing as dressing one's age. Of admitting who one actually is.

But he didn't throw the shirt away. No; suddenly, out of nowhere (*in a moment*, one might say) he regained his power of decision. Perhaps it was the memory of who he'd been when he'd first pulled on that check shirt, blushing with daring at his own attempt to appear handsome as he did so – some kind of determination to keep faith with that fresher-faced and smooth-skinned young creature, who'd been so ruddily amazed by the sight of himself dressed at last like a man – or perhaps it was simply a stubborn reluctance to let himself be swamped by the random. Who knows. Putting it firmly back on the rail in its allotted place amidst all the other fifty-seven witnesses of their lives, lives lived both apart and together (how many was it now, he wondered; how many days, how many separate remembered and unremembered mornings had there now been when they had got dressed *together*?) he picked the shirt immediately to its left, and began to put it on. This shirt was black – tailored from an expensive-looking, heavy black cotton – and had double cuffs, a wide collar and six real bone buttons. He remembered this one, and had no doubts at all about how well it suited him. He'd worn this one on the happiest day of his life.

He'd only kept it as a memento, really, never intending to give it another outing, and certainly not to ever wear it to work. But why not, he thought? Why not dare to wear it again, and why not on this day; this day, when he felt he knew nothing about himself. Was happiness something to be ashamed of too?

As the fabric of the sleeve slid up over his skin (he looked down and watched it), for some reason or other he found himself remembering a half-forgotten phrase from his childhood; *the quick and the dead*. The quick, he supposed, was his white skin, and the dead, the chilly black cotton sliding over it.

As he buttoned the cuff, he remembered a picture, too; something the guidebook had called a *Doom*.

At the top of the picture, two furious-looking angels were blowing into a pair of unconvincing trumpets, and at the bottom, like so many maggots from a piece of hole-ridden cheese, the dead, blank-faced with astonishment, were rising from their graves. The pasty rich were still all clutching the attributes of their earthly rank – crowns, tiaras, gold-tasselled mitres – using them as props to cover themselves as decently as they could; but the common people, who the artist had depicted as being uniformly brown-skinned, were all stark bollock naked. The men, he remembered, had all been given the same square chin, and workmen's hands as big and blunt as spades; the young women at their sides were all painted with identical cornflower-blue eyes and child-bearing hips as round as eggs. The few old ones – the worn out, the used-up – were crudely labelled as such by their dog-teated, hanging-down, triangular breasts. Ah yes, he remembered; when the time comes, we will all be labelled according to our lives.

With this thought in mind, as he did up the first five buttons of the shirt, he tried to decide what his label would be (the slight resistance as each button slipped firmly through the stitching of its well-made button-hole gave him, each time, a distinct pleasure). His *appropriate attribute*. If not an item of clothing (if not a shirt), then what? His bank card, complete with signature? His phone number – after all, that's how we mostly list and sort people, he thought, these days, by number. Did that mean he would be depicted rising maggot-like from the ground with a mobile phone clutched in his upraised right hand? Hardly… Well, what then? What about him could possibly sum him up? The ring? The tattoo he'd crossed his heart with to celebrate the first time he'd ever been proud of his body (the ink was smudged now, spreading under the skin)? The hard-to-pin-down colour of his eyes? The sound of his voice, perhaps – but how would you paint that? How could you paint the taste of a man's tears, or the peculiarly despairing cry he always made when he came? The feeling, the physical sensation, when love overcame fear?

Frowning at himself in the mirror, he tried to concentrate; really concentrate. To force himself to do up the last button, he tried to imagine the actual sound of the trumpets. When this was done, he'd be very close to being dressed, to having to leave the house. To being the man he was, today.

Trumpets.

Trumpets.

Let's leave him there, shall we?

Troubled

Sebastian Beaumont

1977 started for Gary Gilmore with his execution by firing squad as the US reintroduced the death penalty. For David it started by falling in love with Ian Young, a boy in the year above him at school. David did not consciously become aware of either of these until much later in the year.

In the summer, Anchor Records released the punk classic, 'Gary Gilmore's Eyes', by The Adverts, and David heard Ian singing it in the corridor in the week before the holidays started. Ian had just taken his A levels and David, who was in the year below him, was feeling bereft that he would never see him again. In fact it was this strange emptiness that gave David his first inkling that he was in love. David had hardly spoken to Ian, and they had no mutual friends, so David's feelings were entirely of the sighing-into-his-coffee variety.

David had bought The Adverts' single the day before and was caught up in the macabre imagery of the song, in which Gilmore's eyes are transplanted into an unsuspecting patient who only gradually realises that he's seeing with the eyes of a murderer. Perfect horror stuff for an understimulated sixteen-year-old.

As Ian sang, David spontaneously joined in with the chorus, and Ian laughed and turned to him, impressed.

'The Adverts are playing at Tiffany's at the end of the month,' David said, 'do you fancy going along?'

And so started a summer of gigs and minor underage drinking. They went to see The Adverts, The Boomtown Rats, The Stranglers, Blondie… Ian borrowed his dad's Hillman Super Minx on Thursdays, which was punk night at Tiffany's, and they would drive into Coventry and pogo to the music. Ian usually had a friend or two who would come along and so the two of them were rarely alone together at that point. Ian treated David as he might a younger brother, with hearty but patronising camaraderie.

They didn't have much money in the first few weeks. Enough for their entrance and a single pint of lager, so it was a pretty sober affair, but an incredible time for David. He felt that he was part of something exciting, musically, and that, mingled with the exhilaration of being in Ian's company, created a heady mix of happiness that managed, nevertheless, to contain within it a certain unrequited hopelessness. Ian was handsome, and slim, and in his ripped T-shirt and drainpipe trousers he looked great. When he leaped up, David would catch glimpses of the musculature of his chest and it took his breath away.

In August, David turned seventeen and started taking driving lessons. They put L plates on his mother's metallic brown Mini Metro and David would drive to their Thursday night gigs with Ian supervising him. This worked well as it coincided with Ian getting his first job as a trainee on the production line at the Rover plant in Longbridge. This meant that, after he'd got his first pay packet, Ian could drink as much as he wanted, whilst David's solitary pint – sometimes supplemented by a later half – was fine for him as the driver.

In September, Ian discovered amphetamines and that added something to the buzz of their evenings out. He always let David have some, and they would end up arriving back at David's place, still speeding, at around two-thirty a.m. Ian would sometimes stay over and go to work in the rather battered Morris Marina he'd just bought, without having slept, managing somehow to get through Fridays at the plant, though David wondered about the quality of the work he did on those cars, and of the drivers who must have paid the price for the nights out that he and Ian enjoyed.

Once back at school for his A level year, David found that Fridays were a nightmare to be negotiated with strong coffee and sheer determination. At least he didn't have any practicals to do in either physics or chemistry on that day, and so he could usually manage to remain silent, inconspicuous and at least semi-conscious.

On the third night that Ian stayed over, they ended up having sex. It's strange that, later, David couldn't really remember how this happened, only that they somehow drifted into kissing and then into a rather prolonged mutual masturbation. David hadn't known that amphetamines delayed orgasm, but that was all to the good as far as he was concerned. Ian seemed to genuinely enjoy it. In the morning, after that first time, he gave David a quick kiss before leaving for work.

The next week, however, as they left for Coventry, Ian didn't mention their tryst of the week before. It was as if it hadn't happened. One of Ian's friends was with them and Ian completely ignored David for the first part of the evening, which felt hurtful and unnecessary. That week they were there to see Richard Hell and The Voidoids. When the band did their anthemic single 'Love Comes in Spurts' it seemed wildly apt, somehow, and elicited the first friendly interaction between them when Ian winked slyly across at David.

That was when David realised that Ian was terrified of being seen as gay. It hadn't really occurred to David to think about it one way or another for himself, although in retrospect, of course, he was as firmly in the closet in his silence as Ian was. But the difference was that he would have been happy to come out if it might mean coming out as Ian's boyfriend.

They slept together again that night, and that was how the pattern was set. Ian wouldn't mention anything about what they were going to do, and wouldn't show David any affection until he was halfway through his third pint and he was up on his speed. Then, he would become very tactile, in a 'we're straight mates' sort of way, which would bleed quite naturally into even more tactile, almost hungry, sexual contact once they were back at David's house.

David kind of knew this was no way to conduct a relationship, but for those weeks until Christmas, he didn't care. His Fridays became a haze of tiredness and erotic afterglow that would last for the whole weekend, after which he would look forward to Thursday with increasing tingles of anticipation.

Of course, it didn't last – it couldn't. David was aware of that on some level. But the end came too quickly, and too shockingly, for him to take it easily in his stride. His parents had probably been suspicious about them from the start, and confronted him one Friday night in early December. In 1977 homosexuality was a no-no in rural Warwickshire, in David's parents' milieu at least. But when they asked if David was gay he saw no reason to deny it.

'It's not against the law,' he said, defiantly.

'What you've been doing with Ian is, until you're twenty-one,' his father told him, and forbade him to go out with Ian to Tiffany's again.

Perhaps David should have realised by then that Ian was a coward. Perhaps it would have made it easier to forgive him for abandoning him like he did, because Ian made no contact whatsoever and David was left with a great emptiness that he found impossible to fill. He ended up listlessly moping about the house, sulking really. He wanted to turn his unhappiness into a punishment for his parents and he guessed it worked because they withdrew from him and both became snappy, with David and with each other, and with his younger sister, too. She turned sixteen in the Christmas holidays, and tried to comfort David in her own way. He was impervious to her sympathy and snapped at her when she tried to be kind to him, which he regretted even as he was doing it.

It was easy for David, on the way to school, to do a detour and go past Ian's house on his bike. He did this several times over those first few weeks. But Ian's Marina was never in the drive. David dropped off notes for him once or twice asking if they could meet up for a drink in The Stag at Offchurch at a designated time later in the week, but Ian never turned up.

In the week before Christmas David went to Ian's house and knocked on the door. His mother answered and smiled a little shyly at David when he asked where Ian was.

'He's not living here any more,' she told him.

'He's moved in with his *girlfriend*,' his father shouted from the lounge.

'I'm sorry,' his mother said, and closed the door.

To say David felt betrayed is an understatement. His rage seemed uncontainable. He cycled home and banged about in his room, playing music incredibly loudly and being furious with himself because he couldn't stop crying. There was something about the angry energy of songs like The Clash's 'White Riot' or Slaughter and the Dogs' 'Cranked Up Really High' that managed to express his feelings for him, and stopped him from simply detonating. He also listened to The Rezillos' 'Can't Stand My Baby' over and over… At dinner, nothing was said, but there was a quietness round the table that was curiously respectful of his pain.

It wasn't quite the Christmas he'd expected. He didn't know it was possible for a person to be so relentlessly miserable. The fact that he passed his driving test on 28 December was hardly helpful, as he had no reason to drive anywhere now that he couldn't go to Tiffany's. But there was something that started to happen as the New Year dawned and he began to realise that he wasn't cut out to be unhappy.

He was aware of other people in his year at school who'd been unhappy in love, or friendship, and who became depressed and withdrawn, stuck on a downward spiral that seemed to have no end. But, in the end, David bounced back with a kind of battle-weary chagrin and returned to school for the spring term with a feeling of resignation that had a touch of dark humour to it.

But he decided to give up on love.

What a waste of time it had been, and so painful, and anyway there were no other boys that came even close to Ian in the attractiveness stakes, so it wasn't as though he had to waste any energy in sighing over anyone. He just put his head down and got on with his work. He knew, somewhere, that he was still young and that 'being gay' was something that he would be able to explore once he'd left home. All he had to do was wait until he went to university in the autumn and he would be free to do as he pleased.

In May he heard from someone at school that Ian had signed up to join the army. David felt a real jolt of distress as he heard this, and wondered why he was so affected by the news. Ian was quite able to make up his own mind about what he wanted to do. What did it matter? They'd had sex a few times, that was all. David couldn't even bring himself to think of it as an affair because it hadn't existed in between their Thursday nights out, except as a sense of anticipation. But part of him wanted to find Ian, shake him, and shout, 'You fool!'

David knew Ian was gay. *Ian* knew he was gay. He might have been terrified of what was happening between them, but there was no way that he'd been able to hide his desire from David when they were in bed together. And now, what was he trying to prove by having a girlfriend and going into the army? You couldn't make desire go away just by hoping hard enough.

David was surprised to get an invitation to Ian's farewell party, which was to be held in the Pump Rooms at the bottom of The Parade in Leamington Spa. It was a venue that could be hired, along with a mobile disco, and at first David was very clear that he wouldn't go. But as the day approached, he began to be curious, and it was this curiosity — to see Ian's girlfriend mostly — that eventually decided him.

All Ian's 'pals' from school were there, quite a number of whom had come to Tiffany's the year before, and there was a lot of bravado about what they were all doing now. Only one had gone on to university, and he was teased about it. The others were working in factories, retail or were in trainee management schemes.

Ian was as handsome as ever, and his girlfriend was beautiful, which was somehow rather comforting. Her name was Charlotte and she knew who David was, and at least something about his connection with Ian, because she was solicitous towards him, and friendly. But she couldn't hide the fact that she pitied David, and she made a point of being particularly tactile with Ian when she knew that David was watching.

Ian only said hello to David in the most cursory manner when he arrived, and David thought to himself, 'He obviously hasn't had three-and-a-half pints yet.' Ian could never show affection before that… And, of course, there was a moment at around ten o'clock when Ian glanced across at David with that odd, trapped look, and David realised that this was why he'd come. To see if Ian would look at him in that way, and he felt a sad pang that Ian should be so inhibited and so self-destructively stuck in trying to pretend that he wasn't feeling this desire. There was an anger that went with this, too, because David looked at Charlotte and thought, 'That should be me.'

Back at the bar, he ordered a pint and sat alone for a while until someone of about his own age came up and said hello. His name was Stephen and he turned out to be Ian's first cousin. They exchanged pleasantries for a few minutes before Stephen said, 'You're in love with him, aren't you?'

David was shocked, and said, 'What do you mean?'

'It's OK,' Stephen said, 'I was in love with him, too. I fell in love with him when I was seven. I saw the look in your eyes when Charlotte kissed him just then and I recognised the pain of it immediately. But let me tell you, you're on to a loser, falling in love with someone as fucked up as Ian.'

David shrugged.

'I'm resigned to it,' he said. 'It still hurts, but I find I can cope with it.'

'Wise words.' Stephen drank some of his beer and then smiled ruefully. 'I had to hate him for a while before I could even begin to start liking him again. Why did you come here this evening, if you still find it painful to be around him?'

'Because I wondered if I *would* find it painful. And I do, of course. But then I also find that I'm not heartbroken either, which is a relief.'

At around eleven-thirty David went to the toilet and Ian followed him in. David could see by Ian's heavy movements that he was drunk, and when he came to stand at the urinal next to him, he mumbled something that David didn't catch.

'What?' he asked him.

'You heard me,' Ian said.

David laughed.

'I'm sorry, Ian, I *didn't* hear you.'

He looked at David, and his expression held so much pain that David was breathless for a moment.

'I love you,' he mumbled again.

David zipped up his jeans and went to the washbasins. Ian came and stood beside him and said, 'I love Charlotte, too. I *really* love her. But in a... different way.'

David turned to him.

'You had a pretty funny way of showing that you loved me, disappearing without a word like that,' he said. 'I love you too, but I've kind of come to terms with the fact that we're never going to be together. You'd never be comfortable enough with yourself to love me when you're sober. That's pretty crap, really, when you think of it.'

David turned to leave, and as Ian came out into the pub with him, David said, 'This conversation just makes me sad. I'd like to say that I hope you'll be happy with Charlotte, and that I hope you'll be happy in the army, but what's the point in lying? We both know that you won't be.'

There seemed to be no point in staying, so David went back to say goodbye to Stephen only to find that Stephen had bought him another pint.

'Thanks,' he smiled, 'I'll have this one and then get off home.'

Their conversation was easygoing and David was hugely relieved to be able to pass the time so pleasantly when it might all have been so ghastly. When he'd nearly finished his drink, Charlotte came over to say hello.

'Thanks for coming,' she said. 'I know it must have been difficult for you. It meant a lot to Ian.'

David tried to smile, but failed.

'It seems so sad,' she said, 'to fall in love with someone like Ian, who's straight. I mean, it's so impossible, right?'

She hugged him drunkenly.

'I hope you find a nice gay boy to fall in love with. I'm sure you will, David. I mean, you're a good-looking guy.'

She staggered off and Stephen laughed.

'Don't say anything,' said David, 'it's too sad to even make a joke about it.'

He downed the last of his pint and stood up.

'I'm off,' he said.

'Look,' said Stephen, 'maybe I could give you my number? I don't know many other gay people round here and it would be great to have someone to go out for a drink with once in a while.'

It took David most of the rest of that academic year to fall in love with Stephen. Love crept up on him, really, and when it became obvious to them both that they were in love with each other, they were already good friends. In the autumn of 1978, David went to Imperial College to study geology and Stephen went to the University of Surrey, in Guildford, to study French. They saw each other most weekends and settled into what might be described as a 'stable relationship'. London's gay scene was tiny and underground at that point, but Heaven opened in 1979 and a new air of confidence was burgeoning in the capital, although there was clearly a long way to go.

David introduced Stephen to his parents in early 1980, six months before his twenty-first birthday, and they took to him immediately. They still wanted to pass them off as 'friends' to the neighbours, but nevertheless it was a huge step forward from 1977.

By the time they both graduated in 1981 they were ready to live together, and they moved to Camden and bought a small flat not far from Camden Lock. David stayed on at Imperial College, in research, and Stephen started a teacher-training course to become a French teacher.

They heard of Ian sporadically. In early 1981 he was posted to Northern Ireland, and suddenly watching the news became more poignant. The 'Troubles' – a word that was a strangely anodyne understatement for what was happening – were on TV almost every night, with the Maze prison hunger strikes, and Bobby Sands' election to Westminster whilst still incarcerated, and his subsequent death by starvation. It was all highly charged. British soldiers had been dying out there in dribs and drabs for years, and it was impossible not to look out for Ian when they saw footage of soldiers manning road blocks or patrolling the streets.

It was a relief, in 1982, to hear that he was back on the mainland, and even more so to hear that he'd left the army. He'd also, it seemed, left his wife, and David hoped that perhaps he would now be able to come out and settle down to accepting his sexuality. Perhaps he would be able to find a place for himself now that he was a bit older, and the world had changed. The gay scene in London was getting bigger and more visible all the time. Heaven was a gay club on a scale that would have been impossible to imagine only a few years earlier, and pubs and bars were beginning to vie for gay custom. Not that it was all plain sailing. With the greater visibility came more anti-gay violence and queer bashing, but there was also a feeling of a need to *demand* acceptance rather than to hope that it might simply arise. David and Stephen joined a local branch of the now-ailing CHE, the Campaign for Homosexual Equality, and felt they were doing something proactive to get things moving.

One weekend at the beginning of 1983 David got a phone call from Ian. Stephen was on a training week in Manchester, and so David went out on his own to meet him in a pub on Regent's Park Road. Ian was twenty-four and David hardly recognised him. He was still handsome. Even more handsome, perhaps, now that he'd grown into his physique. He'd gone for the 'clone' look – short hair, Levi 501 jeans, plaid shirt and a moustache. It kind of suited him, but it looked like yet another uniform. The thing that took David aback, though, was the hard look he had. This wasn't just because he had a bruised cheek and the remains of a black eye. There was also something taut and sinewy about him that looked as though he was ready to snap, as though he was existing on a regime of heavy exercise, strong coffee and cigarettes. There was something a bit trembly and hesitant in the way he spoke, too, which hadn't been there before.

He had an air of sexual assuredness coupled with massive personal vulnerability, which, even whilst he wasn't attracted to it himself, David could recognise as attractive in an emotionally dangerous way. He could imagine people getting sucked into his unassuageable neediness. Fortunately, David's spark of sexual interest in Ian had well and truly died. It was almost like meeting up with a wayward elder brother, rather than an ex-lover.

Ian drank more heavily than David – he always had, now that David thought of it – and there was something a little desperate about it. There was also a sense of bravado in Ian's bragging about his sexual conquests that David found disturbing. David and Stephen had a number of gay friends who slept with quite spectacular numbers of men, so it wasn't disapproval on David's part that made him feel that there was something wrong. It was just so painfully obvious that what Ian was doing was neither making him happy nor meeting his needs. It was clear, as far as David was concerned, that Ian needed to be loved, not just slept with.

Like clockwork, at three-and-a-half pints, Ian became flirty, and David, in spite of a certain amusement at having predicted that this would happen, had to be stern in letting Ian know that nothing was going to happen.

'Why not?' Ian asked, lighting another cigarette and looking both puzzled and, suddenly, very young.

'As you know, I'm going out with Stephen,' David told him, 'and we're happy together, so please leave it alone.'

Ian shrugged at this, and moodily drank some more, and David realised with sudden clarity that Ian never had sex with anyone unless he was drunk. This was the saddest insight of that sad evening.

'So,' David asked, 'how did you get your black eye?'

'I've taken to hanging around some of the gay pubs and clubs after closing time,' he said, 'looking for a bit of… entertainment.'

'Entertainment?'

'There are quite a lot of people who sneer at or taunt guys who are leaving places like the Salisbury or the City of Quebec, or Bang, late at night, and if I come across that kind of behaviour, I go up to them and make sure they… apologise.'

'I see,' said David, 'you mean you go looking for fights.'

'That's one way of putting it,' said Ian. 'But I also like to see it as being socially and politically useful. Giving the bastards a lesson. You can't disapprove,' he added. 'I'm offering a much-needed service.'

'I don't know what I think,' said David truthfully. 'I just know that you're miserable. Unhappiness is spraying out of you in all directions.'

Ian downed the rest of his pint and got up to go and buy another round. As he stood at the bar, David could see him as a man in crisis. The way he held himself was so posturing and false that it would have been risible if it wasn't so tragic, and yet David could see why he would be wildly sexually successful, with that mix of taut muscularity and heartrending vulnerability…

When Ian came back with the drinks, he looked intensely at David, and spoke through gritted teeth, with barely concealed contempt.

'You know fuck all about what's important in life,' he hissed. 'You live your bland life in Camden, and you never have to think, even for a moment, about what it means to be alive. Well I *am* alive, and I know what it feels like to think you're going to die. A friend of mine was shot dead by a sniper as he stood beside me at a check point in Fermanagh. We were in the middle of a conversation, joking about something, and then, bang, he was dead.'

David looked at him and was unsure what to say. He found himself reacting to Ian's anger by becoming defensive, but he could tell that this was what Ian was hoping for – a fight, even if it was only a verbal one – and so he forced himself to smile gently and said, 'It's true I've never faced death. At least not in the way that you're talking about.'

Ian lit another cigarette.

'It's not that,' he said, 'not that you think you might die. I knew I might have to face that at some point. I joined the army after all, so I'd be stupid not to think it was a possibility. But it was something else that made me grow up. The whole thing of being in it together. My commanding officer risked his life to keep me covered while I got out of an ambush. Then there was a time when I crawled nearly two hundred yards through mud on my belly to get to a man who was wounded. I almost certainly saved his life.'

He took a drag on his cigarette and looked down into his beer.

'No one really understands that about Northern Ireland – how many soldiers have died out there. Because it happens in ones and twos. No one gets a feel of it as war. But there was no one in my regiment who didn't have a friend who was murdered.'

David sat silently, waiting for Ian to continue.

'And then you come back into civilian life,' Ian went on, bitterly, 'and it all seems so fucking pointless.' He repeated the words, spitting them out: 'So *fucking pointless*. No one cares. No one knows what it's like to sacrifice yourself for someone else. *Nothing* is important. I go out to bars and no one has any idea what's really important. And then you get these fucking yobs thinking they're so smart calling us names, people who've never faced a moment's real danger in their lives. So, I go and give them an opportunity to experience what fear is really like.'

He nodded to himself and smiled. David tried to feel the poignancy of what Ian was saying, but really what he was feeling was a deep sadness that the beautiful seventeen-year-old that he'd fallen in love with, the young man who'd given himself up to love so hesitantly and so fearfully, should have become so full of hate.

There was no way of redeeming the conversation after that, or of finding some common ground. David mentioned the punk gigs that they'd been to together, but it was as though Ian's past had been subsumed by the hugeness of his experiences in Ireland. Everything else had become so small in comparison that he could no longer see any of it or regard it as important. Love seemed to have fallen into that category, too, of comparative insignificance, so that all that was left was anger and violence. And sex, although David started wondering, looking at Ian's bruised face, whether these weren't all inextricably linked.

David walked home later that night, to an empty bed, and felt truly alone for the first time in his life. He felt a need for loving comfort, and Stephen's absence was particularly poignant. He wondered, as he lay awake in his double bed, if Ian ever lay alone in bed at night yearning for someone's tender touch.

Stephen returned at the weekend, and David told him of his meeting with Ian. They decided to write to him, to invite him over for a meal, or to see if he wanted to go for a walk on the Heath. They worded the letter to be friendly but neutral. Stephen phoned his mother to get Ian's address and then they went out together to walk along the canal and to post the letter. They'd definitely decided to avoid suggesting meeting up in a gay bar.

David was relieved when Ian did not respond, and was a little ashamed of his relief. After a while, though, it almost seemed that the meeting hadn't happened, and that David had been mistaken or had dreamt it. His memory of Ian was not of taut anger, but of an earlier frail neediness that he could remember with affection.

In the summer of 1983, Stephen got a call from Ian's mother. Ian was in hospital. Accident and Emergency, in fact. He'd called to get her to contact Stephen, to ask him to come to the hospital. It was only a couple of miles from where David and Stephen lived, and so they set out in a taxi at eleven-thirty on a Tuesday night to the Middlesex Hospital. Ian, it turned out, was on one of the holding wards by that time. His head was swathed in bandages so it was impossible to see how injured he was, but he slurred when he spoke.

'I didn't do so well tonight,' he managed, and gulped a few times, painfully. 'They're keeping me in over night, and maybe for longer. I don't know.'

Stephen sat on the single chair whilst David took the edge of the bed.

'Look,' Ian said, gesturing carefully towards the clothing in his locker. 'Can you go back to my place and pick up some more… suitable clothing? Take this lot away, will you?'

David could see the plaid shirt plus the black leather jeans and leather waistcoat, and smiled.

'I'm sorry,' Ian said, 'I didn't know who else to ask. I didn't want Mum to see my clothes. Or my room.'

'That's OK,' Stephen told him, 'we're happy to do this for you, Ian. How are you feeling?'

'Tired,' he said. 'Tired.'

They went to Ian's flat, which was actually a tiny bedsit in a basement off Caledonian Road. There were three bedsits down there, and Ian's was at the front. There was a narrow bed across the back wall, a chest of drawers and a single wardrobe to the side of it. In the window was a small table, with a tiny Baby Belling electric cooker at the back of it. On the other side there was a sink which had a plate and a knife and fork in it, with toothbrush and toothpaste in a glass between the taps. There was an armchair, taking up a lot of the available floor space, which was positioned in front of an old television.

'Oh David,' Stephen whispered, 'this must the loneliest room in the world.'

There was no sign that Ian had ever had a guest here. The room was simply set up for sleeping and watching television. In his wardrobe he had some 'sex' clothes – a black leather jacket with chains on it, plus chaps and a leather peaked cap. They also found some Levi 501s which they took, along with a pale blue denim shirt and a crisp white T-shirt, plus some Marks & Spencer Y-fronts and fresh socks.

Stephen hugged David, briefly, silently, as they stood in the room which smelled slightly of rancid fat from the cooker, and David thought to himself, *I will never take love for granted again.*

In the communal hallway, just as they were leaving, someone was coming in, a gay man who looked to be in his mid-thirties, and stopped when he saw them.

'Oh hello,' he said, 'who are you?'

'I'm Ian's cousin,' said Stephen. 'He's in hospital, I'm afraid, and we've come to pick up some clean clothes for him.'

'Is he OK?'

'I think so,' Stephen told the man, 'though he may be in for several days. He seems to have been quite badly beaten up.'

The man nodded.

'It was bound to happen some day,' he said, then paused and glanced towards his door. 'Would you like to come in for a moment? For a coffee or something?'

Stephen glanced at David, and then said, 'Yes, OK, thank you.'

They went in and the man introduced himself as Jamie. The room was similar in size to Ian's but utterly different. It was full of clutter – ornaments, pictures, posters for musicals; there were framed photographs of Judy Garland and Barbra Streisand, and a record player in one corner, surrounded by stacks of vinyl.

Jamie busied himself making them coffee, fussing a little in a camp way, and as he did so, he spoke of Ian.

'He's a saint, that boy,' he said. 'Deserves a medal for what he's been doing to help people like me... like us.'

He looked across at Stephen and David, as though expecting them to contradict him, but they remained silent.

'Ian kept himself to himself, though, if you know what I mean,' Jamie went on. 'He was never one to talk much. He just smiled in that sad way of his when he said hello. And so handsome! But so troubled. There's that look that some gay men have, when you can see that it's all been too much for them. Some people just go bitter, and I can understand that. I have my moments, I can tell you.'

He laughed briefly before handing them their coffee.

'Some people just have to do something about it – go out into the world and bash back. I could never do that, myself, and so I admire it in Ian, even though I worry about his safety and about what's going to happen to him in the long run. He says to me, "I can look after myself, Jamie", but he can't, you know. He can't at all. I don't suppose he's ever been able to, that's the thing. People who are troubled, like he is, don't know how to let the world in.'

He perched on the edge of the small sofa on which David and Stephen were sitting.

'I cook a meal for him every now and then,' he told them, wistfully, 'and he's grateful for it, but his gratitude is the gratitude of a soldier who's still fighting.'

He nodded to himself as he said this, and sipped his coffee.

'He'll accept a little comfort from me, from time to time, when he's lonely, which is lovely. Of course, he'd be embarrassed to have a boyfriend like me, who's so much older, and so... different. He occasionally brings home these hard types, men who know how to *take* sex without giving anything, and I suppose Ian knows where he stands with that sort. When he's with them he can get by without giving either. I suppose there is something raunchy about all that muscle, but, well, there we go, I can't offer him that, can I? So, I do dinner for him every once in a while and sometimes he stays over. I hope that one day he'll find a steady chap who'll do nicely for him. He deserves that, at least.'

David felt Stephen take his hand, surreptitiously, as they sat on the sofa and talked some more with Jamie about other things. David wondered at what he was feeling. There were all sorts of things in there – sorrow that Ian had never managed to find love; there was also some pity, for Jamie as well as Ian, and a kind of irritation at himself for the patronising edge to his pity. There was some more pity in there, too, for his own seventeen-year-old self who had wanted so much more from Ian than he'd been able to give. There was gratitude for the relationship he had with Stephen, and underneath that a brittle sense of fear at the fragility of everything.

'Ian has to fight his own wars in his own way,' Jamie said out of nowhere, and laughed sadly.

David nodded in agreement and felt helpless, suddenly. What could he do to genuinely help Ian? He had no idea, but he found, as he sat, that beneath the helplessness, and the fear, there was a small spark of love for Ian that seemed to just sit there and exist, without purpose, and without being altered by what had happened between them.

Every No One

David Patrick Beavers

The winter wind bit through him. His thin cotton jacket was no more protection from the cold wet air than bare skin. Skin that felt the stinging barrage of shrapnel-like sand and bits of eucalyptus that blew off the shoreline and dunes. No shoes. No socks. His jeans were wet up to the knee. The black sky above was brilliantly clear. The iridescent half-moon and the fiery bright of Venus were the only familiar signs. Familiar through his right eye that was slowly swelling shut as the left one had. His nose ran freely, the salty mucous trickling down over his lips, sometimes into his mouth. He brought the back of his hand up to wipe the wetness away. He winced. His hand was swollen, bruised, lacerated. The rumbling waves broke and washed up around his ankles. He could no longer feel the penetrating cold of the water. Shelter. He remembered he had to find shelter. A shadowy grove of old eucalyptus and cypress was not far ahead. A black hole darker than the night sky. An abyss to fall into and never be found.

He hunkered into himself and trudged through the sand, up the dune and into the trees. The wind still soughed through the branches and leaves, but the pelting sand subsided. Things crunched beneath his bare feet. Sharp things. Woody things. Stickery things. Without the brightness of the moon, he was walking blindly in the darkness. He slowly sank to his knees and gingerly felt the ground before him. Cold sand, patches of solid soil, leaves, twigs, burrs, berry vines... God knew what else... He didn't. His parched throat and tongue felt even more swollen than his eye. The pain in his body was numbing. He wanted to sleep. Couldn't sleep. Not there. Not after all that he'd been through... Been through... What had he been through? Someone was after him. Had been after him. That's all he could recall. Someone had been after him because… His mind drew a blank. He suddenly realised he didn't remember much of anything. He'd been on a boat. With João.

João.

The name shot through his brain. João. Disjointed images flashed in his mind in a nanosecond. Portuguese man. Broad smile. Bronzed skin. Shaggy brown hair. Clear, penetrating gray eyes. He'd been with this João on the boat. That's what he knew. That's all he remembered. He couldn't think. Couldn't see. Couldn't hear anything but the rapid clacking of his teeth. He was shivering violently. All of him that had been numb now stung with an icy hot tingling of nerve endings protesting against him remaining still. The dull ache in his left eye throbbed. The vision in his right eye was lessening. He had to keep moving.

He crawled slowly through the increasing overgrowth deeper into the wooded area. Something cool and clammy raced over the back of his hand then skittered into the underbush. A lizard? A mouse? Something that needed water. And food. The rumbling growl in his stomach was loud. He drew up and leaned back against a tree. His entire body shivered violently when a cold breeze stirred the canopy of the trees. Leaves snowed down on him.

His right eye focused as best it could. Bracing himself against the tree, he pulled himself back up onto his feet. The inky blackness of the grove was pierced by the all too familiar bright black sky. An opaque white glow made him squint. A light in a window.

Anxious excitement knotted his gut. Fear wanted him to remain hidden. Survival pushed him to move his feet, slowly at first, but in a minute he was practically running like a loping rheumy drunk towards that rectangle of light. So blind was he to anything else as he stumbled out of the grove that he didn't see the chain-link fence. He slammed into it and fell back onto the ground. The back of his head hit something hard. He lay there dazed for a while, until the new pain subsided and blended in with all the dull, throbbing pains within his body.

He groaned as he strained to sit back up. His scalp tingled like a thousand ants were racing over it. His face flushed hot. Just as he fell back towards the ground, he felt arms catch him under his shoulders. A vortex of blackness wiped out the world.

His voice is hoarse. Raspy. Damaged. A lifetime of complete exhaustion growls out of him. His tired anger leaks out, seeking to make sense through words. Words I cannot understand. His mumbling. Is he speaking to me? I can hardly hear. Can't see. Just feel… pounding… tympanic pounding deep in my skull. I want to tell him to shut up. Just shut up. Leave me to my silence, please. I just want to go home.
   Home.
   Is this home? Cinnamon. I can smell. My nose feels raw. It was running. I was running. From what? To where? My God, my body aches. The cinnamon is making me hungry. I'm so tired.

Uri stared down at the young, blond man all battered and bandaged in his bed. He had washed the sand and salt from the fellow's tattered clothes. The jacket was threadbare. The old chinos and plaid shirt were too big. Second-hand or stolen clothing. The man was more of a boy, really. Maybe twenty, twenty-five at best. Compresses were on the young man's eyes. They had been swollen shut. Coagulated blood had almost fused his pale lashes together. He had been cleaning the lad's eyes and applying a salve to them for the past two days. He'd cleaned the young man's body as best he could. His feet and hands were in a horrible state. The boy had had a fever. It was all he could do to trickle water and weak cinnamon tea into this stranger's mouth while swabbing him down with cool water and diapering him with old tea towels.

Uri felt the wet chill in the air. He found a few more scraps of kindling and put them in the old iron stove. He then pulled on an old weather-worn leather jacket and looked through the cupboards of his small cabin. Just a cabin. One big room and one tiny bathroom that he had installed a few years prior. An illegal addition to the place, but no government official had ever come out to tell him to tear it down. People kept to themselves here, he thought. That amused him. He laughed at the thought of all the convoluted rules and regulations townships and cities can impose upon their citizens. Rationing. Everything. And then some.

He glanced once more at his sleeping charge. He'd almost shot the kid's head off that night. The wind had blown the shutters off the window, letting the light slip out. Had the long arm of the law spotted the faint light, he'd have been fined by the city and the country. But no one saw the bit of lamplight. No one saw or no one really cared. He had raised his rifle when he heard something slam into his old chain-link fence. Then he heard the groan – an unfamiliar sound within the normal music of the wind. He carried the young guy in, then quickly and quietly repaired the shutter.

And here, two days later, the young man remained. He ladled out some vegetable broth into a bowl, then sat on the edge of the bed and did his best to spoon some nourishment into the unconscious fellow.

'Who are you, boy?' he muttered. 'Soup's not much. Celery, bit of spinach, carrots, garlic, onion, some herbs, salt 'n' pepper.' All he could do was to trickle teaspoonfuls slowly between the stranger's lips. The young man's body seemed to reflexively swallow the wetness.

Uri studied the man's battered face. His blonde hair was close cropped. No lice. His body had no distinguishing marks. He'd said something once. Something that sounded like a name. *Joaõ*. Like the French 'je'. Zsh… wow. Portuguese, though, Uri thought. Not French. He'd heard the name. Lots of Portuguese in the east side of the bay. Fishermen and farmers. The blond stranger didn't look Portuguese. He looked German. Quite a few Germans and Italians in the camp up in Benicia.

Joaõ. John. John the fisherman.

As Uri spooned yet another trickle of broth between the blond man's lips, the man coughed. Uri set the broth aside and wiped away the residue of spit-up fluid. It was time to apply another compress to the fellow's swollen eyes, then he would allow himself to go to sleep.

He's been silent for hours. My head hurts still. A dull, persistent ache. He's still here, tending to me, watching over me as a guard does. I can feel my body again. Feel the cloth of the covers of a bed. It is a bed, not a cot. I'm not back there. I can hear the ocean, faintly. It's dark. I can see that it's dark. My eyes are open. My fingers work. I have to move. Have to go. He speaks English.

The crash and howl of pain woke Uri. He reached up and turned on the lamp. In the dim, yellow wash of a twenty-five-watt bulb, he saw the young man, sprawled naked over a tipped chair. A fresh gash in his forehead where his head had struck the edge of the old oak table.

'Hang on, lad. Hang on,' Uri whispered as he left the small divan where he slept and made his way over to his stranger. He grabbed a dishtowel from the back of another chair. The young man looked up with a horrified, frightened expression as he tried to right himself. He ended up stumbling backward, onto the edge of the bed.

'Softly, my friend. Move no more. I'm not going to hurt you,' Uri said gently as he crouched down beside the young man. He reached over to daub the wound.

'Don't!' the young man snapped as he drew up his knees and hugged them.

'OK.' He proffered the towel. The young man reached out with a shaky hand and took it. Uri sat down on the floor. 'You speak English.'

The young man gingerly blotted the blood from his wound. 'My clothes, please.'

Uri got up and ambled over to the small closet. He'd washed the fellow's clothes on an old washboard, in a washtub out in his yard. He'd even pressed them as best he could with his old iron. Yet, even cleaned and hanging on a hanger, the garments looked pretty tattered.

'You didn't have any skivvies,' he said, 'nor any wallet or identification or loose change or anything.'

The young man braced himself against the bed and slowly rose to his feet, his embarrassment of being nude suddenly gone. 'I have to go, please.' Pressing the towel against his forehead, he tried to take a few steps towards Uri, towards his clothes, then faltered. He almost stumbled against the table again, but clumsily found his footing and sank back onto the edge of the bed.

'You're in no shape to go anywhere,' Uri said quietly as he hung the clothes back onto the top of the closet door.

'Where is this place?' the young man asked.

'How about you tell me your name? You muttered the name João. Thought that might be your name, but you don't look Portuguese to me.'

The young man cast a suspicious eye on Uri. 'And just what do the Portuguese look like?'

'Most here'bouts aren't as fair as you.' Uri moved to the small wood-burning stove. And old cast-iron pot was off to the side of the burner. 'Got a few old bones from seven bone roasts from a butcher I know. Traded him a lug of wild blackberries I'd picked out there. The marrow in the bones helped flavour up this vegetable broth. You ready to eat something by yourself?' He opened the warmer next to the small oven and pulled out a partial loaf of bread. 'Got a bit of cheese, too.'

'Call me João,' the young man said. 'What do I call you?'

Uri dropped the bread on a cutting board, then pulled some flannel pyjamas from a small chest of drawers. He took them over to the young man. 'Put these on. You're shivering a bit.' He took the bloodied towel from him and inspected the wound. 'Stopped bleeding.' He picked up an old plaid bathrobe from the foot of the bed and handed it to the young man, then returned to the stove to serve up their meal.

The young man slipped into the pyjamas and robe. They were a size too big. He watched as the older man dished out their meal – soup, cheese, bread. In the faint glow of the dim lamp, he finally focused on this stranger who'd tended to him. A little taller than himself, maybe two or three decades older. Grey hair with bits of pale brown still showing. Brown eyes. Thin, but muscular. The ropes of veins in his arms and hands were very pronounced. The young man hesitated a moment, then joined the older fellow at the table.

They ate in silence. Uri got up once to get them water. A simple dinner, but one the young man found extremely satisfying. Uri took the dirty dishes to a small pump-fed sink and washed them. The young man just watched him.

'You drink coffee?' Uri asked as he filled an old enamelled pot with water.

'You have coffee?'

Uri let out a little laugh. 'Chicory. And some old coffee grounds.'

The young man shook his head. 'No. Thank you.'

Uri pulled a pouch of tobacco out of a tin and rolled himself a cigarette. 'You smoke?'

The young man nodded. Uri handed the cigarette he'd rolled to the fellow, tossed a box of matches onto the table, then rolled one for himself. The young man lit the cigarette, coughed upon taking the first drag, then fell into an old habit.

'My name is Uri.' He finally answered the young man's question.

'Russian?' the young man said, a bit accusingly.

'Ukranian. On my father's side. My mother's people are mostly Romanian.'

The young man nodded rather absently as he exhaled a plume of smoke. 'Where is this place?'

'What's your real name?' Uri pressed again.

The young man let out a defeated laugh. The type of laugh that almost slipped into tears. He drew up a deep breath and leaned back in the chair. 'I am No One,' he said with a certain amusement. 'I am Every No One.'

Uri leaned back in his chair and rolled another cigarette. 'Every No One…' Uri repeated. 'Every No One who washes up on shore and staggers through the dark all battered and half-dead. Every No One in second-hand rags and barefoot with nothing to his name that's his, save for his own soul. Every No One who is scared as hell that some shadow's gonna pop up and grab him. That Every No One?' The young man said nothing. He just stared intently at Uri. 'And what about João? That John the fisherman? That man you say is you. Is he also Every No One?'

'Yes,' said the young man. 'I am tired again.'

'Someone is after you.'

'If that is what you believe, then why are you keeping me here?'

Uri was stunned into silence for a moment, then let loose with a raucous laugh. He laughed so hard he started coughing. He got up, poured himself a cup of water, drank some of the cool liquid down, then cleared his throat.

'You know what I think, Mr Every No One? I think, worse than running from the camp up in Benicia, worse than running from the law, you're running from yourself.' The young man said nothing. Uri sat back down and spoke as he drew the ashtray towards the middle of the table. 'The army's pretty lax up at the camp with the internees. Thought you might have escaped from there.'

The young man felt mighty old. He watched Uri's lips move as he continued to talk. Deafness was rediscovered.

God, why does he persist? I need to go. I want to sleep. I have to find João. What happened to the boat? I can't answer his questions. I can't answer my own questions. We were on his boat, heading south. His boat? Was it his boat? A smaller trawler. A small harbour. Choppy water. But… something else… There was something else.

His deafness melted away. Uri was now just staring at him.

'You can't leave in your condition. Not yet,' said Uri.

Something snapped in the young man's mind. A spark. A thought. He scrutinised Uri through his troubled eyes. 'How is it that you're here alone? How can you remain here to play nurse to me, a stranger?'

Uri regarded the new surge in this fellow, his young charge. 'I'm alone by choice. I have no place that I have to be.'

'And how did that come to pass?'

Uri got up to check on the pot of coffee heating slowly on the stove. 'That's just how it worked itself out.'

'You seem to want to know about me. I could tell you anything. That I've had some sort of accident. That I'm a bit battered and bruised. That, I think, you'd believe.'

'I don't believe you're this João. I don't believe you're a fisherman,' he said as he sat back down at the table.

'I could give you any name. Willie. Jack. Robert. I could do that because I can't remember my name right now.'

'And that could be a lie,' Uri said as he rolled and lit another cigarette.

'Yes.'

'But you're the one who stumbled upon my cabin. You're the one fleeing something like some battered old tomcat needing to hide. Fleeing from what? A dog? A hawk?' Uri extinguished the cigarette. The tobacco left a sour taste in his mouth. 'Maybe you're fleeing from this João.'

'No!' the young man barked. He slapped his palm hard on the table as he pushed himself up out of the chair. 'No!'

The outburst caused his wounded hand to sting and throb unmercifully. He tried to shake the pain out. It lingered. His eyes started to water. He dropped back into the chair, keeping his hands hidden below the tabletop as he tried to massage the pain away with his other sore hand.

Uri leaned back in his chair. 'That hurt, didn't it.'

'Lots of things hurt.'

'I know.' Uri checked his wristwatch. 'It's almost three in the morning.'

'I can't sleep,' he said hoarsely as he reflexively tried to rub his eyes. He winced when he touched them.

'Go back to sleep, kid.' Uri moved to help ease the young man to his feet and guided him back over to the bed. 'So, I'll follow your lead, for now, João.'

Uri remained seated on the edge of the bed, waiting until his charge fell asleep. He then ambled back to his too-small divan.

Wind. Again. I can hear it out there. It's got eyes. I have to pee. Where is he?

The young man slowly rose from the bed. The cool wood of the floor soothed his pained feet. Uri wasn't there. He ambled cautiously through the room, past the table, the small stove, the ice box. His clothes still hung on the hanger hooked over the top of the closet door. Another door. He hesitated, then opened it. A tiny bathroom. Toilet, sink, shower stall – all

46

crammed in there. He loosened the pyjama bottoms and sat down on the commode. Not only did urine flow, but also his bowels. Diarrhoea. He had to flush the toilet three times before he could even think to look for tissue to clean himself. There wasn't much of it. Some sheets in a box. A fourth flush. He needed to shower. There was a bit of a cake of soap in the dish on the sink. A small shaving mirror hung above it. For the first time in a long while, he saw his face. Lumps, welts, bruises… chapped lips and nose… dark circles beneath his still puffy eyes. He looked like a walking corpse.

Over the toilet he saw a narrow shelf unit. A shaving mug, shaving soap and brush, and a straight-edge razor. He opened the razor, cut some of the soft soap into the mug then went to the sink. He trickled water into the mug then used the brush to froth up a lather. He had to be careful. His hands were trembling slightly as he gently pressed the blade to his cheek. He felt every pale whisker tug under the edge of the blade as they were cut. As careful as he was, the blade nicked the side of his chapped nostril. It bled a bit. He let the blood run down his cheek and drip off his chin. An image flashed through his mind – a fist coming straight into his face. He flinched. The flashback unhinged him. He stared at his reflection again in the small mirror. The nick stopped bleeding. A shiver raced through his spine. A shower. He needed a shower.

Uri parked his rusting old pick-up under the makeshift carport next to the cabin. He looked down at the box of meagre supplies he'd managed to get. Some artichokes, a half-dozen eggs, butter and a quarter rasher of bacon. These he'd gotten from a couple of old farmers that he periodically worked for – mostly doing repairs on farm equipment, coops, fences and the like. They were all shorthanded these days. He was still collecting payment from them for past services rendered.

He climbed out of the pick-up, snagging the box with one hand. He looked around. Even with the wind, he could hear the sound of plumbing. The shower was being used. That was a good sign. The kid was better able to get around. Still, he hadn't learned any good news for his visitor.

He'd gone out the morning after the young man appeared. He had walked through the grove and up the beach for quite a long while. He'd seen no signs of anything unusual. He had gone out that morning again, thinking that maybe if there had been some accident with the boat the young man had mumbled about, he could call the local authorities. Again, he found nothing. He found the same while out procuring the box of provisions. The farmers generally knew every farming and fishing family for fifty miles around. There had been nothing of any men missing in the local newspapers either. That's when he made some discreet calls from a payphone up to the camp. He heard the water stop running. The kid had finished his shower. Before going inside, he made one last look around his property.

The young man slid on his pants. He couldn't remember where his underwear had gone, nor his shoes and socks. He pulled on the old shirt and hung the threadbare jacket over the back of a chair. While in the shower, he saw just how tore up his feet were. He'd found toothpowder and a couple of old worn toothbrushes behind some bottles of iodine that were on the small shelf in the bathroom. He pilfered a toothbrush and scrubbed his teeth as best he could, then applied iodine to the cuts and abrasions on his feet. The yellowish red stains were dry now. He rummaged in Uri's closet and found an old pair of slippers that almost fitted him. He would wear them now. Hopefully Uri would allow him to keep them until he could find shoes of his own.

Food. He had to eat something. He checked the warmer on the side of the stove and found a bit of the old loaf of bread left. He opened the ice box – he remembered his grandmother had had one of these old things – and found an old apple and a small hunk of cheese. Hunger commanded. He ate the apple greedily, core and all, then made short work of the cheese and bread. He felt bloated from eating too fast, but was still hungry and thirsty. He went to the sink and pumped a glass of water and chugged it. He noticed water on the floor. The old ice box had a drip pan that evidently needed emptying. As he bent down to pull out the pan, the front door flew open.

He saw Uri standing there, with his arms somewhat raised. Another man was behind him. It was João. In the time it took his heart to skip one beat, everything came back to him. João pushed Uri into the room and kicked the door closed. He had a German Lugar in his hand.

'Hey, Benjamin,' João said with a grin. A crooked grin. His right eye had been blackened and his jaw had a huge welt on it, just to the right side of his mouth. He motioned for his two captives to sit at the table.

48

Uri cast an angry glance toward Benjamin. 'So this is your Every No One friend João?'

João laughed. 'I trained him good, I see.'

'I sank the boat,' Benjamin suddenly confessed.

'That you did, you fuck.' João paced around the table with the gun trained on them. He suddenly coldcocked Benjamin in the head with his free hand. 'Fucking bitch.' He looked at Uri. 'You get yourself a piece of this skinny white ass, old man?'

He stared at Uri's puzzled expression. He pointed the gun at Benjamin. 'He's a dutiful bitch if you fuck him hard. At least he was, 'til he flipped to play G Man.'

'I have no idea what you're talking about,' Uri said calmly. 'What do you want? Him? Take him.'

'Good, old man. Good.' João paced around the table again. 'Would've been good, except you stuck your fucking nose into stinging shit when you made those calls up to the camp. Those of us in the trade got a network, dip fuck.'

'I don't give a crap about whatever it is you're black-marketing, João,' said Uri.

'I believe you, old man. A few quick calls to me and I find out Mr Ex-Lieutenant almost got himself court-martialled after the first big war. Almost. Your CO couldn't come up with proof positive, though.'

Uri turned slightly in his chair to face João. 'And your ass, my resident alien friend, in now branded. Information flows in many directions.'

João stuck the barrel of the Lugar in Benjamin's ear. 'Yeah. Lots of things flow in many directions. Splattered brains and blood, for instance.'

'I'll go with you,' Benjamin said flatly.

'Oh… how sweet,' João said sarcastically. 'Because you love me, faggot? Huh?' He pulled the gun back. 'You should hear him beg me to fuck him. Sometimes worse than having a real bitch around. I'm his first, you know. Got something easy going, then he got all involved in me and my business.' He wagged the gun in Benjamin's face. 'Not too smart for a PFC army translator.'

Uri scrutinised Benjamin. 'You're army?'

'He's army, G-Man spy, Every No One faggot,' João said. 'I turned him in anonymously. Ratted him out to everyone in your stupid military at that camp. Faggots are No One. And he's every bit a no one, now. He was gonna come with me. Work with me. 'Cause he loves me and I made sure he can't stay here.' João slapped Benjamin hard. 'The he gets some fucking patriotic conscience when I tell him the Krauts are in Mexico, working on the government there, trying to negotiate an alliance like they got with Italy and Japan. We could've been a third of the way to Central America by now. But he goes below deck and finds a way to sink my boat.' He squared off across the table from Uri and looked him square in the eye. 'What kinda fuckin' love is that? Huh?'

Uri leaned back in his chair. 'So, what're you going to do with him now?'

'I wanna kill him,' João said. 'But I can't.'

'Because in your own way, you love him,' Uri said.

Benjamin finally spoke up. 'I sank the boat because I didn't want to go with you, João. I got scared.'

'I got scared, too, you fuck. I thought you were running back to have me arrested. That made me nuts!'

'So you start hammering on me like some rabid grizzly?'

'You betrayed me!' João shrieked.

Benjamin jumped to his feet and shrieked back in João's face. 'You betrayed me, you shit! You turned me in!'

The two men were so engaged in their anger towards each other, they missed Uri slink over to pull his rifle from behind the ice box. He pointed it at João's head.

'Put the gun down, please.'

João complied. 'Smooth, old man.'

Benjamin sat back down. 'I'm sorry, Uri.'

Uri moved forward, keeping the gun levelled on João, forcing him to back up. He picked up the gun, pocketed it, then indicated for João to sit. He stepped back, lowered the rifle a bit, then just stared at the two men before him. Finally he spoke. 'I said before, I don't give a good God damn what you black-market, fisherman. I don't give a good God damn if you like to fuck ass and suck dick. What I do give a good God damn about is you shoving a piece in my face, in my house, in the face of my guest.'

João burst out laughing. 'Your guest? That's a good one.'

'And I give a real good God damn about strangers sticking their noses in my business.'

'So what? You gonna shoot me, old man?' João let out a laugh.

Uri backed over to the ice box. He opened it and pulled out a small bottle. He set it down on the table. He pointed the rifle at Benjamin. 'Give him a dropper full.'

'Poison?' Benjamin asked

'It's Hex-something-barbital. Just a type of sedative,' Uri said. 'But first, fisherman, tell us where your boat is.'

'I'd rather you shoot me.'

Uri fired the rifle. The bullet whizzed past João's head, just nicking his ear lobe. João flinched wildly. Uri laughed. 'If you'd done more snooping, fisherman, you'd know just how good of a shot I am. I can kill a man cleanly and quickly, or I can shoot him in any number of places where he'd die a slow, agonising death. Either way, it's your choice.'

'You're fucking nutso, old man.'

'Where's the boat?'

Benjamin opened the bottle and drew up a dropper full of the liquid. 'He's a creature of habit. It's at Half Moon Bay. Slip four.'

'You sure about that?' João said with a cocky smile.

'Yes.'

'Take the drops,' Uri pressed, 'and you'll wake up on your way down to sunny Mexico. Or maybe drifting out to Japan. You'll figure out how to survive.'

'Why should I believe you?' João asked.

'Because your choices are simply to do it, or be shot, or be turned over to the local cops, who don't much cotton to black-marketing aliens.'

João looked at Benjamin. 'You comin' with me, Benny?'

Benny stared at João long and hard. He finally shook his head. He handed the dropper to João. João seemed very disappointed. He shook his head as well, then took the dropper and downed the sedative.

'How long?' he asked Uri.

'Takes some time. We just wait.' Uri said as he sat down.

Twenty minutes later, Benjamin and Uri loaded João into the pick-up. He looked like a passed-out drunk. Benjamin touched João's black eye, then kissed him on the lips. Uri climbed into the pick-up and fired up the engine.

'You can stay or go, kid,' Uri said.

'Maybe I should come with you,' Ben said.

'No.' Uri backed out onto the road, then sped off.

Benjamin watched him leave. In a minute the pick-up was out of sight. He looked around at the cabin. The box of provisions was overturned on the shaggy grass. He walked over and picked up the box. The artichokes, bacon, butter and eggs were all intact on the grass. He carefully put them in the box and carried them inside.

It's been hours. The day has gone. Night has taken over. He isn't back. I have nowhere to go. We were both Every No One. Every person like us who isn't seen because we can't be seen. I couldn't go with him. Can't remain where I had once been. It's all changed now. I hope Uri won't be angry. I can feel the sedative. It's taking longer with me than it did with João. More of it than he had. Much more... I'm tired. God, I'm tired. I never wanted to be a soldier. Never wanted to be in any army. Never wanted to be in any war. I want to be no one.

A Casualty of War

Scott Brown

I laughed as I kicked him. We all did. It wasn't funny but I guess that laughter was subconsciously our way of dealing with the fact we were kicking a man to death. The human body is a complicated thing. The human mind even more so.

My eyes had met with those of my victim as he had looked up at me from his place on the floor. I saw the look in his eyes; well, it wasn't a look, more a silent pleading for me to help make it all stop. For me to make it end. Pain and pleading conveyed in one silent stolen glance, all of which would disappear with a single blood-soaked blink. A final, closing, blood-soaked blink. In that look I had seen his soul. In that look I had seen what I already knew; he was going straight to hell. The look in his eyes in that final moment confirmed to me what I had always known.

I remember that I had squared up to him – only he was on the floor and I was standing over him. With ease and grace I lifted my leg back, I took aim, then I swung. Swung with force and might. I swung with all of my six-foot-two in height and all of my two hundred pounds in weight. I kicked at the defenceless body lying limp on the floor time and time again. I was like an animal attacking its prey. Whilst my body did this to the human on the floor the rest of me sat and watched from a faraway place high above. Somehow my mind making a disconnection. It wasn't me, I wasn't there. Or at least some part of me didn't want to be. I watched myself from above as my booted foot slammed repeatedly into his face. I watched myself from above as I laughed like a madman whilst doing this. I watched myself from above as the others encouraged it, encouraged me.

That doesn't mean I wasn't involved and it doesn't mean it wasn't justified. It just means I did it in a detached way. I did it because it needed to be done not because I wanted to do it. That's a very important point to remember. Sometimes things just need to be done.

He died right there on the dusty dirt road just outside the camp. No ceremony, no honour and no medal for bravery. Another dead soldier. Another casualty in America's War on Terror. Jake, another soldier killed by his own. We left him on the ground, dead at the roadside. No colleagues would rescue him; they had been his assailants. No Stars and Stripes draped over him; it wasn't fitting. We simply left him crumpled on the ground, hunched into the foetal position he had assumed as he tried to defend himself and save his life from the people who were supposed to be looking out for him. American blood bleeding out on Arab soil, al-Qaeda would rejoice at such a vision. We would blame Jake's death on the Iraqis, the insurgents. It's easier that way; death is everywhere and it doesn't mean anything. That excuse would wash without question. Another dead soldier is just an aside on the evening news nowadays. The bigger story of streets full of dead Iraqi civilians doesn't even make the news, so go figure. Someone somewhere had decided that an American life was more valuable than an Arab one. I wonder if that was God or Allah. Whoever it was, I wasn't afraid anymore, not after nine months of being here. I used to be scared of dying but it no longer bothers me, not like it used to. Here you can touch death, feel death and smell death. It's so normal that it really just becomes something less in your life to fear. And when you don't fear dying life can become pretty dangerous. Right now I'm in that small percentage of people who think life is just too long.

Killing Jake wasn't hard. Killing isn't hard. I don't have nightmares about killing or about the people I've killed. I don't have nightmares. I do however have sweet dreams that in waking hours are my biggest nightmare.

Killing is weird. It's a defence mechanism that can go so wrong when you engage it too much. And you do here. You engage it. Too much. Your own mortality powering you along. Powering you along because of the thrill. Powering you along because it's a drug. And powering man along because it gives him the power to make the kind of decisions that should only be vested in God; namely the power to take the life of another without retribution. I remember my first kill, but then we don't really speak about it. Not here, not to each other. Soldiers don't discuss how many people they have killed – it's kind of rude to ask or talk about it. Kind of like the old days when it was rude to ask how much someone earns. Just not done, not proper in polite society. But then this is not polite society. It is Iraq, and this is still a war regardless of what George W. Bush may say. A very big, very costly and very real war.

As for me, well I've killed seven. Three for real and four for fun. You can do that here and get away with it, you just simply shoot the bastards stone dead without justification or reason. It's a hot melting pot of shit out there on the streets and nobody cares, tell the boss the fucker had a gun and you almost get a medal for bravery. It's fucked up, but it's fun. It's the thrill of being God. Of playing God. Of understanding God. Maybe if I get close enough I can find out why.

Death in real life is the most certain thing I have ever seen. Regardless of the mystery surrounding it, it is the end and when you see it up close and personal you realise just how very final it is. When you see the life vanishing from their eyes and the person disappearing forever you know and understand the finality of it all. It's not like the movies show it, not when the victim staggers around and then hits the floor, dying slowly, telling everyone he loves them on his way out. In reality it's quick, it's definite and it's final. The ones I've killed I can still see in my head, each of them the same; they all fell to the floor in a bloody heap in one limp movement. Like a puppet whose strings had been cut. I remember one time the rag fell off of one dude's head as the bullet fucked his face up. I almost came in my pants. Just another dead Iraqi as far as the army was concerned. Just another dead Iraqi as far as the world was concerned. One less mad Muslim walking the streets. The patrol didn't even break its speed; we just carried on with the job in hand, making the streets of Baghdad a safer place. As soldiers, we do all we can to win the hearts and minds of the Iraqis, it's important for them to see us as something completely different to the oppressive murderous regime they were so used to living under. I remember looking back at the dead body on the ground as we moved into the distance, a time machine moving forward as that dude was left there, stuck forever in history, blood spilling onto the pavement. He was gone forever and that was the power I had vested in me by the US Army. I was a soldier in this war, and that is why the rest of it is all wrong. I can't be a soldier because the two don't go hand in hand. That was fucking Jake's downfall and it was going to be mine.

My first real kill was weird. It left a bad taste for a while, the sheer magnitude of what I had done washing over me. My very own little inner struggle questioning whether I should be allowed to take the life of another. I was jittery for a while but then it sank in that I had killed another human, that was my job, that was now my right. In no time it started to feel like it did when my dad had taken me shooting as a kid, first at the range and then out hunting for deer and shit. I remember killing that first fucking deer, looking in its big dark eyes. Most kids love the movie *Bambi* and cry at it, not me; at ten years old I was the cunt that shot Bambi's mother – and it made me so fucking happy. I killed that deer, we dragged it back and we cooked the thing. It was the best meal I ever had. Out here in Iraq, it's becoming the same; you're hunting, just it's not deer, it's the bad guys – and they are everywhere. Just like deer and just as expendable. I confessed to Jake about killing an unarmed man, I confessed my inner soul to him about killing a dude when he had no fucking weapon at all. Jake was cool, I loved him in every way possible. He was an amazing guy, a great friend and a fantastic soldier. It was a shame he was a fag otherwise he would still be alive today.

So Jake sucked my cock a few times, shit happens, most soldiers do it. Fuck no, all soldiers are capable of it. You're away from home, away from everything for a long fucking time and you face death daily, for me that is horny, for most it is sexual. There is a difference between letting a guy suck your cock, shooting your load in that dirty cunt's mouth and between what Jake wanted, which was to fuck, to touch and to hold. Fuck that shit man, I fucked his mouth and he could do what the fuck he liked with his own cock; I just wanted a warm hole to get off in. If you do more than that and start touching the other dude's cock then that's a different thing. That's queer. And there can't be fags in the army – it's a simple rule we have to adhere to. Soldiers don't like fags. The army doesn't like fags. Mainstream America doesn't like fags and, from what I gather, God isn't too keen either. Basically, fags got dealt a bad hand. I'm a soldier. That is all I've ever wanted to be. That's all I ever want to be. I can't imagine not being a soldier and I know what that means.

I remember the day that Jake died for being a fag. It wasn't my fault, but he had told me he was queer. That was fine. I'm no fag hater, but I knew that he couldn't be a soldier. I know you can't be gay and be a soldier. I *know* that, but I let it go with Jake, he was different. Then one day he touched me in the wrong kind of way. In a bad way. It was too much, him holding me, the kissing. His tight black hole. The last time he touched me I punched him square in the face and knocked him across the hooch. He cried; he would, he was a fag. It was that next morning that I told Lieberman and Fitch that Jake was a fag. It was that same night that we kicked him to death like he was a diseased dog.

There was a curfew. There are always fucking curfews. At least it means that these bastards have to stay in their fucking houses and take a day off from hating us and trying to kill us. But that's when you get complacent. That's when your guard drops. Curfews are a good day to catch the bastards though – you can always get a tip-off from these pigs, that's the thing, you can never trust these Arabs, always betray each other, always on the lookout for a bit of cash. They would do anything for a bit of cash; turn in their own mother, kill their own brother. They are scum. I hate them, we all do, every fucking one of them. These cunts flew planes into the World Trade Centre for fuck's sake, how mental is that? That's why I'm here, that's why we are all here. Fucking revenge. Revenge and to teach these bastards how life really should be lived.

Regardless of the curfew I keep my finger on the trigger as we move through the el Jihad district. I don't trust these nutters not to come out and take pot shots at me. It happens. That's when you die. By taking your eye off the ball. This whole fucking city is alive with killers and mental cases. I'm sure they say the same about us. United? We are supposed to be but it will never happen. It's a city full of rats all dancing to the tune of Osama bin Laden. He was the sensible one, he fucked off to the mountains; you don't see him with a suicide vest on, do you? It surprises me that no one questions that fact, no one questions the fact that he is the one who tells all these dudes to go blow up planes, to go blow up themselves, to go blow up innocents; he tells them how glorious death is and yet he runs like a pussy. Cunt. Why don't they see it is all about money and fucking power? I see something move and instinctively shoot. I miss, three rounds clap out of the chamber, thud, thud, thud. You never know how dull a bullet sounds until you hear it. The Humvee slows but doesn't stop; I look to shoot again but see nothing. Probably a cat. We move on, no point looking for one insurgent when we are about to round up a whole houseful.

We wait, the team waits; we are together inside this metal vessel. Waiting for orders, waiting to slide out and attack. My heart pounds through my ribcage; it must be loud. I think I can almost hear everyone else's heart pounding too. We wait, wait to slide out of the back of the truck; waiting, nearly ready to go now that dusk has fallen. Waiting, almost ready now that a cloak of darkness is enveloping everything. Waiting for the word to go. These are the longest, hottest moments of my life, they always are. My stomach feels the excitement, my groin feels the excitement, I look at the other guys, I wonder if they too feel the way I do. I look at each of the five of them in turn, even to me it's a scary look, all these dudes sitting in full combat gear and body armour, they grip their guns in their tense hands and you know they would kill anything that got in their way without a second thought. I close my eyes and think about Jake, dead Jake, murdered Jake – this is Jake's revenge. I'm aware the guys around me are talking about girls, about fucking those Iraqi girls inside the house. The wives of the terrorists. Call it a perk of the job. Why do I think about Jake? Then we go. One by one, out of the heat of the truck into the heat of the night. In turn we slip out of the vehicles and onto the dusty road, one foot at a time, slowly, quietly. The dust is soft but now familiar beneath my boot. The air is hot on my body. Or I imagine it would be if I could feel anything on my skin, but I can't due to the armour. It's stifling and I can't breathe; I feel sick.

'These cunts are going to die,' Martinez whispers into my face, his breath hot and stale. I nod. We spread out and form a single-file line following the lead – it reminds me of a game we used to play when I was a kid. We move along the road under the cover of darkness.

We move slowly and sporadically. Silently. I am like a drunk in the night as I list and lurch along the empty dark road under the weight of my equipment, hands out for balance, gripping and grabbing at the small stone wall that runs beside me, the wall having somehow thus far avoided being damaged by the war. There are not many things in Baghdad that can claim that fact. The road surface is uneven and the stones turn my ankle over several times. The wall is needed by me, but then I'm not the only one struggling in the heat of the night; ahead and behind we all stagger, a line of drunks, overloaded with bags and weapons, masks and armour. It's not easy. In fact it's hard. Fucking hard. I trip and fall against the wall, it hurts, but I push up and carry on. It's what we all do. It hurts. Everything hurts, but we just push up and carry on.

I shuffle along in the darkness. I notice that I am both aroused and scared shitless at the same time. Physically I feel that I am half-crouching, half-crawling, half-hunched, but I can't be because that would make me one-and-a-half people. Maybe I am carrying Jake too. But that would make him half a person, or maybe more likely me half a person. The air is full of fear, from me, from the other guys, from the Iraqis. I know that these right now are the moments when I am most likely to get killed. These are the moments that my parents should worry about. This is the time I want to stand up and scream. This is the time to say fuck you all, go mental and kill all these fucking towel heads, kill all these fucking soldiers, kill every cunt for just fucking up everything. But I don't scream; I move forward with my gun in my hand and those stinging tears in my eyes. I move forward because it's my job to move forward. I'm a soldier. America's finest. And this is what I do although I shouldn't be doing it because of what I am. It doesn't make me a bad soldier, because I'm not, I'm one of the best. But that doesn't matter, not here, not in the army. It's not a case of being good, it's a case of being right, and somehow I know that I am not right. It's not right. So pushing forward in the way I am, pushing forward to reach and destroy our common enemy is right for the country but it's not right for me to be doing it. I may be willing to die for my homeland, but my homeland regards my life as less worthy than that of the other soldiers. Somehow I know this is true and in my heart, the place where I know I have always wanted to be a solider, I can't understand this. I don't understand this bloody-minded determination to remove from me all that I ever wanted to be just because I am me. For something that neither interferes nor matters. But it does matter. It matters a lot. And I know my life doesn't work anymore.

I notice that the silence on the street is deafening. It's funny how that happens. How silence can be so loud. I look at the houses that I crawl past, for I am crawling now, but these houses are nondescript and loudly silent too. I can't believe these people practically live under house arrest due to us invaders. I can't believe what these poor bastards have to put up with because it's America's will. The will and quest for black gold and keeping oil below ten dollars a barrel. It's all about America. These fucks live in their little houses with no power, no phones and no electricity because that is America's will, a will that is enforced because we invaded this country in order to keep our cars running. I'm sure that it's great that we got rid of Saddam, and I'm sure that this kind of freedom is exactly what they had in mind when the US troops invaded. Liberation and freedom. It's no wonder some of them want Saddam back. To most it's quite the preferable option. But that's a secret, isn't it?

'Hughes.' That's me. Sergeant Anderson is in my face and talking to me.

'Sir,' I reply. My head swimming with the fact that he is a useless piece of shit I only call sir because it is what I am trained to do.

'As the plan.' Sweat runs down his face and his breath is cooler on me than the night air that surrounds me. 'On my command, you follow in fourth and you take the upstairs room to the right.' His words gush but I know the plan, we've been through it twenty times. 'OK?' He seeks confirmation that I know what I am doing. Why is he questioning me? Do I look like I'm hearing voices in my head and losing the plot? Can they hear that too? I thought all of that stayed in my head. The sergeant's drawl snaps at me, it's thick and slow, his voice saying absolutely everything there is to know about the man within. That deep southern drawl grates at me, I'm from the south too but I don't speak like it. But then I guess again I am in the minority; every other cunt around me is from the deep south and has the drawl, in fact most of the fuckers in the army are from the south, the deep south… a breeding ground for the army, a place where you are born with an expiry date on your fucking forehead. I wonder what percentage of the war dead are kids from the south. I hate my country. I hate this army. I could have done something else with my life but chose not to; for the rest of these poor fuckers this is as good as it gets.

'Sir.' I nod and look in his eyes. One word is enough to assure him I am on the ball on this one. He nods and moves on. I look at his fat arse as he scrambles off in the dust, watching as he relays the message to the other drunks leaning against the wall. He's off in the distance and once more I wait for the word to go. Always waiting for someone to tell you when to go. I'm getting fucked off with being told when it's time to go. Very soon it's time to go, and it will be my own voice that tells me when this time is. The sarge scrambles back past; he doesn't stop this time and I know it's almost show time.

The word 'Go' from the front means we are up again. I see the arm motion forward in a kind of medieval charge movement. And we do – charge, that is. Up and moving. Suddenly I'm with it and suddenly I seem much less wobbly on my feet, the perpetual motion doing its job of keeping me from falling flat on the ground. I don't use the wall at all as we rush forward; I'm standing higher this time, boots stomping on the ground, not worried about noise now as the ragheads couldn't flee at this stage even if they wanted to. We move faster, I feel Morse behind me, running into me, snapping at my heels; he is a greyhound that has seen the rabbit.

We turn and I follow. My heart beats faster. The wall, the path, the house, the door, the bang. It happens in seconds. I glance over my shoulder, the whole distance we have covered in the last ten minutes is no more than two hundred yards, I see the trucks; they sit in the distance and suddenly it's real. Suddenly it's real and I am here doing my job, doing what I pledged to do for my country. It's a shame my country won't do something for me.

Regardless, I do what I am told – I would, I'm a soldier. Here to help. Here to liberate Iraq. That is my duty and I'll do it to the bitter end. Whichever end that may be. I mean, who am I to question what goes on – surely someone would have thought about things, someone at some stage would have said, 'And you're sure Iraq will be stable if we topple Saddam?' Well maybe not those words but the thought must have crossed their minds right? Did someone believe that Saddam was the problem between Sunni and Shi'ite across this Arab land – was this all his doing? Did someone honestly think these savages I see killing my friends and killing each other give a fuck if Saddam was around or not? I'm crying now but nobody sees.

My goggles are on. We are in, I hear shouting, I see people running at me. I remember my orders; upstairs and secure the front room to the right.

'Allah! Allah!' The woman is in my face, she claws at me as I hear one round of gunfire being discharged somewhere in the back of the house. I want to take her in my arms and hold her, but I don't. Instead I swing the gun and the rifle catches her on the cheek and her face splits. She hits the floor. Her husband, I guess it's her husband, runs to her and bends over her in a gallant show of love and protection. I wonder which number of the four wives Islam permits him to have she is. I kick him in the ribs like you would a rabid dog. He yelps and rolls over and the next thing I know is that my rifle points into his face, the metal touches his head between his eyes; all I have to do is squeeze, it would be a simple, clean, justified execution. I know he would pull the trigger and kill me in a heartbeat. But I don't. I'm not like that. His brown eyes sigh the relief that flows though his veins. I simply look away from him, lift my gun and walk off. I had the power to give him life or to take it away. Like I said, being a soldier here gives you the power of God. As my feet hit the stairs I hear another gunshot behind me. It was him or her that got killed. The order didn't matter, the other wouldn't be long behind. I hear a second shot.

I reach the top of the stairs and see Hummer and Bruno pushing a teenage girl back into the bedroom. I feel hot, I feel dizzy. This place is bare. Bare and dark. This is no home. The cries downstairs are drowned out by more gunshots. No neighbours come to help, no one dares, most have fled, or those that could afford to have. Those that remain now cower behind blacked-out windows not wanting to be involved. This is what is left in Iraq; people who have no skills, money or talent. Those that could run went straight out of the back door when Americans came in the front. What is left is a land of the poor and unlucky which is run on fear and corruption. Good job for the coalition. Some would say these raids and rapes add to the hatred of us. I would probably agree.

I turn to my right and see nothing but outlines and shadows, my gun is cocked and my finger on the trigger. Like everyone else, all I want to do is kill. It's been only seconds but seems like minutes, I'm in a bedroom. A boy. He shouts at me in Arabic. I say *'Durka durka'* back in answer to him; it's a piss-take from a movie I saw. I can't speak Arabic and have no intention of learning it, as such I have no idea what he shouts at me. Probably something like don't butcher me and my family. What he wants is to run but I'm not going to let that happen. The rifle butt to the face works and he hits the deck. I stand over him in my full armour with my M16 pointing in his face. What is he? Old enough is what he is. That said, it really didn't matter if he wasn't.

I say he was a boy but here he is all man. Probably fifteen but you can never tell with these ragheads. He has a beard growing. His is different though, you know, that patchy, wiry hair that young men grow. Well, young men here, they all grow it, the facial hair thing, it's to do with religion. Fuck that religion thing. The facial hair thing looks cute though, and unlike the other bastards around here he still has a look of innocence about him. I want to touch it, to touch him.

I lift him from the floor by the arm, my hand gripping his wrist as he tries to twist away from me, my other hand takes his whole throat in one simple manoeuvre. I have control here; this is just the struggle you expect from anything that fears for its life. I squeeze his throat and hold him there at arm's length, his eyes on mine and then my eyes wandering down and taking in the fact that he wears nothing but a pair of pants, the old-style Y-fronts, blue. Blue I think, but the light is bad. Back to his eyes, those Arab eyes. Are they mysteriously beautiful or deeply devious – I never can tell and fall off the fence on to the side of caution. He is a rat like the rest of them.

I hear the girl scream next door and then I hear laughing from Bruno. They are fucking her. Downstairs is quiet which I take to mean the inter-rogation has begun. We will be here for no more than thirty minutes. The Americans will be the only ones that now leave this house alive.

I let go of his throat but he stays close. I don't know if he is being brave or stupid. Probably brave because he is an Arab and would want to show the infidel he is not afraid. His torso is slim and I can see the goosebumps on it – I sense that his olive skin is actually perfect and blemish-free; on these Arab boys it usually is. His face is more European than Arabic and those shadowy features framed with the hair beyond his years are utterly desirable and completely beautiful. I can't stop myself wanting him and I really don't want to. I'm back over the fence and now find those eyes mysterious. I hear Bruno laugh again. I have a hard-on. I grab the Arab boy by the wrist but he knows already. I sense he has been here before. Probably raped by all the elders in his family since he was young, and if he has been really unlucky he would have been raped by a couple of American soldiers since the occupation too. If that's the case then it'll be easier for me, and so I push on. I don't take my armour off, experience has taught me that you don't need to, not to fuck. I fucked Jake in the Humvee once in full armour. It's not hard to get your cock out of the battle-dress uniform. I slide my gun onto the floor, making sure it is far enough from him and close enough to me for when I need to use it. He doesn't fight. He doesn't protest. My hand on his wrist is firm and I walk him backwards towards the bed, the small cot in the corner of the room. As I walk him with one hand I pull my dick free from my combats with the other. It is hard. Throbbing. The thrill of the fight, of the chase, of the war. The thrill of beating these cunts.

He bends over. I didn't push him over. It throws me a bit that he rests his own weight on his elbows and presents his bare arse to me by pulling down his own pants. I take my glove off, I'm not allowed to but I do. We can't break code by breaking uniform rules, but if I'm quick no one will know. I spit into my hand and rub it into my cock. God, I'm fucking hard. I spit again, a mixture of spit and chewing tobacco comes out. This time it lands square between the boy's arse cheeks at the base of his spine. I'd always been good at spitting. Daddy taught me. I used to spit with Tommy at high school. But back then most high school and college nights were spent sucking and swallowing rather than spitting.

I traced my thumb through the groove of his arse cheeks and then my thumb disappeared inside his firm but welcoming hole; I love arses. My cock was wet and I simply stepped forward. He relaxed his arse as the tip of my cock touched his hole and with ease I slipped inside. He didn't make a sound. I pushed my cock all the way home, which is not easy for someone to take, but he did, in silence. Not even a whimper. I placed a hand on each of his hips and held them there, I wasn't gentle. I pulled his arse to me and I fucked him. I fucked him raw and hard. My cock was sore because of the way I fucked him. That spit soon dried. My cock soon dried but I fucked him regardless. Fucking them. Fucking those Arab cunts. I'd fuck them for fucking killing my friends. Fuck them and fuck their religion and their rules. I was hard and high. I wanted to fuck him because of what they had done. But that wasn't it, was it? My gloveless hand traced the arch of his back, traced the curve of the boy's arse cheek. I slowed the fuck into sex. I touched him, my hand on his shoulder, on his arm and then his face. My index finger brushing through the hair on his chin. I fucked and touched him from behind but this was still intimacy. He let me do it and he didn't respond. But then my finger touched his lips. At first it was a quiver and it was slight but it was definite, he kissed it, his lips kissed my finger and my heart skipped.

It was the head rush that I felt. And the flutter in my heart. I rubbed a finger over his lips again and once more he kissed it. My other hand moved down, down on to his cut cock and heavy hanging balls. I touched them, his cock was rock hard, not so big but as hard as anything, yet he didn't move, his arms still holding on to the bed frame as my cock slipped in and out of his battered arsehole. I stroked his cock once, twice and then took hold of it in my hand, a third and fourth stroke before his arse started to buck into me, his arse intensifying my strokes into him, him getting off… me… getting off. I slowed, I pulled at his cock, touching, feeling, enjoying him. But what was this? Me getting off, I was hard, I wanted to… what? I wanted to fuck these cunts. I wanted to fuck them all. No, I wanted to fuck him. He trembled as he came in my hand, my free arm holding his waist as he shot time and again, his hot come in my hand made me explode, and I filled his arse, probably twice over. My dick flopped out. I fucked him. And it wasn't because I wanted to fuck them, it was because I wanted to fuck him. That boy. That boy. Any boy. I always wanted to. I did with Tommy but that was school fun and learning about the birds and the bees. I did with Jake. I did with others but that was army fun. I'd been a soldier for twelve years now and that was all it was, army fun. It was all it was allowed to be. But it wasn't anymore. I wanted him, I wanted a man, a boy, someone to love but I had never been allowed to.

He didn't put his pants back on. He was too scared to move. I could see some of my come running down his leg where it had dribbled out of his arse yet he didn't brush it away. He looked at me with those beautiful eyes and simply said, 'Thank you, sir.' His English was poor but that was what he said. Bruno shouted, a girl screamed and then there was a gunshot. I put my knob back in my pants and picked up my gun from the floor. The boy watched every step but didn't move from that spot, he stared at my face as my come ran down the inside of his leg. He was beautiful. He was God's creation. He was a stunning Arab kid who would do nothing but be part of the cycle of violence destined to go on forever. I looked into his eyes and had an urge to kiss those heavy Arab lips, and so I did. With an M16 most people let you do anything. I kissed him full on the lips, slightly at first and then passionately. He responded with a kiss that was more than anything I would have known how to do when I was fifteen. It was the most intense kiss of my life, and it was a kiss goodbye. I knew that it was the kiss of death. I pulled him close and smelled his hair. I felt complete and I knew who I was. Physical contact; that thing you miss most. That thing I miss from Tommy, that thing I miss from Jake. That thing I want from this boy. And so the time was now.

Tears rolled down my face. This boy, this room, this house, this country. It's not real. It's all shit. This was it though. I let him go from my embrace but he didn't back away. I know what I've been taught from day one, and being taught the rules doesn't mean it is something written in a rule book. It's the way of the army. But it's what I am and it's not good enough for them. So what I am is wrong and what they do is not. Women scream downstairs and then more shots go off.

'Moving out.' The cry comes from the sarge. The code and clue that everyone is dead and the mission is accomplished. Another group of terrorists killed by the Iraqi police helped out by American information. Bullshit announcements like this one are frequent. It's an excuse for us to use our guns and get laid.

'Moving out.' There's a bang at the door. It's time for me to go.

They raped and killed a whole house here tonight. But you know, for me, what is worse is what I now know. I know they will hate me more than the Arabs they just slaughtered. And what I also know is that I deserve it. I used to think I deserved it for being what I am. But things are different now. I deserve it for doing what I did and for letting them do it too. For being involved and for not stopping it. I deserve all that comes my way because I am, and always have been, so fucking weak. I'm a soldier. And I'm gay. I can be nothing else and those two things don't go hand in hand.

I fucked that boy because I wanted him. I loved Jake and they made me kill him because he was a fag. I did it because I'm a gutless cunt. Not anymore. I'll face the consequences of my actions right now. See how America reports me, you won't see those fuckers crying when I return home, America's latest fallen soldier.

'Get under your bed and shut the fuck up,' I whisper to the boy and kiss his lips one last time. I point under the bed and with tears in his eyes he does as he is told. America has killed his whole family, he is now alone in this world and all I want to do is look after him yet it is my job to kill him. I find that now just simply too hard to swallow. He is Jake, he is lying there and this is my chance to do the right thing. My chance to put things right at least.

'Moving out.' The bang on the door again. 'Finish up with whatever you're fucking and get your arse out here, Hughes.' The sarge is getting pissed at me, I hear three more fisty bangs on the door and then his footsteps going down the stairs.

They are all waiting for me.

But I'm a fag. And if they knew that they would never wait.

And so I'll never come because I don't belong.

I wanted to fuck him. I wanted the boy. I wanted Jake and I wanted to be free. But I am a soldier and the two just don't mix.

Baghdad never sleeps, the air is always filled with gunfire. Strangely enough you don't hear the gunfire anymore, it's white noise, a noise that is there so constantly and expectantly until it is gone. For me Baghdad and gunfire remind me of Texas and the birds. A noise, a sound. The sound of the birds is around us every day we spend on this earth but we don't hear it unless we listen, we don't appreciate it, but it is there. It is only there until it is gone and only then do we appreciate and miss it. There are no birds in Baghdad and I miss that. But now I don't hear the explosions or bangs and I wonder if one day I would have strangely missed that noise too. Will I ever let the birds back in? One more shot is all it takes. I look at the bed, the boy lies under it, his little legs stick out from beneath it. I lift the gun and take as best an aim as I can. One more shot and it will all be over. The metal of the gun barrel is strangely warm and somehow already tastes of blood. I swallow. I hear birds instead of explosions. I think of home, of growing up. I hope Daddy feels guilty, as this is all his fault. I bite the barrel and close my eyes. Life is too long. I squeeze the trigger knowing nothing in life will please me more than death. Suddenly I know what the suicide bombers have flashing through their minds just before they die. And now I have, for one split second, a whole new understanding of this fight. Maybe it is all better when it is all over.

I don't hear the bang. Just the birds.

Atti Innominabili

Michael Davidson

The newspaper reported the affair in the phrases which Italian journalism keeps for the sexual involvement of the young. The two boys were *mini-bruti* – 'mini' being the current adjective for anything exiguous or juvenile, and 'bruto', beast or animal, the invariable pejorative for a person sexually interested in the immature, even if immature himself. The girl, a sweet-faced but hardened whore of fourteen who got no worse than a slight stab wound, was in one paragraph the 'dainty victim' and in another a 'mini-Messalina'; and all three of them, in the headlines, were *ragazzi terribili* – almost any youngster before a judge is 'terrible' from the word go. The catalogue of accusations which the press found the boys guilty of long before they got to court was so carefully comprehensive that while acquittal was probable on most charges, conviction was certain on some. The charges included: *atti innominabili* in a public place; obscene behaviour in public; abetting prostitution; abetting prostitution by a minor; carnal violence; libidinous assault on a minor; corruption of minors of both sexes... since in this affair all three were minors, though in different grades of minority, the police could construct a triangle of cross-corruption. (The 'unmentionable acts' of the first charge generally connote in police language some form of masturbation, solitary or in company.) Against the younger boy who unluckily flourished the knife, these charges were preferred in addition: attempted murder, malicious wounding, armed assault, possession of an unlawful weapon, carrying a blade more than so many centimetres long...

The bigger boy, seventeen years old, was sent to prison. The judge said that no person of either sex in the town was safe from moral contamination so long as he was among them. The other, just sixteen, was put away in an 'institution for re-education', the judge remarking that he was corrupt, violent and perverted and required a long period of re-education. The girl, 'for her own good and that of the boys in her neighbourhood', was placed in the care of some nuns who specialised in the 're-education' of delinquent girls as well as in their spiritual salvation. The newspaper called the affair a mini drama of juvenile jealousy over a girl. In fact, it was a story of a boy's jealousy over a boy.

A small fishing town, hardly more than a village, called San Cataldo del Golfo stands just inside the south-eastern heel of Italy in the Gulf of Taranto, where the Italian waters of the Ionian Sea quickly merge with the Greek. The houses, stacked like dominoes over a low rocky plateau and bright with balconies, are washed in pale tones of blue, lemon and pink and seem to hang twenty feet above the harbour. Two paved jetties of solid stone enclose the port; in the morning the fishing smacks lie alongside and their catches of the night are auctioned there and then to the wholesalers waiting on the quay. Almost the whole town lives from fish, the catching or canning of it or the selling and packing and freezing and marketing of it, or from the culture of mussels for which, like Taranto further up the Gulf, San Cataldo is famous. At certain parts of the foreshore, where the seabed is suitable and the water shallow and sheltered, the mussels are strung from poles in festoons like flowers garlanded over a pergola, a kind of marine rose-growing which one might fancy some retired triton taking up as a hobby in his old age. With Taranto, too, San Cataldo shares as patron saint the adventurous and frequently miraculous Irish missionary after whom the place is named.

A high sea wall screens the southern jetty from the south-east gales; and is reinforced on the weather side by a tremendous bulwark of concrete blocks piled along a foundation of natural rock. These rocks and huge cubes of concrete make a perfect scampering ground for certain boys of the neighbourhood and also, in the parched days of summer, provide innumerable couches of stone on which they can lie supine between swims. Throughout the three baking months, the same group of boys daily speckled these rocks with their bodies – like a club, they were, exclusive and clannish; they all lived in the *palazzo*, a modern block of flats clad in brutal ferroconcrete, which towered above the sea wall; it wasn't often that a 'foreigner' to these flats came onto the rocks. By climbing onto the top of the wall, the boys could shout out messages to their mothers and sisters hanging out the washing on the balconies.

One of the first to arrive on the rocks in the morning, once the school holidays had started, was Dante: a solemn yet cherubic blond who by July had the skin off his nose and a fantasy of freckles over his white shoulders. Though hardly fourteen, Dante was already at a high school, a studious and insatiably lubricous scholar; he would bring an armful of books and pass the hours studying either Latin syntax or his own genitals. His friends called him 'Dand–day', an inflexion puzzling to a stranger. Asked what this nickname stood for, he repeated 'Dand–day', himself using the local pronunciation, and added crushingly: 'Alighieri, you know.' Towards eleven o'clock, Alduccio (a double diminutive for Cataldo) would arrive. He was about fourteen, had left school and was working as a *pescivendolo*, a fish-hawker, a mousy, silent person whom everybody liked and nobody bothered about. Next Tonino and Tanino (Antonio and Gaetano); they almost always arrived together, but if one was there first, he would seem restless and distracted until joined by the other. Tonino, who was seventeen, was employed at night, watching over an uncle's 'mussels garden' a mile down the coast. Tanino, not quite sixteen, helped his father in the fruit market in the early hours of the day.

Then half a dozen more: Mimino, Ninino, Pepino and the rest. The biggest was Mimino, who must have been eighteen, and the youngest his eleven-year-old brother. They were all friends; their few little quarrels but loud and short. Along this sequestered 'lido' of concrete and polished brown rock, the boys disposed themselves over the most comfortable slabs they could grab – first come, first served; or in the niches in between. Only Tonino and Tanino had a pitch tacitly reserved for them, a smooth slope of rock, ample and slightly concave and looking full into the southern sun.

At one point the foundation rocks of this rampart were indented to form a tiny creek, its sides just right for plopping into the water like a seal or leaping from it like a salmon. One overhanging boulder made a good diving platform. This was a perfect bathing place, where few strangers intruded. Droves of large jellyfish called 'medusas', fortunately without sting, swayed slowly by with the current and their own curious muscular impulsion, like obese and slightly tipsy dowagers. Under the lip of the little creek, sea slugs lay blindly, like disagreeable sausages; and a cuttlefish was sometimes dosing, ready to vomit ink if disturbed.

Sea urchins encrusted the rocks below the waterline, limpets and the like above; the boys would borrow Tanino's knife for gouging these creatures free so as to eat them raw. On a still day the translucent sea was like glass through which every detail of the bottom could be seen and clouds of small fish flashed. Fifty yards offshore a small 'mussels garden' stretched its garlands; and beyond that a reef of dark rock ran parallel with the coast, just topping the water so that in a breathless sea the lapping ripples were like fingers running through brown hair. In this channel, between shore and reef, an old grumbling boatman laid his crayfish pots, shaped like wicker lanterns and weighted with stones. He dropped his pots in the evening, and each mid-morning, when the boys were on the rocks, sculled himself over the course, picking up each pot with a boathook and extracting his prey. This sour octogenarian daily accused the boys of interfering with his pots: they did often dive down like ducks to have a look, like any boy would, but never hauled one up nor touched a fish. Yet a continuing war was fought between this crusty old man and the young tritons of the rocks; he ranted at them and told them he would 'tell their fathers' and they replied by shouting back obscenities and derisively wagging their cocks. This put him in a frenzy of exasperation; he would row in close and try to hit them with an oar; and he'd scream at them about the indecencies he had seen them performing: *he* knew what they got up to among the rocks and he'd tell their fathers about that too! Porkers, animals, that's what they were! He must have forgotten the games he got up to some seventy years ago.

In these circumstances of titillating indolence some display of sensuality was to be expected (they'd have been odd boys if there hadn't been); the luxury of nakedness; the feeling of burning sunshine on the body and the dazzle of a white-hot sky; the warm submission of the velvet waters; the sensuous roughness of hot concrete (whose pitted surface would leave patterns like pokerwork on the boys' flesh); the voluptuousness of physical liberty: these were pressures of delight that few adolescents could be tempted to subdue. But mainly it was a mild boyish sensuality that hardly merited the word sexuality; and basically it was a manifestation of one of mankind's earliest mystic preoccupations. When boys find themselves free of the prohibitions of convention, they instinctively reveal that same fascinated curiosity about their own and their friends' phallic attributes, which is identical to the age-old obsession with the eternal phallic mystery. It

76

isn't 'sex'; it's an involuntary probing of the vast quandary of sex. Of course there was sexual performance too; '*na bella pugnetta*' ('a nice little fistful') was a recurrent matter for merriment and often for action. Occasionally a general, almost competitive, session would spontaneously be held; or one of the boys, perhaps two together, would slide their thin bodies through the slit loopholes of the 'pillbox' that stood above the junction of the sea wall and shore, a forlorn relic of the war. Tonino and Tanino would clamber up to this chamber now and again: their friends tactfully let them go without comment, as if they were a pair of *fidanzanti* going off hand-in-hand for a cuddle. But most people who felt the need of *una pugnetta* did it in front of their mates as unashamedly as blowing their noses. And yet, although such things were pretty frequent and though one could almost smell the suffusion of sensuality that seemed to rise like a heat-haze from the very stones of their languorous sea wall, frankly sexual exercises took a back place: the boys usually were too absorbed by their exertions or delicious inactivities: in and out of the water or simply lying luxuriously doing nothing; absorbed too in their endless gossiping about schools, work, themselves, their friends and the doings in the *palazzo*. Their conversation sometimes soared towards the metaphysical, but it seldom condescended to women and never slumped to politics: probably none of them could have given the name of the ruling prime minister.

'I wonder...' began Alduccio one morning, in that tone of his which indicated that he'd thought a lot before opening his mouth. 'I wonder if there really *are* women with fishes' tails living on the rocks near Punta Grossa?'

'Sirens, you mean,' said Mimino with authority. 'Of course there aren't. That's all legend, just stories they tell you.'

'But after all,' Alduccio pursued, 'there's San Cataldo, and the Madonna, and God – they're real...'

'Oh *God*,' said Mimino contemptuously. 'I grant you San Cataldo and Maria, yes... we know they're real. But the rest's all legend.'

'Well,' said Alduccio with something like Catholic logic, 'if we know San Cataldo and the Madonna are real, why shouldn't the fish women be real too?'

Hare Dante lifted his head from the close scrutiny of his scrotum and observed: 'Our *maestro* says the sirens weren't fish women. In Homer, he says, they were half-woman, half-bird.'

'*E cazzo "I tu" maestro,*' said Mimino flatly. 'Your *maestro*'s a prick. Of course they were fish women, the mermaids were, everybody knows that.'

'But you said just now they weren't real, Mimino,' Alduccio complained.

'Of course they aren't real. They were fish women in the legend. Dand-day's *maestro* is a prick…'

At that moment Tonino and Tanino hoisted themselves like jack-in-the-boxes out of the sea, so that water gushed off their bodies.

'Well anyway,' said one of the others, 'Tonino's got his tame mermaid… look how the water's running of Tanino's arse like off a fish's scales…'

And indeed Tanino's purple-brown skin (its natural swarthiness so deepened under the sun) was darkly glistening like a dolphin's, while water ran in runnels from his buttocks to his ankles.

At this remark the corners of Tonino's mouth turned down in a small amused pout; but the perfect line of Tanino's dogged jaw seemed for a second to harden, as if tightening its grip.

Tonino was a big, loose boy of seventeen, with dark straw hair and the blue eyes of a northern heritage: a thousand years ago this Apulian south was overrun by Teutonic and Norman brigand soldiers. Good nature, indolence and a lazy delight in physical pleasure were written into his rather florid good looks; his body was still slim, but had the lushness of flesh that suggested he would grow over-plump too early. His affection for Tanino was evident; yet one could guess that, like a bee, he would take his sweets where he found them without a backward thought.

Tanino's temperament was as different as his appearance. The darkness of his skin was matched by an almost Eastern beauty and by a perfection of profile that one sees in some Indian dancers. The grace and subtlety of his body was almost serpentine. His devotion to Tonino seemed more emotional than physical: as if his desire lay rather in Tonino's gratification than in his own. It was he who lit their cigarettes, first Tonino's then his own, between his lips; he who fetched bread from a pocket when Tonino was hungry, or, with his penknife, sliced off a piece of the watermelon they'd brought with them; he whose fondling finger ran over Tonino's skin, giving him an ecstasy of luxurious sensation: and he never asked for similar attentions for himself. It was Tonino, not he, who gave the word for a move up to the 'pillbox'. This wasn't because he was younger and smaller and therefore the underling. It was his role to serve the person he wanted: he *needed* a soft and self-indulgent friend who would be made happy by his services. Tonino had become necessary to him, and so had Tonino's character. He wasn't quite sixteen: a stolid-minded boy, simple in most things and with few desires, but stubbornly tenacious of anything he wanted to keep. In the expression of his classic face there was something dogged and clenched, as if once he'd got a hold he wouldn't let go. He knew nothing of his own beauty; the only beauty he knew was what he saw in Tonino.

These two, though members of the *palazzo* 'club' and friends of all the others, seemed somehow isolated within the circle of their own affections. They would shout and play and swim with the other boys, and yet always as a pair, never singly; and then they'd lie down to dry in the sun and slowly snuggle closer to each other in the warm concavity of the slab they'd appropriated. Then the other boys left them to themselves.

The long parched summer moved slowly round, apparently as endlessly as a chain of cogs, each fresh day a duplicate of its forerunner, yesterday forgotten and tomorrow never thought of. To the boys on the rocks the summer seemed to pass in a brazen haze of enjoyment, pass yet never finish.

But for Tonino and Tanino, by the time the first heavy drops of thunder rain were falling in August like shaken almonds, the end was abrupt. One morning they didn't come to the rocks; and they never came again. What had happened came out bit by bit in the boys' talk afterwards; and, later, from the stories of people who had been in court. In one thing the boys were lucky: the case was heard within only a few weeks, instead of months or even the year so many are kept in prison 'awaiting trial'.

A block of flats, in southern Italy, becomes a kind of hamlet on its own, a self-contained colony where people use the same shops and run in and out of each others' homes and where the boys find their friends within the flats and don't look elsewhere. A *palazzo* generally, therefore, has its own *ragazza perduta*, its 'lost girl': one of its daughters who, having had the ill luck to lose her socially indispensable maidenhood, with it loses all reason for not making the best of the loss and turning it to advantage. She becomes, that is, the resident tart. The *palazzo* above the sea wall too had its *ragazza perduta*: a sweet-faced child of fourteen unfortunately named Fortunata; parents in these parts seldom realise until too late what perils may lie dormant in the choice of a name. She looked like a child madonna but had a dangerous temper and kept her fingernails long. There had often been, on the rocks, a bit of banter about poor Fortunata, from crudely guessed-at details of her anatomy to gossip over which boy had been seen whispering to her and which returning conspiratorially from the bomb site behind the *palazzo*. Sometimes the others twitted Tonino: 'Why don't you have a go at Fortunata?' they'd ask. 'Tanino wouldn't mind, would you, Tanino?' But Tonino would grin, with that little turned-down pout: he seemed to say, 'I'm all right as I am – I've got plenty of time ahead...' And Tanino would pick up a stone and throw it, whether in joke or spite it was hard to tell from his set face.

Tanino happened to be passing the alley leading to the bomb site just as they were coming out of it. The back of Fortunata's dark red frock was flecked with the dust of rubble and old whitewash. Some boys who were watching said Tanino looked as if he suddenly flew right off his head. His face seemed to go white under its dark skin and his eyes looked 'like a madman's'. For a moment he stood without moving; then, moaning and blubbering, turned and ran. Nobody saw him again until the next evening when the carbineers brought him home... they'd found him on the road between Lecce and Brindisi. Some boys who went to his house that evening said he wouldn't utter a word, and looked more dogged than ever. He refused to eat; and left the flat almost at once, after getting some cigarette money from his mother.

He'd been waiting outside the *palazzo* half an hour before she came up the hill from the cinema. Fortunata had long made a point of knowing her neighbours' secrets; she kept, in reserve, a mental file on everybody in the flats, and there wasn't much she didn't know about Tanino. At that moment it was misery he was feeling more than anger; but when he began to plead with her, begging her not to take his friend, his mate, his *compagno*, she burst out laughing at him, perhaps out of pique because this beautiful male creature hadn't ever looked at her twice. She shouted at him in dialect a dozen brutal names meaning catamite and queer; and told him spitefully she'd even peeped through the loophole slits and seen what was going on. This turned his wretchedness to rage and he hit her; in a second her fingernails were out and then his knife. They were separated before she got worse than a nick on the arm and he a bleeding cheek. The families would have smoothed the affair over and hushed it up if left to themselves; but suddenly it was too late: the screaming had brought a couple of police whom chance had placed in the nearest coffee bar, and once the police have come into an affair there's no stopping it, and the handcuffs are on. The police came down to the rocks and questioned the boys, from whom they learned little. They also interviewed the old fisherman, from whom they learned a lot. The old man thought they'd caught one of the boys interfering with his crayfish pots, and was anxious to help all he could with any evidence required.

People in court said that Tonino, before and after he was sentenced, appeared totally bewildered; he couldn't understand how he'd done any harm to anybody, nor why he was being locked up. Fortunata kept repeating *ma perchè? ma perchè?* – 'but why, why?' She wanted to deny their right to take away the liberty she'd gained by the great sacrifice of her virginity. As for Tanino… they said he simply looked dazed, as if he'd been left with a lasting concussion; he didn't listen to anything being said about him and wouldn't answer questions. He wasn't interested. That was how three young people started their re-education.

Down on the rocks the boys were talking. 'A pity,' said one, 'Tonino had to have Fortunata. Or a pity Tanino had to mind when he did. Doesn't seem *right* in the *palazzo* now, without them…'

'Tanino was silly not to know he wasn't interested in her beyond the quick poke – like eating a bit of bread between meals…'

'They were saving up to buy a *motoretta* between them, cheaper than a scooter. They used to pool all the money they had…'

'Tonino used to say that what he lost on cigarettes he made up on ices…'

'Don't suppose they're getting many ices where they are now…'

Then Mimino said: 'It's kids' stuff really, two boys together like that. A man wants a woman, that's how it's meant to be. It's all right for kids…'

'It isn't only kids' stuff,' said another. 'Look at those men who come to the Ariston cinema and sit among us boys. And look at Signor Bevilacqua who pays for Vito's clothes and has bought him a *motoretta*. Vito's parents know all about it and don't mind.'

Here Dante interposed. 'It wasn't kids' stuff in the old days. Our *maestro* says it was the Spartan custom for a man to take a boy and teach him and all that, and we're all Spartans here, did you know? Our *maestro* says the Spartans landed at San Cataldo ages ago, and so all of us and our families are really from Sparta.' And he added magisterially: 'In 708 BC, if you're interested.'

'*My* mother didn't come from Sparta,' said Mimino, 'she's from Milan.'

A wind had got up from the north-east, blowing across the peninsula from beyond the Adriatic. There was already a chilly bite in it, and the sea was slapping heavily against the rocks. It was time to go; the boys began lazily putting on their clothes. They were into September: the days of the rocks were almost over.

'It all just shows,' Alduccio observed meditatively, 'how even an ordinary *bella pugnetta* can lead on from one thing to another and another and another…'

The Other Half

Hugh Fleetwood

In theory they had lived together for twenty years. In practice, they probably hadn't spent more than six months under the same roof. When Jean was away, Henry was home; when Henry was off in some obscure part of the world, Jean tended to be in London. It was probably just as well, they agreed. The flat was so small they might have irritated each other if they had spent too much time sharing its limited facilities. As it was, they got on perfectly, and had hardly had a single disagreement in all those years.

The attraction of opposites, some people who knew them said. Henry so dark, heavy, wild-looking and given to gloom; Jean so apparently lightweight not to say superficial, always smiling, charming, and as hard to get hold of as an eel. Others said they complemented one another, were two sides of the same coin.

However they were described – there again, some saying they were lovers, some calling them partners, others merely close friends who found it convenient to share a flat just because they were rarely in it at the same time – everyone agreed that they constituted a perfect couple – and that appearances were misleading.

For while brooding long-haired Henry, who liked to take himself off to lonely places, looked like an archetypal romantic, he was in fact a devout classicist: an essayist, journalist and author who saw it as his task to champion the art, music and literature of Europe's past, and for whom that past had come to an end in the middle of the twentieth century, and been in decline for some time before that. A stickler for correct grammar who believed one couldn't write good English without a knowledge of Latin, he claimed to admire the polished surface rather than the murky depths, and to be by nature a critic rather than a creator.

Jean, in contrast, who played the part of the social butterfly in his daily life, in his work, for those who wished to see it, was anarchic, nihilistic and as bleakly comic as only the serious can be. Most preferred not to see it; a novelist who claimed he was incapable of writing non-fiction because there was no such thing, his books were generally shoved into categories by reviewers and then dismissed for not abiding by the rules of those categories. 'Thrillers that do not thrill.' 'Horror stories that fail to chill.' 'Farces that aren't funny.'

Still, there were enough people who did more or less make out 'the figure in the carpet' that Jean hoped he had woven, and who bought enough of his books – two of which, somewhat surprisingly, had been made into films – to enable him to live without doing any other work except write.

Neither Henry nor Jean was jealous of the work of the other, since professionally too they complemented one another and were not rivals, and both were the other's most perceptive reader and editor.

'Were one of us to encroach on the other's territory,' Henry once said to a friend in Jean's presence, 'I suspect that would be the end of our relationship.'

Words that Jean was to recall one July morning, in the twentieth year of their co-habitation. Just six days before, Henry had departed for his latest 'drift'; this time around some of the states that had once formed part of the Soviet empire: Belarus, Ukraine, Georgia. He was hoping to gather enough material for a series of talks on the BBC World Service if not for a book, and was planning to be away 'Who knows? Three months? Six months? Longer, maybe'.

Going downstairs to check on the mail, Jean found a letter addressed to H. Morton Esq. And since it looked like a business letter, and the two men had always agreed that when they were away business letters should be opened and dealt with, personal letters left for their return, Jean opened it.

It was indeed a business letter of sorts, in that it came from the secretary of the *Societas Carolus Dickensius*, and read as follows.

My dear Henry,
Double apologies. First, for having mentioned this matter to you nine months ago and then not getting back to you immediately, as I

promised. Second, for now having the gall to ask, if you are still interested, whether you could provide us with a couple of thousand words by the end of next week. In case you have wiped the matter entirely from your mind, I would remind you that I proposed asking fifteen or so writers – some Dickens experts, some not – whether they would play but the latest version of that perennial parlour game: suggesting how the other half of *The Mystery of Edwin Drood* might have gone, if Dickens had lived to write it. I procrastinated for the usual and most depressing of reasons: money. That is, a lack of. However, I was talking to one of our members the other day, who has just been left a respectable sum by his late father. He said he would like to underwrite the project in memory of said father – a Dickens lover and one always fascinated by the fragment of *Drood*. The only trouble is: our friend would like the special edition of the magazine to come out on the first anniversary of Papa's death, which is alarmingly soon. Hence the rush.

If you do not have the time or the will to participate in our game I shall quite understand, though I would be grateful for a word to that effect even if I do not deserve one. On the other hand, should you be off on one of your jaunts, obviously you will not see this, and if I do not hear from you fairly soon I will assume that to be the case. In any event, and whenever you read these words, I trust you are in good health and spirits, and look forward to hearing from you and seeing you sooner or later.

Yours very sincerely,

John McFarland

P.S. A further favour. If you *do* feel able to contribute, if you could send me your piece by email I would be most grateful. There again, to save time.

Jean's first reaction was of course to get in touch with John McFarland and say yes, Henry was away, and thus would not be able to write two words on *The Mystery of Edwin Drood*, let alone two thousand. His second, however, was to smile, tell himself, 'Oh, what the hell,' and go to Henry's computer. He couldn't really account for his irresponsibility, but guessed it sprang from a combination of mischievousness and vanity.

The mischievousness was in turn explained by his having met John McFarland a couple of times, and having found him earnest, well-meaning and very dull. It would be fun, he told himself, to pull the leg of such a dry stick. The vanity, on other hand, was the result of his having come late in life to Dickens, having but recently read *Edwin Drood*, and having views on the subject that he wanted to air.

As a slender half-French pupil at an English boarding school, who was despised by most of his thicker classmates – despised still more after he had managed to seduce a number of them – Jean Delacoste had heard in Dickens, when first he had dipped into him, the voice of those very oafs and hypocrites alongside whom he was being educated. A facetious, blustering voice it had seemed to him, that frequently lapsed into senti-mentality, and had the heavy-handed humour of the essentially humour-less. With time, however, just as he had learned to see behind the masks his 'friends' adopted – to see that the man within was someone altogether less confident, brave, charitable and indeed sane – so Jean had come to hear that behind the annoying public voice of Dickens, there was another more insidious voice. That of an author who paid tribute to the kindness, unselfishness and even nobility of which humans were capable, but was ultimately more interested in mankind's cruelty, fear, greed and madness.

Nowhere could that other voice be heard so clearly, as in the first, the only half of *The Mystery of Edwin Drood*.

Jean started his piece much as Henry, he suspected, would have. Saying that in the 1940s, Edmund Wilson had put a cat among the Dickensian pigeons by suggesting that the figure of John Jasper in *Drood* was the embodiment of Dickens's own erotic and violent impulses. Here Jean had paused, and rereading his opening sentence, had wondered whether he should add, after the name of Edmund Wilson, 'the distinguished American critic'. Henry wouldn't have, he knew, either assuming that his readers were familiar with Wilson and his work, or thinking that if they weren't, they should be. Then, having decided that in this case Henry would have been right, and it would be patronising to assume that readers did *not* know who Edmund Wilson was, Jean was just about to continue when he said once more 'Oh, what the hell', deleted his opening sentence and started again.

'Did John Jasper rape his nephew Edwin Drood before murdering him? Yes, I think we must assume that he did. He had probably got near to doing so after the first dinner he had prepared for the young man and Neville Landless. A dinner at which, it is clear, Jasper had served his guests drugged wine. On the night of Drood's disappearance, however, following the young men's second dinner *chez* Jasper, nothing but a violent sexual assault can explain why the opium-addicted music master feels he must kill the person he loves most in the world. (And he undoubtedly *does* kill him, though the murder is not described and some scholars over the years have asserted otherwise.) Of course Dickens would have us believe that Jasper carries out the carefully planned crime because he assumes that Edwin is going to marry "Rosebud", with whom Jasper himself claims to be in love.

'Given however that Rosebud herself is terrified of the twenty-six-year-old music master and sees him – rightly – as a malevolent figure, it is surely more likely that in truth Jasper hates the young woman; hates her just because he thinks she is going to take Edwin from him.

'Throughout that second dinner, Jasper remains unaware of the fact that in reality, Edwin has broken off his engagement to Rosebud. All he does know is that after they have eaten, the hitherto antagonistic Drood and Landless go for a walk together down by the river – having presumably been reconciled. After the walk, Drood returns alone to his uncle's lodgings; whereupon Jasper, unhinged equally by jealousy and by the opium he has taken, declares his love for the young man, carries out his violent assault, and, determined that if he cannot have Edwin Rosebud certainly shall not, strangles him. As he has known for some time that he will have to kill him if he wants to: a) have sex with him, and b) stop anyone else having sex with him. For if he murders Rosebud herself, there will soon be some other young woman after his handsome nephew. (Not to mention the fact that Drood is planning to go off to work in Egypt, so being equally lost to Jasper. That too must be prevented.)

'After the murder, Jasper takes Drood's body down to one of the vaults he has been shown a few days earlier by Durdles, the gravedigger and mason, and covers it in quicklime; unaware that Edwin has a ring in his pocket – the ring he did *not* give to Rosebud – and that it is this ring that will ultimately prove his undoing. Though further evidence of the crime will be provided by the psychotic child Deputy, who has not only seen Jasper burying Drood's body – and tries to blackmail the man on account of it – but has himself been the victim of the music master's advances.

'When in due course Jasper learns that Edwin and Rosebud's engagement had been broken off, he goes nearly mad with grief, thinking for a while that he has killed the young man in vain. Imagining too, perhaps, that he might have persuaded Edwin to give himself to him voluntarily, and that the two of them might even have gone off to Egypt together. For we know that Jasper is bored and frustrated by his life in Cloisterham, and longs for wider horizons. Then, realising that of course this is a fantasy, he concentrates instead on trying to pin the blame for Edwin's disappearance and murder on Neville Landless; before going to Rosebud and telling her that if he cannot have her, he will pursue and destroy not only Neville, but Neville's sister Helena – who has become, in the meantime, Rosebud's friend.

'I would further contend that in this tale not just of violence and eroticism, but of violence and *homo*eroticism, had Dickens lived he would have had Rosebud offer herself to the diabolical (and himself handsome? It is suggested so at the start) Jasper, in an attempt to buy off his wrath. She would have failed, of course, earning only his further contempt and hatred. And having been forced to admit that the dish placed before him that he purportedly covets in fact disgusts him, Jasper would further have realised that he has only pursued the girl, and got her to humiliate herself, so Neville shall not have her. For at this stage he has transferred his lust to Landless, the exotic young man from the East, and in a replay of what has gone before, is determined both to have, and to kill, him. As, almost certainly, at the end of the book he would have; whereupon all the "good" characters in the story – the clergyman Crisparkle, the lawyer Grewgious, Helena, the sailor Tartar – who will end up marrying Rosebud – and Rosebud herself, urged on by the opium-dealing Princess Puffer, by the abused and demented Deputy, and by the mysterious Mr Datcherty (Jasper's natural father?) would have hunted the beast down and, beastly themselves at last, destroyed him.

'It is said that Dickens didn't finish his last book because he was exhausted, in poor health, and had a stroke when he was halfway through it. Surely, though, it is more likely that Dickens was exhausted, in poor health and died because he didn't dare to finish his book, didn't want to, and could see no other way out but death. Either he had to betray his art or his life; and he preferred to do the latter.

'By saying which, I am not trying to suggest that Dickens was a suppressed homosexual, or that he should be included amongst the ranks of "gay writers". He wasn't and he shouldn't – even if, like most people, he could be attracted to those of his own sex (see Steerforth in *David Copperfield*).

'What I would maintain, however, is that Dickens's alter ego, his other half, his double – that is, indeed, his art – is monstrous, and feeds off a knowledge of monstrosity. And though throughout his life the author had pretty much managed to disguise the true face of his art – to put a sometimes sentimental, sometimes comic mask on it – by 1859, he no longer had the will to. For all that he tried to portray Jasper as a drug-taking, black-hearted fiend, he loved Jasper, and Jasper's opium-induced dreams were his dreams. Dreams that, having taken him far around the world, deep beneath the earth's surface, had now taken him too far, too deep. He was afraid that were he to complete *The Mystery of Edwin Drood*, it must have become obvious to all what the real nature of his art was, the real nature of his vision. That of a harsh, pitiless universe in which the stench of the dunghill on which civilisation is built may be relieved by the flowers of humour, love and grace. A universe, nonetheless, and a civilisa-tion, that sustain themselves on violence and murder, and would perish on any other diet. Should he thus betray himself, Dickens was afraid, he too would be hunted down by the good of this earth and destroyed. So he dissimulated until he no longer had the strength to dissimulate.

And then he died.'

Jean dashed all this off in one go, hardly stopping to read through what he had written, hardly bothering to think about what he had written. His essay might well be bunkum, he admitted; even more probably, many of his views might already have been expressed by others. However, while he had been wilfully contentious here and there, and maybe should have organised his thoughts more thoroughly before starting, the ideas he had set down had been pretty much those that had occurred to him when he had read *Edwin Drood*. And they were ideas that, as he had told himself before starting, he had been eager to set down in some form, or at least to express to someone, for a while. Had Henry been around when he had read Dickens's last and uncompleted novel, he would have expressed them to him. But Henry had been in London at the time, while Jean had been staying with his grandmother near Toulouse, trying to get on with a novel. And when, two months later, he returned to London, initially he forgot that he *had* read the book, and then, when he remembered, it was too late: Henry himself was off again.

Something else Jean realised: that he should wait a day or two before looking again at his essay, and either polishing it a little, or – more likely – deleting it. To write *then* to John McFarland and explain that Henry was away. Instead, still feeling mischievous, still because it amused him to imagine McFarland's face when he read his opening sentence, he attached the piece to an email that read simply 'John, herewith Drood piece, hope you can use it, best Henry,' and pressed the send key.

Oh, everyone would be very cross with him, he knew, but, for the third time that day, Jean Delacoste said under his breath, 'Oh what the hell.'

He was already regretting what he had done an hour later, and felt he should phone McFarland, and apologise. The following day he regretted it still more – since still he hadn't got round to making that call.

Four days later regret was compounded by embarrassment; when a further note arrived from the president of the *Societas Carolus Dickensius*. 'Dear Henry, Many thanks for your contribution. I have to confess I have been so frantic I haven't yet had a chance to read it. But knowing how meticulous you always are, I have forwarded it as is to the printers, and told them to get on with it. I look forward to perusing it at leisure in three or four weeks' time, after we have published. In the meantime, may I express again my deep gratitude, and send you my very best wishes. Yours, John.'

Yet – Jean had to admit that his shame was shot through with a certain glee. If Edmund Wilson's innocuous remarks on the subject had caused a rumpus – albeit nearly seventy years ago – how would the readers of the special edition of the *Societas*'s magazine that McFarland was bringing out react to his little effort? Always assuming that the magazine *had* any readers beside McFarland himself. Of course nowadays most people were unshockable; but he had the feeling that the members of the absurdly named *SCD*, should they exist, would by and large resemble their earnest president and editor, and prove exceptions to this rule.

He certainly hoped so.

A month later, when a friend phoned Jean to ask if he had seen an article in that morning's *Daily Mail*, denouncing Henry Morton for his disgusting treatment of a national hero in a little-known literary magazine, Jean felt even more gleeful. If he had hoped to create a bit of a stir in the tiny enclosed world of die-hard Dickens fans, he certainly hadn't imagined that it was possible in the wider world to cause controversy about such matters. Not only were most people unshockable; a still greater number, he assumed, had never read a word of Dickens in their lives. Yet here – on a presumably very slow day for news – a national paper had chosen to blow up his mildly provocative words, and denounce him for trying to do just what he had stated he was *not* trying to do: that is, make out that Charles Dickens was gay. It was almost too good to be true, Jean told himself after he had read the article, and too hilarious for him to feel only shame.

He still felt some degree of shame, however. Not for the piece itself, that really was nothing more than a *jeu d'esprit*, that had the *Mail* not chosen to expose it would have attracted as little attention as thistledown blowing in the wind. Rather, because he had signed the piece with Henry's name, and hadn't bothered, in the weeks since he had committed his folly, to set the matter straight. To begin with he hadn't done so partly out of laziness and partly just because he was embarrassed; then, when he had convinced himself that no one at all, no, not even McFarland, would read what he had written, he had thought it better to let sleeping dogs lie. Now, though – it was not he who was being pilloried in the popular press, made out to be some sort of hysterical proselytising gay fanatic, who was casting aspersions on A Great British Writer. It was Henry. Henry the diligent. Henry the retiring. Henry the respected. And though with any luck by the time Henry returned from wherever he was the controversy would have died down and been forgotten, it was inevitable that he would hear of it and be, rightly, furious. Oh God, Jean thought, what have I done? And perhaps I am guilty not just of mischievousness and vanity, but of unforgivable foolishness and arrogance.

He became still more ashamed when, another month later, the novel he had been working on in France when he had read *Edwin Drood* was published, and to his great surprise was widely reviewed and universally praised. Praised even by – especially by – a critic in the *Daily Mail*, who wrote, amongst other things: 'Delacoste has always been what is called a writer's writer, a cult figure. That is, one whose books do not appeal to and are not read by the general public. *The Other Half* should change that. In the past it was easy to dismiss the underlying seriousness of Delacoste's novels as no more than a mosquito bite on the smooth skin of an otherwise sweet-complexioned tale. Here though, even the least perceptive reader must be aware that the bite is the subject of the book, that the mosquito was carrying some deadly disease, and that however lovely the skin at first sight appears, soon it will be pockmarked and scarred. It is a tragic and compelling story, made more so by the fact that much of it is hilariously funny.'

In the *Guardian*, meanwhile, another critic wrote something that struck Jean as such a coincidence as to be scarcely believable. 'Jean Delacoste has always been obsessed by doubles: by identical twins, egos and alter egos, *doppelgängers*. Just as Dickens at times was similarly obsessed. Think Charles Darnay and Sydney Carton in *A Tale of Two Cities*; think the two faces of John Jasper in *The Mystery of Edwin Drood*. But in Delacoste's previous books, one half always seemed to dominate the other, so that if one wished one could pretend there *was* no other. Here though both halves demand to be recognised, to be taken as the two parts of a whole, and the book is all the better for it.'

Could this critic be a member of the *SCD*, Jean wondered. Could he have read his essay – or perhaps have read the articles about his essay, in the *Mail*, and then the *Sun*, the *Express* and the *Telegraph*? It seemed unlikely. Nevertheless, the mention of Dickens, and of *Drood* in particular, was very strange, and might have led those who believed in the supernatural to see some hidden hand at work.

Something else to talk to Henry about when he returned, Jean thought.

There, though, was the rub. Stung by what he saw as Jean's frivolity and underlying hostility in sending out that essay under his name, or jealous of the success of Jean's new novel, or the victim of some crime or accident, Henry did not return.

And just as neither Jean nor Henry himself were ever to receive any comment from John McFarland about that article that had appeared and the brief stir it had caused, so Jean was never to receive another word from Henry. The man vanished so completely that had his clothes not still been in the flat, had mail not continued to arrive for him, had he not had a sister who became first concerned about his absence, and then frantic, it might have been doubted whether he had ever existed. But existed he had, and now he was gone, and the mystery of his disappearance was to haunt Jean for the rest of his life.

Six years after Henry Morton had last been heard of, and after he had been officially declared dead, one of his nephews, a young English teacher who was not notably witty and was given to using expressions that had long passed out of general usage, wrote to Jean. 'Dear Jean,' the letter started, 'Like you, I can never stop asking myself, what the dickens happened to Uncle Harry?'

Brothers in Arms

Stephen Gray

We were filling in time before Johnny had to do his show at the Festival, taking side routes, so that we would be together a while before the frenzy started up again. I had toured most of South Africa with him by then, but this time his type of show was to be on the main programme.

I was going on about my childhood stay on that branch of the family's farm, along on the right somewhere. Half a century ago the road was all gravel and corrugations, instead of this national security tar. But there behind a clump of cactus was the old grid under the railway bridge. Johnny braked and reversed, but I thought not. There was no radio reception to phone down into the valley and check if it were convenient for my very distant, last surviving relative to receive us. But Johnny insisted.

Down the track my first impression was: overgrown, eroded. The long tin house on its ridge was infested with giant eucalyptus, dying now in the perennial drought. And these days you do not hand over to Old Klaas the sweating horse you were learning to ride and run up onto the veranda for tea and scones. You park with your windscreen full of caution notices and have to beware while half a dozen varied dogs try and savage you through the barbed wire fence.

'Let's go, she won't realise it was us. She will not really remember me,' I said. 'She doesn't want one ever to visit anyway. It was after the war, Johnny, and only because of my bad chest.'

'Let's try a bit. There she comes to investigate.' Johnny jumped out.

'No, stay in the car, please.'

But Johnny was already projecting over to her that he had a big, big surprise, after so long, and sorry to be intruding, but please call the dogs off.

She cracked her whip at them and with snarls and gurgles off they skulked. So she was to have the unexpected pleasure of meeting her long-lost nephew once again. Whether she was still the same body as that spiky war bride, and I in any way resembled the coughing prep school lad of old, was an open question. We would have to tick off the gruesome register of all our dead. Johnny had asked for this.

Turns out that, even though I had never really taken to her, she was lucid and admirably sharp as ever. We had just kept up the Christmas cards in the interim. Only now she had sold off the farm around her, as her beloved son, I gathered, wished not to inherit any of it. She had the right to live on in this desolate enclave. There were some dark shapes in the kitchen, stoking up the same old Aga for a kettle.

We'd had it; now it was going to be family trees and my late husband Ronnie and oh do stay over, no trouble at all. And it had to be separate bedrooms, Johnny's down by the broken gutter at the one end of the veranda, and mine at the other with the special piece of the past, a mosquito net.

'I'll shuffle across when all's calm,' Johnny said, unloading our bags.

'You'll wake the dogs,' I replied.

We explained over tea about Johnny's show, how a one-man performance is no such thing because it needs at least three people: the actor in all his roles (*voila!*); the one at the controls in the light-box; plus me as prompt in the wings, holding his hand, only psychically though. She regretted she never got down to the Festival. But, as she liked to keep in touch, she always received the programme and had noted Johnny's success, although she did not realise I was the one who supported him. These days she couldn't get out much; in fact, not at all, because if she left the place everything would be stolen.

'Just helping out,' I said, meaning the show.

'I suppose everyone brave as Johnny needs a fan,' she replied.

I didn't have the heart to tell her for how many years he had been my partner, nor that these days he was well-known on TV, etc. I signalled to Johnny to be quiet, as it was not our task to update my relative on contemporary mores, marooned as she was, not only in space, but in period. The photo albums were going to appear; she went for them.

There was also to be a raw thunderstorm; duly it came. We certainly couldn't leave in that.

We went through the photo albums twice, once before dinner and once after by lamplight. Johnny enjoyed babbling on about this one was your late husband Ronnie, in the uniform; must have been when he came back, demobbed – after El Alamein, up north. She had been left alone, a newly-wed and pregnant, stuck on their African farm for the duration; she had learned to run it like a man. Ran it ever since. Pages of her blond, puffy-cheeked warrior against the pyramids when he should have been home, supervising the dam-builders; she had over fifty convicts following her instructions... And the time she broke down an airstrip with rollers to get the crop sprayer to land, and how the veld down here bloomed – an orchard of navel oranges, and those mandarins we call them – while up there good men were just ploughed into the dust by Rommel. Hard to believe any of the pointlessness of it now. Gave women their opportunity to prove themselves, she concluded. There was one snap of me as a bag-of-bones in a baggy costume.

Turning in that night I felt glum with appalling revivals of memory. How my late parents had dispatched me here to convalesce, since they desperately wanted me to stay alive – that sort of thing. A teardrop kept accumulating on the edge of my left eye. Gone now, the lot of them, and all the old colonial struggling post-war life. We used to listen to Winston Churchill's voice live, and General Smuts regularly.

Johnny came across with his bare feet all muddy, but I asked him please not to risk it tonight. This was no time for flaunting his gay activism, thanks very much.

'And you used to ride that pony handsome Uncle Ronnie assigned to you, right across the valley, to buy an ice-sucker at the trading store, all on your own. Just to prove you could recover.'

'What of it? Go to your own bed.'

Come to think of it, I had never yet turned Johnny down.

'No one'll notice,' he said.

'Trouble with you is, if I know you, you'll make sure everyone in the whole district does know.'

On his way back he set off the dogs, which meant the worried aunt came out with her hair up. He explained he had been peeing under a shrub, just so as not to disturb her. They had to search the grounds with a torch for intruders.

In the morning I woke to the railway engine's whistle – the daily milk train, still collecting the cans from the bare sidings. On such a farm there was never any rationing as we city children experienced it: for starters there was mealie meal porridge to build me up. Then fried eggs galore, rashers and juices and homemade jams. Then my asthma pump and deep breathing exercises.

Then I heard the old aunt say exactly the words in her slightly cracked voice she had uttered at the other end of my life, at that very loaded table: 'Go and call the master.' It was a command, routinely addressed to whichever maidservant in her frilly cap was bringing in the rack of toast. 'Go and call the master.'

Once Johnny was woken up and duly fortified, I could see how he'd so taken to the aunt that we'd stay another night. But on one condition: run-through on the lawn in the shade of the palm tree, with me in a canvas chair with the script, as audience. There was no point in the aunt being invited to a preview: all she would have seen was a few lewdish contortions, as Johnny always rehearsed mute to save his voice. I lipread, reminding him with gestures. Some of the labourers from the kraal at the back, on their way to the old manager's house, peered through the fence. When Johnny started on his physical theatre bit, they were highly chuffed.

I asked her if we could still hike up to the caves. She didn't think the new owners would mind, even if it was their property now as a sort of consortium. Well, it wasn't *hers* any more, since everyone she had shared it with was dead. Of course there were no longer horses to ride up on (all hacked to bits ages ago).

The cowsheds and paddocks were ruined and thornveld seemed to have reclaimed most of it. But still we managed to toil up the rocks and find one of our prehistoric national treasures: the faintest of Bushman paintings on the sandstone overhang. There were eland and other buck charging in a frieze – Johnny couldn't believe it – with ochreish blobs for, I guess, ant heaps to hide behind. Then the inevitable small stickmen with bows and arrows, following up, their penises pointing forward to their quarry. Although it was all grievously faded, I remembered every item in the puzzle.

Over lunch Johnny kept charming the dry old duck, genuinely delighted with her. I could tell he was a tad jealous of my having such a last limb of a family, which I'd never really told him about. He also actually liked such stern, pickled old ladies; would turn into one himself. He was telling her his heartstring story of how he was an orphan and all, although he did add that he had always been brought up and supported by kind people and lacked for nothing. He did not add that then I had adopted him, as it were, when he was sixteen.

'Relationships never quite go as they're meant to, though, do they?' she commented.

I looked at Johnny; Johnny looked at me.

'Better not to marry at all, I say, if you're not going to make a proper go of it,' she concluded. 'There are plenty of other ways to organise life.'

Johnny's eyes widened.

'Oh, I quite agree,' I added quickly, clearing my throat.

'Especially in South Africa at that time,' she continued. 'It was the war, you see, messed everything up rotten. The Second World War, I mean, Johnny – before you were born. Not the Border War, you know, in Angola, or Mozambique, or what have you. Never the same again. We should not have been caught up in it.'

'You must mean Korea then, do you?' Johnny was getting lost.

'No dear, hardly Korea. But William volunteered for that too, you know, and off they went.'

'Then who is William?' Johnny insisted.

'Oh, leave it,' I said.

'The swarthy one in the photos?' Johnny asked.

'Yes,' she said without batting an eyelid. 'He was my husband's batman at the very start. Then he trained as a fighter pilot later on. People used to think he was coloured, but he wasn't actually.'

'Must have been Welsh,' from Johnny.

'Not with hair that kinky,' I said.

'Earned more medals than your blond and blue-eyed uncle ever did, I may tell you. Couldn't kill himself if he tried. When they returned from the front, Ronnie thought William should be installed as manager. We didn't have to pay him or anything. It was tough on my four year old, who didn't know who Ronnie was, let alone how William fitted in.'

We played dominoes till the cows came home, not that there were many real dairy cows there any more. After dinner, while she was rootling out a nightcap – her own orange liqueur – I flipped the top album open again.

I pointed out the photo to Johnny: my uncle in his military gear, cap as horizontal as the plain about the Sphinx, buttons shining, belt tight, boots aligned, baton under his elbow. As much of a smile for the photographer as such an erect body of his could afford. He had trouble finding razor blades. The faint line under his lower lip indicated he had grazed himself shaving.

Behind him his batman was posed, a step back and to his right. He was equally alert as to how the lens might betray him should he let his shoulders down, his backbone unbend. That was said William from the Cape, who for all those years tromped through the desert with his farmer's son, grinding his blades sharp again on the inside of their tooth glass.

A few cracking pages on there was actually a photo of their foreman – Old Klaas himself – the huge, cranky black man with his sisters and wives and numerous progeny, posed in their Sunday best under the oak tree by the goldfish pond (long gone). Old Klaas, when he wasn't picking me up off that horse, I now realise was the one who actually ran everything day-to-day on the farm. Except my aunt, that is, who relied on him from when he checked in at the kitchen door at dawn until he locked up the chickens and everything else at nightfall, handing over the keys.

'Couldn't have done without Old Klaas,' she said for the umpteenth time. She took out of the archives a copy of *Farmer's Weekly* – with her on the cover as the first Karoo woman farmer to receive their trophy for yields per hectare (of cotton now, I'm sure it was). And there alongside her, but keeping a respectful distance, was battered Old Klaas himself, holding the cup for her. If ever there was a married relationship, that was it – not that the readers of *Farmer's Weekly* could ever have imagined such an accommodation. She had sold all around to the late Klaas's descendants, which explains the derelict surroundings. But one of them had done very well in the city and a luxury hunting lodge was planned, down by the stream, and some wildlife had already been imported. We saw the prospectus; they were disease-free.

'I just get some usufruct,' she explained to Johnny. 'My son gets a bit of timeshare in the game lodge itself as compensation. He can come down and take out up to five head per annum. His wife'll like that; she's the real killer. And their son, he's a genuine Tarzan. Nothing stays alive when he's around.'

'I suppose it'll be gay-friendly too,' said Johnny. I prodded him under the table.

Through the blinds I could see the roofless old manager's house under the quite unbelievable sunset, with a beer drink and dance starting up on the old parking place and a bonfire rising. Whether this was a do to celebrate the return of the tribe to take possession, or a rehearsal for the performance expected to entertain the tourists to come, I could not be sure. I remembered in a panic running flat out in my bare feet, down to the bungalow, my toes pierced with thorns. I was rapping on the little window that was William's bedroom.

'Go and call the master,' she had commanded – but not to me, to the kitchen maid. I had had to outrun her there. I can vividly remember having to prise out bits of thorn from my soles, drawing blood with one of my aunt's sewing needles. Hobbling thereafter.

Later that second night I was the one shuffling across the veranda in what I realised must be a great secret family habit. Every time one of those vile dogs growled at me, I tried to pacify it and proceed a few feet further.

At Johnny's window I saw he had two candles burning inside for cross-lighting. He was mouthing out his very last lines in the direction of the stable door. Then he came to the final gesture, held it.

I opened the top and gave him a fervent (silent) clap, whereupon he retreated, came out for his curtain call and tripped on a slipper. Laughing and being silly, we just fell on the bed, as we liked to do.

The sound was on again. 'Ho hum, guess who's been eavesdropping without a ticket.'

'I'm sure it'll all go all right tomorrow,' I said. 'Don't get all neurotic now, please.'

'With you there it will,' he said. 'You know I have to thank you for *so* much.'

'Oh, shush,' I said.

Later when the candles were sputtering out and it was incredibly dark and quiet, Johnny sat up and said: 'But did she ever discover?'

'Discover what?' I said. 'You shouldn't pay too much attention to all that old stuff. She's got her version of things sorted out all right. When she dies, they'll probably turn this into a curio shop full of native dolls and basket-weaving for the tour buses, shouldn't wonder. Don't worry, she'll have seen to it that they keep a place for her in the family graveyard. She'll be happy to be past history.'

Johnny kissed me; I kissed him. As was our custom, we mimed various endearments to one another, like the sign language of two deaf-and-dumb. Not that we could see much; we worked by instinct.

'Just make sure you don't end up there too before your time,' he said.

I held on to him and started to weep a bit, I'm ashamed to say – which is how soppy I get over Johnny.

But then he pushed me off a bit and asked the question he had to, in order to put it all together: 'Why were you running then – over the pebbles and sheep droppings and prickles? Why with such urgency?'

'I had to warn my beloved uncle.'

'Because he would be caught in bed with his old batman?'

'Yes. I was panting, but I could see past the corner of the lace curtain, in the dark little window. If I shielded my eyes against the daybreak and stopped breathing and stretched up.'

'Why, for God's sake? How old were you? It must have been a hell of a shock.'

'I told you I was only ten, Johnny, and it was very touch and go with me then. Their stupid son was always sent off to boarding school, so that he couldn't be a witness to any such things.'

'But you came through all right – your chesty problem, I mean.'

'Of course,' I said. 'Ah, but it was just a false alarm. It's all way over now.'

Johnny wasn't going to let go. 'So you had to get there *before* that maid came to call her master, and discovered what most probably everybody in the entire neighbourhood knew anyway.'

'Including my aunt.'

'Including your aunt.'

'That the master was actually in the same bed as Sweet William, his manager. William, you know, was quite a husky guy with a great hairy black chest, and pink ankles. And there was my uncle sprawled all over him, as if he'd passed out on top of him. I could see his one bare shoulder was all shiny, and the side of his face was unshaven, inevitably.'

'And it was summer so there was no sheet.'

'Exactly, not a sheet over them. But also I could see their cocks. I don't think I'd ever seen an adult cock of any kind before, but all squashed together, with sweat gleaming and tangled hair. So I banged and shouted for them to hurry and separate and get dressed, before the maid caught them.'

'So that was *your* defining trauma,' Johnny said. 'Why didn't you ever tell me? You just had to find out for yourself what the hell was going on. And you decided which side you were on by letting them know not to be discovered. They were both so playful with you: butch things, like holding you up as you learned to swim in the dam. That was your moment of coming out, even then.'

'Not really,' I said. 'But after that each in his own way was terribly nice to me. So that I wouldn't splab on them to auntie, I suppose. William I fell for with such a crush – could only be unexpressed, of course. But when he had his flying jacket on, and his goggles, boy, was I head over heels. For years my uncle used to cross over late at night, I guess, once the official guests were gone or whatever. William'd shoo him back to do his duty by her every so often. I never saw them again, though, once I was cleared of the TB. But I knew that they'd head off to fight together, whenever they got the chance, and just leave her to it. Neighbourhood watch they ended by organising, so that they could spend nights out on patrol together. When uncle was diagnosed with the cancer, William was the one to nurse him through it all, right to the very end.'

'While she had that Old Klaas to look after? It's highly irregular.'

'More or less. Let's get some sleep before tomorrow.'

Johnny nudged me and gave a stagy sigh: 'Oh, yet another premiere – gasp.'

Lightning was striking now, so that I would have to be careful crossing back, so as not to disturb my aunt's watchdogs once again. Johnny was quite resigned to my leaving, by instinct keeping up appearances before the old-fashioned principles, although these days we made no secret of our liaison (perfectly legal, believe it or not) – unless we should unnecessarily offend others. Johnny was such a performance artist on his own by now, he was becoming better off without such an elderly hanger-on, anyway.

A huge lightning strike across the landscape made me hesitate. It must have wiped out the traditional dancers. You could smell its burn before the rain clattered on the roof.

Johnny grabbed me back for a last hug, 'I suppose when your uncle finally croaked, she kicked suitor William off the domain. She'd had quite enough of all his pampering by then.'

'Not quite,' I remembered. 'She'd had that son out of Ronnie, never mind how useless he was too on the farm. And she had Old Klaas keeping things up. She told William he could stay on if he wished, marooned in his cottage, just as she's stayed on now. At least, that's what I heard.'

'And so then, happy ending?' Johnny persisted, as he always did when relishing someone else's privacy.

'Well, not really,' I tried to shut him up. 'May I use your slippers to ford the puddles?'

He scuffed them towards me.

'Thanks, sweetest,' I said, clutching my pyjamas together against the damp air. 'But you should also know that, after the funeral and uncle was finally planted in the two-hundred-year-old plot – he had the circle over a cross on it, true military style to the end, and all their medals on his coffin – we should go on and check it out tomorrow before we leave, maybe put a flower on it… Apparently Sweet William just took off in auntie's biplane. He had enough fuel to get from here to over the Indian Ocean, emptied his tanks and waited till his engine cut out.'

No applause for William. Bed.

Awkward Relations

John Haylock

'Here comes Cuthbert,' said Barry.

'He looks worried,' said Fred.

'He always looks worried.'

'And he hasn't more to worry about than most of us.'

'Less, I'd say.'

Barry and Fred were sitting on the pavement outside the Café de Paris, Tangier's main observation post. It was between eleven and noon on a bright September morning; there was no wind, but the sea was cold enough for a middle-aged British bachelor not to feel guilty about eschewing a bathe.

Cuthbert, lean, in his late fifties, approached – most of the foreign residents fell within the wide bracket of middle-age, if they weren't downright ancient.

'You look worried, Cuth,' declared Fred.

Cuthbert winced at the abbreviation, sat at the little table and faced the two friends.

'Have a coffee,' suggested Barry.

'No. I don't think I will, thanks. Just had breakfast. What shall I have? Don't want anything, really. Perhaps a mineral water?'

'*Garçon!*' sang out Barry in an imperfect accent to the old, tarbooshed waiter.

'What's the matter? Boy trouble?' conjectured Fred, who was more down-to-earth than Barry. 'Is it Seven League Boots, Curio Shop or Lemon Trousers?' Fred listed the names of Cuthbert's Moroccan friends,

111

nicknamed for convenience since two of them were called Abdul Salam and one Abdul Karim.

'No, nothing like that,' replied Cuthbert, a little haughtily. 'I had a letter yesterday from my brother. He and his wife are coming to stay with me.'

'Hasn't he been knighted?' asked Barry, a respecter of titles.

Cuthbert nodded. He was both proud and ashamed of his brother. 'He has just retired. They're thinking of getting a place abroad. Don't want them here.'

'Course not. What will you do about your Moroccan friends?' asked Fred.

'Certain callers can, I hope, be passed off as grocers' boys and repelled with a banknote. What honestly worries me is that I don't know any presentable people to introduce them to.'

'There's us,' said Barry, indignantly.

Cuthbert had in fact decided that his two English friends were just a bit too camp for his brother and sister-in-law to meet. They were so 'obvious'. Nonetheless, Cuthbert said, albeit without much conviction, 'Of course you, but who else? I don't know any women. Miles and Monica will expect to meet staid married couples.'

Barry put forward a name. 'There's Barbara Palmer. She's been married.'

The aged waiter in the fez, who looked older than the café, placed a glass on the round, steel-rimmed table, opened a plastic bottle and slopped out the mineral water.

'Yes, I've thought of her. She is presentable, but she won't go anywhere without her Moroccan postman.'

'Mohammed's all right,' said Fred. 'He looks very nice out of uniform. I saw him at Colonel Hubbard Wright's the other day and he was better dressed than most of the foreign guests.'

'Were you at the Colonel's?' asked Cuthbert, a little enviously. 'Yes, they could meet the Colonel too. After all, even though he's unmarried and there are suspicions about the way his army career ended and his subsequent activities in the City, he was a colonel; at least, he passes for one here. But my brother is bound to wonder why he never married.'

'Doesn't he worry about you, ducks?' asked Fred, waspishly. 'Grow up, for God's sake! We're in the eighties.'

Cuthbert sipped his mineral water as if it were vintage wine. 'You may be in the fortunate position of having understanding relations. I haven't. I simply couldn't admit to my brother my *penchant* for Lemon Trousers, say. Incidentally, talking about Lemon Trousers, I haven't seen him for weeks. Have you?'

'No,' said Barry. 'We haven't seen him, have we, Fred?'

'No.'

Cuthbert went on brooding over his predicament. He had long ago decided it was prudent to keep his high-minded brother ignorant of his inclinations; his brother, who had led such a different life, a life of hobnobbing with directors, chairmen, lord mayors, cabinet ministers, ambassadors, a routine of shooting grouse, fishing salmon, playing golf, going to Glyndebourne. Nor had Cuthbert ever felt like confiding in his wife, Monica, who to him, partly because she was a woman, had always seemed unapproachable, so utterly decent, so impossibly correct.

Cuthbert left Barry and Fred, crossed the Place de France and seeing old Eustace Colshott sitting alone in the Café de France (it was rumoured that he lusted after one of the waiters), he went over to him.

'My brother and sister-in-law are coming to stay,' he informed Eustace.

'What?' The old man was deaf.

Cuthbert repeated his statement.

'Oh yes.'

'I'd like to bring them up to see your house.'

'Bring them for a drink.'

Eustace lived in a house on the Old Mountain. Rather dilapidated, like its octogenarian owner, the house had a terraced garden, mostly gone to seed, and a splendid view of the Straits. In spite of his unmarried state, Eustace was presentable: because of his years, his aristocratic connections, his distinguished manner and his hobby of painting flowers; it was said that he also painted male nudes, but Cuthbert had never seen any of them. Yes, Cuthbert said to himself as he walked up the Rue de Fez, I can safely introduce Miles and Monica to old Eustace.

What would Monica's reaction be to his first-floor apartment in the Rue des Vignes? The rooms weren't exactly poky and if one went out onto the balcony and looked to the right one could see the foothills of the Rif, but the lavatory tended to regurgitate alarmingly, the bath was stained and the furniture was shoddy. There was nothing in the form of decoration except a pair of banderillas, which Cuthbert, fearing they might be used as weapons, had intended to remove but never had.

Cuthbert's lunch of ham, salad, cheese and a glass of the cheapest Moroccan red wine was over in ten minutes and after another five he was lying on his bed with a three-day-old *Daily Telegraph*. He did not sleep, for each afternoon he hoped the doorbell would ring. It did now and he rose quickly and opened the door to Lemon Trousers, a rather spare young man with a farouche look, a regard that came from the hills. He was about twenty and was not in fact wearing yellow pants but close-fitting jeans; the nickname stuck, however, no matter what colour enclosed his legs, in Cuthbert's mind at least.

Cuthbert said, 'Where you been? You no come long time.' Knowing no Arabic, he found pidgin more effective than grammatical English.

'Casa,' replied the young man.

Invariably Moroccan friends said they had been to Casablanca when they had failed to turn up for a long period. Cuthbert guessed that Lemon Trousers had found a tourist who was more generous than he – it was tacitly understood that residents gave less than visitors; understood, that is, by the residents, not always by the young men.

'Where you get those?' Cuthbert indicated the jeans.

'Casa.'

'You work Casa?'

'Work finish. *Pas travail.* I want passport. You help me get passport.' Lemon Trousers caressed Cuthbert, putting an arm around his shoulders and giving him a rough kiss on the cheek. Cuthbert sighed. He knew he would give the young man twice the normal fee, and a promise to do something about the passport in order to stave off having to part with a larger sum.

'We see,' said Cuthbert.

They went into the bedroom. Lemon Trousers undressed, throwing his shirt and his jeans onto the floor, and there he stood in his swim shorts, which he wore instead of underpants, ready and eager to dive into bed with Cuthbert, who was nearly three times his age.

'He seems to enjoy it,' Cuthbert had often told himself and others. 'It can't only be the money, can it?'

After Lemon Trousers had bathed and dressed, Cuthbert slipped a fifty-dirham banknote into the tight pocket of the jeans. The young man did not examine the money, but he did say, 'You help me get passport, yes?'

'Yes,' Cuthbert weakly agreed.

Lemon Trousers gave Cuthbert a grubby scrap of paper on which in a childish hand was written 'Abdul Salam Salmi' and the name of an official in the local government office.

'OK, come next week,' said Cuthbert, momentarily forgetting about his relations' impending visitation.

They came in the morning in their Mercedes, having motored from England in leisurely stages. Cuthbert met the ferry from Algeciras. Before they saw him, he saw them drive off the ship and motor into the Custom's shed. How English they looked! Miles wearing a Panama hat and Monica a headscarf. Their faces were red from the Spanish sun; their eyes slate-coloured like the skies of winter in the north.

'Hello there!' cried Miles.

'Hello,' replied Cuthbert, a bit flatly. His brother and sister-in-law in the flesh were more formidable than they had been in his imagination. What would their reaction be to the apartment? Cuthbert kissed Monica's proffered cheek and got into the back of the Mercedes. He directed his brother out of the docks and into the Avenue d'Espagne and then up a steep street that descended to the Boulevard Pasteur, the main thorough-fare of the town. While the car hovered hesitantly at the top of the hill waiting to join the stream of traffic in the boulevard, the hawk eyes of Mr Lemon Trousers spotted Cuthbert. The young man's face burst into a huge smile and he waved. Cuthbert pretended not to notice.

'Someone's waving,' said Monica.

'It's nobody,' replied Cuthbert, feebly. 'You can go on now, Miles.'

The Mercedes purred along the boulevard and into the Place de France, where it was held up by a policeman.

Barry and Fred were in the Café de Paris and they too waved at Cuthbert, who, having seen them, quickly looked away.

'More people waving,' said Monica.

'Where?'

The car was signalled forward and Cuthbert busied himself with direct ing his brother. They reached the flat in the Rue des Vignes.

'Here?' asked Miles.

'It's best to park in the shade on the other side.'

'Let's get our things first.'

115

Monica's face fell when they entered the modest apartment. 'Is this it?' she asked, incredulously.

'Your room is at the bottom of the passage on the right.'

Monica went into the room followed by Miles and Cuthbert, both carrying suitcases. The shutters were closed so Cuthbert turned on the light. 'I hope you like a double bed.' He tried the bedside lamp but it failed to work. 'Have to get this mended. Probably needs a new bulb. Now, your towels are here.'

Miles opened the shutters. 'Good God! Look at that!' Monica joined her husband at the window. 'Look at that filth! Look at all that muck in the garden! Cuthbert, come and look!'

'It's the hippies below. They're always asleep when the rubbish van passes so they throw their stuff there.'

'Disgusting!' exclaimed Miles. 'And you do nothing about it?'

'What can I do?'

'I know what I can do.' Miles stumped out of the flat and down the stairs. Presently Monica and Cuthbert could hear the bell of the downstairs flat ringing away.

'He'll never rouse them. They're "out" most of the day.'

'At work?' Monica asked, innocently.

'No, no. By "out" I mean passed out, in a stupor.'

Miles began to bang on the door.

'They'll never answer'

'Are they dangerous?'

'Not in the least. They're keefed up most of the time.'

'Keefed up?'

'High on hash. Drugged.'

'Really, Cuthbert.' Monica looked unhappy.

Miles reappeared with Lemon Trousers.

'I can't stir those people,' said Miles entering the flat. 'Oh, this young man says he wants to see you.'

Cuthbert's stomach turned inside out. 'Oh yes. It's about the bedside lamp. I asked him to call.'

'You said it only needed a bulb,' remarked Miles.

'I think it may be the plug. Come Lemon Trou – I mean Abdul Salam.' Cuthbert pulled Lemon Trousers down the passage to the spare room and shut the door. 'He my brother. Don't come here. Understand?'

In reply came the tearing sound of trousers being unzipped. '*Vas-y*, Mr Cuthbert. It's ready, see?'

The presence of his brother and sister-in-law excited Cuthbert strangely. 'I can't,' he wailed, gripping the fine organ. 'Come after one week at midnight when they sleeping. *Compris?*'

'*D'accord.*' Lemon Trousers adjusted his dress and Cuthbert slipped a banknote into his pocket.

'Fixed the light?' asked Miles, who was in the sitting room with Monica.

'It does need a bulb. Monica, Miles, this is Abdul Salam.' Hands were shaken and the young Moroccan, quite at ease, sat on the divan.

'Speak English?' asked Miles.

'Yes,' answered Lemon Trousers with confidence.

'I'll have to get a new bulb,' announced Cuthbert, regretfully.

'Can't the boy do that?' asked Miles.

'No, I'll go. Abdul Salam, you come with me.'

'I stay.'

Cuthbert cursed inwardly. Abdul Salam would have gone willingly, but Cuthbert now had nothing smaller than a fifty-dirham note on him and he knew he would have difficulty in getting the young man to return the change. Cuthbert hurried out of the flat to the Spanish grocer round the corner. What would Lemon Trousers say to Miles? What would Monica think? The grocer had run out of sixty-watt bulbs and Cuthbert was damned if he was going to put in a hundred-watt one, so he hastened up the street towards the Place de France to another shop, secured the right sort of bulb and sped back. Coming up the stairs of the flat, Cuthbert heard Miles's chairman's voice booming: 'It's disgraceful. And my brother's done nothing about it?'

Arab charm and winning manners had apparently worked on Miles and Monica and they both seemed genuinely sorry for Lemon Trousers because he had not got a passport.

'Look here,' said Miles when Cuthbert entered the sitting room, 'as far as I can understand what this fellow says, you've promised to get him a passport and done nothing about it.'

'It isn't quite like that,' protested Cuthbert.

'You say you get passport,' said Lemon Trousers, a bit accusingly.

'Yes, no, I er, I er said I'd try —'

'Apparently there's some job waiting for him in Brussels,' went on Miles, 'and he can't get out of the country due to some footling bureaucratic regulation. Who's our chap here, Cuthbert?'

'Our chap?'

'Ambassador or consul or whatever we have.'

'I don't know.'

'Don't know? Good God! Thought this young fellow might like a post in England. I've contacts enough. It might be possible, might be, no promises, mind, the job situation is bad in the UK, it might be possible to fix him up as a trainee. Like to go to England?'

'I like,' said Lemon Trousers.

'I'll see what I can do. First my brother, my brother Cuthbert here…'

Lemon Trousers nodded eagerly.

'…he get passport for you.'

'Thank you very much, Mr Cuthbert.' Lemon Trousers rose, shook hands politely with the Bonningtons and smiled his way out of the room.

At the front door, after Cuthbert, who now had change, had given him a ten-dirham note, the young man said, 'Please one more.'

'No.'

Lemon Trousers kissed Cuthbert warmly on the mouth, put a hand on his crotch and won his request.

'Now, go,' Cuthbert whispered.

'When I come?'

'Shush! Next week, *à minuit*.'

'You ask about passport?'

'Yes.'

Lemon Trousers leapt down the stairs giving Cuthbert a triumphant wave from the landing.

Towards the end of luncheon (Cuthbert had been extravagant and bought three swordfish steaks which had been consumed with satisfaction), and just after Cuthbert had put on the table a wedge of Emmenthal and a chunk of butter (both in their paper wrappings), Miles said, 'What are you going to do this afternoon?'

'Do?' asked Cuthbert.

'What plans do you have?'

'None. I invariably rest. Aren't you tired after your journey?'

'No,' grunted Miles, 'but if you, Cuthbert, want to have a siesta –'

'We are very near, if not in, siesta country.'

'Let's take things easy,' put in Monica. 'I for one want to unpack.'

'I shall go for a walk,' declared Miles, testily.

'Steer clear of empty side streets,' warned Cuthbert. 'There's mugging here.'

'I'm perfectly capable of looking after myself.'

'How did you get on, Miles?' asked Cuthbert, a bit apprehensively, after he had poured out tots of whisky from the duty-free bottle his brother had bought on the ferry.

Miles had returned from his walk, Cuthbert had risen from his solitary siesta and Monica had not only unpacked but she had washed up the luncheon things and tidied the kitchen.

'Have to admit the situation of the place is pleasant,' said Miles. 'The view across the Straits and the splendid *plage*. But the people! I was pestered by brats wanting *baksheesh* all the way down to the beach, and by lewd louts as soon as I'd got onto it. I took refuge in one of the bathing establishments, where I met some friends of yours.'

'Oh Christ!' Cuthbert exclaimed to himself, and then, trying to disguise his anxiety, mustered a casual, 'Oh, yes?'

'I don't know their names,' went on Miles, 'but they knew mine. One of them was called Barry something. They've asked us to drinks tomorrow evening. Decent enough of them. Said you'd know the way.'

'Oh Christ!' Cuthbert exclaimed again to himself, and then to Miles he said, 'Yes, I know the way.'

'They didn't seem to have any wives with them. Are they married?'

That confounded the question! It had cropped up so soon! 'No,' Cuthbert said, adding absurdly, 'I don't think they are. Not at the moment, anyway.'

'I was having a joke at your expense about your having to call in an electrician when all that was needed was a new bulb, and Barry's companion said something like 'trousers and league boots' to Barry I couldn't make out what he meant, so I let it pass. Was it some sort of code, d'you suppose?'

'Course not. You must have misheard. If we don't go to the restaurant soon we may not get a table.'

'Splendid,' Monica said, 'I'm ravenous. Do let's go.' And this made Miles move.

During the meal in the almost empty restaurant Cuthbert had an idea.

After the three had returned to the flat and Miles and Monica had retired to their room, Cuthbert crept down the stairs and slipped under the door of the hippies' abode a hundred-dirham banknote and a message which said, 'Please play your player loudly all night and every night this week. Don't ask me why but doing so will help me.'

Barry and Fred shared a spick-and-span white house in a residential district called California. From the terrace there was a view of a bit of sea framed by two hills, known by the foreigners as the 'coupe de champagne'. Barry had been an interior decorator in London and Fred had run a florist's shop in Eastbourne. Their relationship had started as an affair and mellowed into one of friendship; though lust for each other had long since died, mutual affection remained and was only occasionally upset by one or the other falling in 'love' with a Moroccan. But these lapses didn't last long. For most of the time these two retired, middle-aged bachelors succeeded in living in enviable harmony.

The guests whom Barry and Fred had been able to gather at short notice to meet Sir Miles and Lady Bonnington were not very distinguished. They had only managed to recruit Colonel Hubbard Wright, the City smoothy with a shady past, Eustace and Barbara Palmer, the last without her Moroccan friend for once, which was just as well as he usually ponged to high heaven.

In contrast to the impeccably dressed Knight and his Lady (he in dark-blue, she in a sober, flower-patterned dress), Cuthbert, who, though shabby, looked as if he had made an effort, and Colonel Hubbard Wright, who was in quiet grey, the two hosts and Eustace were dressed in casual bits and pieces. Barbara looked smart but informal in a well-cut, sky-blue trouser suit. Barry and Fred, as well as being slightly faded, had medallions dangling on their chests laid bare by unbuttoned shirts. 'Christ!' said Cuthbert to himself. 'Why *must* they advertise?'

'Oh Sir Miles!' Barry flustered up to greet the Bonningtons. 'I want you to meet Eustace Colshott, who's lived here forever, and Mrs Bonnington – I mean Lady, oh what will I say next – this is Colonel Hubbard Wright.' Cuthbert went over to Fred at the drinks' trolley.

'How are things?' asked Fred.

'There's been one awkward encounter so far.' Cuthbert nearly said two.

'I gathered that at the beach place. Couldn't make out which one it was.'

'It was Lemon Trousers. And my brother said seriously that he'd keep me to my promise to get the boy a passport.'

'My! Scuse ducks, must serve these.' Fred had loaded a tray with drinks. He crossed the room to where Sir Miles was standing. 'I'm sure yours is a whisky, Sir Miles.'

Cuthbert joined Barbara.

'How's it going?' she asked. Although forty-two, with her abundant blonde hair, unstreaked by grey, her bright blue eyes and healthy suntanned complexion, Barbara Palmer looked thirty-five. She would have seemed younger if it weren't for her fullish figure, which her postman adored.

'Touch and go,' replied Cuthbert.

'Bring them to tea tomorrow.'

'Thanks, love to.' Cuthbert forbore asking if her postman would be there.

Fred came up. 'D'you think Her Ladyship would like to see over the house?'

Remembering the very feminine green and yellow bedroom with the huge double bed backed by padded silk, the dressing table cluttered with powders, scents, lotions, unguents and deodorants, the lights that dimmed and changed colour to a sexy red, Cuthbert replied, 'I don't think so. She has no interest in interior decoration. Gardens are more her line.'

'I can't show her the garden in the dark, dearie, now can I?' said Fred, flapping a hand. 'I'll ask her if she'd like to see upstairs.'

During Monica's visit upstairs, Cuthbert was on tenterhooks – would Fred resist touching the switch by the bed that caused curtains on the ceiling to draw and reveal a mirror? And what would his sister-in-law's reaction be to the painting of a reclining male nude whose focal point was so obviously the ephebe's genitals?

Downstairs Sir Miles got on well with Colonel Hubbard Wright, who was quite able to hold his own on the subject of world finance with his confidence trickster's charm. The Knight's conversations with the others went less successfully. Eustace started off on his famous account of his arrival in Tangier in 1925 when he was twenty that clearly bored Sir Miles, who was equally uninterested in Barry's twittering about how he'd covered the armchairs with the cloth used for kaftans ('Lovely fabric. Feel it, Sir Miles!') and Barbara's emotional praise of the people – 'they have such perfect natural manners, they're such gentlemen.' Cuthbert was relieved when his brother got back to Hubbie, as people called the bachelor Colonel, and the world markets.

Monica and Fred reappeared. She did not look as if she'd just emerged from the Chamber of Horrors, but nevertheless Cuthbert wondered what she'd been shown and what she'd noticed. Her return caused everyone to rise, and, after a few moments of platitudes that sparked no interest, there followed talk of the hour and of departure.

As the Mercedes approached the flat, Cuthbert spied his Moroccan friend Seven League Boots, so named because of his remarkable stride, sitting on the doorstep. 'Damn!' Cuthbert cursed to himself. When the car drew up, Seven League Boots rose and grinned inanely – he had a faint resemblance to Harpo Marx.

'Friend of yours?' joked Miles in the teasing tone which he, the elder brother, used to adopt in their adolescence when Cuthbert had served a double fault, done a belly flop, bowled underarm.

The young Moroccan was dressed in a red tartan shirt, jeans and grubby track shoes. He had a pale complexion and a hillock of fuzzy hair. Cuthbert jumped out of the car as soon as it had stopped, winked and said, '*Bonsoir.*'

Seven League Boots returned the greeting and retreated into his fatuous grin.

'This is the night watchman from up the road,' Cuthbert said to Miles, who had been locking the car door. 'He says this is a bad place to leave the car all night. It would be safer if you left it outside that hotel round the corner.'

'What a bore! D'you mean I must move it?'

Pop music was resounding from within the ground-floor flat.

'Yes. And one must drive it around the block as this is a one-way street. Give me the keys. I'll do it,' said Cuthbert.

Miles hesitated. 'Sure you can drive it all right?'

'You know I can. *Viens*, Abdul Salam.'

Seven League Boots got into the Mercedes beside Cuthbert, who drove off down the street.

'Take me Tetuan.' Seven League Boots came from near that city.

'No. Look, here you are.' Cuthbert put two ten-dirham banknotes into the boy's hand. 'I can't see you. My brother here. *Mon frère ici avec sa femme.* Not possible. *Pas possible. Viens plus tard. Après deux semaines. Compris?*'

Cuthbert drove swiftly back into town and came to a halt not far from the Place de France

'You no take me Tetuan?'

'No.'

'I want go Tetuan. My father *très malade.* Gimme fifty more.'

'No. Get out.'

'I stay.'

'Get out!' How often one hated one's lovers! Seven League Boots wasn't usually so difficult.

'Gimme fifty dirham. *Donnes-moi cinquante.*'

'Here's another ten, now get out! Come and see me *après deux semaines, compris?*'

'*D'accord.*' Seven League Boots accepted the banknote without more ado, smiled sweetly, as if there had not been the slightest altercation, and got out of the car giving Cuthbert a friendly wave.

Cuthbert sighed as he parked the car outside the hotel round the corner from his flat. What a day! That awful party! Before he reached his building Cuthbert could hear someone rapping on the door of the lower flat. A locked-out hippy, he presumed, but it wasn't. It was Miles hammering away furiously with his fists.

'What are you doing?' asked Cuthbert.

'I'm trying to get this blasted noise stopped. How can we sleep with it booming like this?'

'They'll never answer.'

'I'll call the police.'

'They'd do nothing. People don't complain here, least of all about noise.'

'Can you sleep through this?'

'It doesn't bother me at all.'

'God!' Miles knocked again. Cuthbert was proved right, however; no one came to the door.

'Either they don't hear,' explained Cuthbert, 'because of the music or because they're keefed up or because they don't want to.'

123

'Damned swine! Why don't you complain to your landlord?'

'He lives in Casablanca,' lied Cuthbert.

'Well, I suppose there's nothing we can do about it. But the first thing in the morning, I'll break the door down if necessary.'

Miles didn't carry out his threat in the morning; in fact, he made no reference to the hippies and their din, which had gone on till five a.m. Cuthbert felt that he had Monica to thank for his brother's reticence.

Over breakfast Monica mentioned that she wanted to see the hotel where Saint-Saens once stayed. Cuthbert said, 'I don't think it's wise for you to go into the Medineh alone, Monica. You might easily get your handbag snatched. So, Miles, let's go to the government's office tomorrow and accompany Monica into the old town this morning.'

Perhaps Miles was having second thoughts about asking for a passport for Lemon Trousers for he readily agreed with his brother's proposal.

They parked the car in the Grand Socco, a square of buses, a cinema, a mosque, the old Fez Gate and an old water seller, whom Monica, to Miles's irritation, insisted on photographing.

Would Curio Shop be in or standing outside his cupboard of a shop? Cuthbert prayed he would not be there; he often wasn't, especially when one wanted to make a date with him. Cuthbert went ahead of his relations down the narrow Rue es Siaghin or Jewellers' Street. Curio Shop was there. Damn! He was standing outside his cupboard and he came forward when he saw Cuthbert. Dressed in his working clothes, a white *djellabah*, a crimson fez and yellow slippers, he looked handsome with his hat pushed back to show a wave of black hair, and saucy with his broad smile and his lustrous dark eyes that twinkled and spelled naughtiness.

'Allo, Meester Cuthbert,' he cried. They shook hands. '*Comment vas-tu?*'

'*Je suis très occupé aujourd'hui*,' warned Cuthbert. '*Mon frère et ma belle soeur sont ici avec moi.*'

Monica and Miles, who had been examining leather goods further up the street, approached.

'*Moi, je viens ce soir?*'

'*Non non non. Ils logent avec moi dans mon appartement. Absoluement impossible.*' Cuthbert felt the presence of his relations overshadowing him like a menace. 'This is Abdul Karim. He sells the most interesting curios and antiques. Do look, Monica.'

Abdul Karim had already unlocked his show case and brought out a filigree brooch, a clip in the shape of a Moroccan dagger and a medallion with a piece of imitation turquoise in its centre. 'You like?' I give you special price. Meester Cuthbert, he my friend.' He gave Cuthbert an affectionate slap on the back. Cuthbert flinched.

Monica behaved wonderfully. To the Moroccan's and Cuthbert's satisfaction she bought seven brooches, three Moroccan stars on silver chains and two medallions.

'What on earth will you do with that rubbish?' asked Miles when they had resumed their descent to the Petit Socco to see the hotel where Saint-Saens once stayed. Cuthbert let them walk on ahead and hastened back to Curio Shop. '*Tu peux venir la semaine prochaine?*' '*D'accord*, Meester Cuthbert.' When he rejoined his relations they had reached the toy square. 'The hotel is over there,' Cuthbert explained. 'It's just a café now.'

'Let's have a drink,' said Miles.

'They only serve mint tea,' objected Cuthbert.

'That'll do fine.' Miles sat at a table on the pavement and Monica and Cuthbert joined him. The other customers were Moroccans in *djellabahs* sitting glumly at empty tables. 'By the way, Cuthbert, doesn't that ghastly racket all night long bother you?'

'I don't notice it,' lied Cuthbert. 'How far apart one grew from one's brother!' mused Cuthbert ruefully to himself. 'I have more in common with Curio Shop than I do with Miles.'

Mint tea was brought. Just as Cuthbert was lifting the hot little glass to his lips, Miles remarked, 'You don't seem to know any married couples, here, Cuthbert.'

'Barbara's married,' countered Cuthbert.

'But divorced, you say.'

A pair of European hippies dressed in *djellabahs* drifted into the square and sat in the café opposite.

Miles looked at them with distaste. 'This place is full of riff-raff.'

Tea with Barbara that afternoon was embarrassing: the smell of Mohammed permeated the flat and in a prominent position on the sideboard in the living room was a dark-blue peaked cap, and on the floor by the door rested a mail bag which could not have been mistaken for anything else as it had a padlock round its neck and P.T.T. stamped on it in black stencilled letters. Cuthbert watched Miles and Monica notice these objects in turn and throughout the visit he tried to think of how to explain them afterwards; also he hoped that in late middle-age his brother's olfactory sense had waned and that Miles was unaware of the very masculine odour in the little flat. Cuthbert did not want his relations to know the truth, which was that Mohammed was probably resting in the bedroom.

Barbara chatted away, apparently oblivious to her postman's accoutrements, even when re-entering the room with the teapot she nearly tripped over the mail bag.

'How are you liking Tangier?' she asked Monica.

'Oh, it's very interesting.'

'When people say interesting they usually mean they don't like the place.'

'One of the things I find disturbing,' said Monica, 'is the mugging that goes on here.'

'Mugging? What mugging?' challenged Barbara, who was hypersensitive to any criticism of her beloved Mohammed's country.

'Cuthbert tells us that –'

'What have you been telling them, Cuthbert?'

It was impossible for Cuthbert to wink at Barbara as Miles and Monica were facing him. 'I only mentioned that it's not safe to wander about dark streets at night, and in certain places, even during the day. There are thugs, Barbara; you know there are.'

'They're so poor. And,' flashed Barbara, who, to Cuthbert's irritation, failed to grasp his tactics, 'what about mugging in London? It's unsafe to go on the Underground. And,' she raised her voice so loudly that Cuthbert was afraid lest Mohammed wake and wander in half-dressed or even naked from the bedroom, 'Tangier is one of the safest places in the Mediterranean.'

'Safer than Costa del Sol?' asked Miles.

'Far safer. The Costa del Sol is crammed with criminals.'

Cuthbert said, 'I believe Majorca is very nice…' and they fell to talking about where to live, a favourite topic among expatriates and would-be expatriates. The three guests rose to leave and at the door Barbara said, 'I love Morocco and what's more it's a monarchy.'

When the three had got down the stairs and into their car, Monica said, 'What did she mean by "what's more it's a monarchy"?'

'Oh she's incurably romantic,' explained Cuthbert.

'What in heaven's name were a postman's cap and a mail bag doing in her sitting room?' asked Miles. 'Had she just held up a mail van?'

Cuthbert had his answer ready. 'They're props for a play some of the foreign community are getting up. She's the stage manager or something.'

'What's the play?' asked Monica, as if she might like to see it.

'I forget its name,' replied Cuthbert, airily. 'Some crime thing.'

'And,' asked Miles, 'does she ever wash?'

'Wash?' repeated Cuthbert, feeling non-comprehension.'

'The place stank with BO, didn't you notice?'

'No.'

'You must have lost your sense of smell.'

They were motoring out to the Old Mountain for drinks with Eustace. Cuthbert was feeling relaxed as a visit to the old man could be nothing more than dull. It was the first time that Cuthbert had brought his relations up the Old Mountain road, a steep, tortuous lane bordered by crumpling residences hidden by walls, eucalyptuses and firs. Through the trees were glimpses of the Straits and the Spanish coast.

'This is lovely,' remarked Monica. 'Do look at the view, Miles.'

'You seem to forget I'm driving,' grumbled Miles. 'One would curse this road if one lived at the end of it.'

'It's the next entrance to the left,' instructed Cuthbert.

They turned through open wooden gates, which were much in need of a coat of paint, and wound up a weedy drive of several twists to arrive at Eustace's once-splendid mansion, now in decay. The old man was sitting on the terrace, whose stone balustrade was mottled with age and spotted with lichen. Eustace rose as the three arrivals alighted from their car. The sober smartness of his neat grey suit was depleted by a little green trilby worn at a rakish angle, a jazzy foulard knotted to make a floppy bow tie and leather sandals. 'Welcome!' he cried from the top of the terrace steps, raising his hat above his bald head.

'This is lovely,' said Monica, after they had ascended to the terrace.

'You've come just in time to see the view,' said Esutace. 'Gib has been sticking out like a sore thumb all day. It's fading fast, though.'

'Can one really see Gibraltar?' asked Monica in admiration.

'There,' replied Eustace, pointing, 'the last tip of land. What'll you have? Whisky? Sherry? Cuthbert, come and help.'

Cuthbert followed Eustace into the drawing room of faded French-style furniture and a warped piano on which were cluttered dimmed photographs in tarnished silver frames, and then the two men creaked down a wooden passage to the kitchen, where at a table sat a young American, whom Cuthbert remembered meeting somewhere, and Lemon Trousers. Both were smoking cigarettes which, Cuthbert knew at a glance, were spiked with keef, and both were drinking whisky.

'Good God!' exclaimed Cuthbert.

'Hi there!'

'Allo, Meester Cuthbert,' laughed Lemon Trousers, stupidly.

Cuthbert had never seen the young man in such a giggly state. 'But Eustace – ' he began.

'Don't worry. They're under strict orders not to appear.' Eustace shakily poured out a sherry for Monica, a whisky for Miles, another for Cuthbert and a third for himself and then said, 'You take those two; I'll take these.'

'Say,' said the American, whose blue eyes were dulled and seemed unable to focus, 'I want to meet your brother, the lord.' He grabbed Cuthbert's arm causing whisky to be spilled.

'Damn you,' said Cuthbert.

'Damn you,' echoed the American imitating rather well Cuthbert's precious English accent.

Eustace came to the rescue. He was still wearing his hat. 'Now shut up,' he cautioned. 'You keep quiet or there'll be no dinner.'

'I don't want any dinner. I want to meet Cuthbert's famous brother.'

'Shut up!' cried Eustace in the tone of an indulgent scoutmaster. 'Come on, Cuthbert! Quick!' He signalled with his head to Cuthbert and when they were on the other side of the door Eustace turned the key. 'The windows are barred,' the old man sniggered boyishly. 'The back door is locked. They can't get out.' Eustace and Cuthbert creaked back down the passage, through the seedy drawing room and out onto the terrace, where Monica and Miles were still standing and viewing, although Gibraltar was now obscure and the nearer Spanish coast had become a dark line.

'Well, here we are,' said Eustace, courteously handing Monica her glass of sherry.

'Thank you so much.'

They sat on the rickety garden chairs and Eustace, prompted by a question from Monica, began to hold forth about his house. 'It was built by a French doctor before the First World War and – '

An American yell came from the kitchen; though muffled by distance it was unmistakably American and it seemed to include the words 'sons of bitches'.

Eustace stopped speaking as if he had forgotten his trend of thought, and there was an awkward silence, which Monica broke by saying, 'We've just had tea with Barbara Palmer.'

'Ah Barbara!' sighed Eustace. 'Dear Barbara! A truly lovely person.'

Monica said, 'I hear she's stage manager in the crime play the foreign community are getting up.'

A cry of 'Shit!' came from the kitchen.

Eustace exploded. 'The *what*?'

'The crime play that the – '

'I've heard nothing about a new production,' boomed Eustace indignantly.

'It's some crime thing, isn't it, Cuthbert?'

'Lemme out, for Christ's sake, you bastards!'

'Yes, that's right,' Cuthbert admitted, uncertainly.

'I call that damned impudence,' fumed Eustace. 'I'm chairman of the Drama Committee and I've heard nothing about a play. It's just typical of that meddling female to go behind my back and – '

'Fuck!' screamed the American voice.

Monica kept her composure, but Miles uncrossed and recrossed his legs uneasily. 'I say – ' he began, but said no more.

Either Eustace's deafness prevented him from hearing the shouted abuse or he shut his ears to it for he seemed unperturbed.

'Well,' said Cuthbert, 'I think we'd better be, we'd better be going – '

'Have another drink,' commanded Eustace, peremptorily. 'Cuthbert, d'you mind?'

The old man held out his glass. Reluctantly, Cuthbert pulled himself to his feet and took the glasses one by one, fitting three into one hand by putting a finger in each like an uncouth waiter; the fourth, his own, he held in the other hand. Thus burdened, he ambled into the house. The kitchen door was being rattled and when Cuthbert unlocked it the young American stormed out like a released wild animal shouting, 'Are you

British bastards playing some private upper-class game?' and bounded down the passage. Cuthbert did not attempt to restrain him. Lemon Trousers was asleep with his head on the kitchen table and his arms hanging down his sides; he looked as if he had suddenly lost consciousness and dropped forward. Not relishing the thought of rejoining the others now that the crazed American was with them, Cuthbert took his time over replenishing the glasses. He regarded Lemon Trousers affectionately; he was not jealous that the young man knew Eustace and the American because it meant that monetary demands for passport fees and so on could be shared. When Cuthbert had poured out the drinks and put them on a tray, he kissed Lemon Trousers on the temple before going down the passage to face the music.

Mercifully, the American was not behaving in the outrageous manner that his language and his violent exit from the kitchen had suggested he might; he was neither bawling obscenities nor rampaging; he was sitting and being polite to Monica, or so it seemed until Cuthbert sat next to him.

'I'm a poet,' he was saying to Monica. 'But I only write when I'm on a "trip".'

'We're on a trip now,' replied Monica with apparent innocence.

'Yeah? I mean a "trip", not a trip.'

Eustace began telling Miles about his arrival in Tangier in 1925.

'You write good stuff when you're on a "trip", when you're really high. I get stoned on hash and write and write and write.'

'What do you write about?' Monica asked.

'My feelings. I write about what I feel.'

'Isn't that what poets write about?'

'Yeah, but you can only feel properly, you can only perceive deeply when your senses are stimulated.'

'*The Doors of Perception*,' quoted Monica.

Eustace went on telling Miles about his arrival in Tangier in 1925.

'Yeah, that's right.' The American drivelled on about how anything, a plank of wood, a stone, can become beautiful when properly observed. 'You can see the parts of the whole,' he explained.

'I should have thought you could have done that equally well under a microscope.'

Cuthbert rose. 'Well, it's getting late and – '

'Oh Jesus!' interrupted the American. 'Your sister and I are having a meaningful conversation. You don't often get meaningful conversations. Most people talk crap.'

'We must continue on another occasion,' said Monica, graciously. With social aplomb she went over to Eustace and broke into his interminable rigmarole about Tangier in the twenties. Miles, trained to act upon his wife's signal, jumped to his feet, goodbyes were made and soon Cuthbert and his relations were descending the Old Mountain.

'There seems to be something funny,' said Miles, 'about everyone you introduce us to, Cuthbert. Why on earth does Eustace put up with that frightful American? Why does he have him to his house?'

'Perhaps he called,' suggested Cuthbert.

'To have someone like that calling. And Eustace himself is senile. For the second time he told me about his arrival in this godforsaken country in 1925.'

'He's eighty-three,' Cuthbert reminded his brother.

'And gaga,' added Miles. 'What a crew!'

To Cuthbert's satisfaction the 'pop' music below was particularly loud that night, and twice he heard Miles banging on the floor and shouting, 'Shut up, damn you, shut up!'

At breakfast the next morning, Miles said, 'We've decided to take the afternoon ferry to Algeciras today.'

Cuthbert feigning shock and disappointment, objected, 'But we're supposed to be dining with Colonel Hubbard Wright this evening.'

'You'll have to make our excuses. I'm sorry in a way as Hubbard Wright seems to be the only decent, straightforward, balanced fellow we've met here. I've made up my mind: we're leaving this afternoon.'

And that afternoon, to Cuthbert's joy and relief, Miles and Monica caught the ferry to Spain. At the docks, while Miles was showing his travel documents to an official, Monica squeezed Cuthbert's hand and said, 'I understand perfectly. I don't mind and I shan't tell Miles.'

Cuthbert swallowed and began to blush, 'He hasn't guessed?'

'No. He hasn't the least suspicion. He just thinks that everyone here is a bit odd.'

Crimson, Cuthbert stammered, 'No more than that?'

'No, no more. He puts it down to the place.'

Cuthbert waved as his brother and sister-in-law drove into the bowels of the ferry boat. 'What a splendid woman!' he exclaimed aloud to himself. 'Far too good for Miles.'

Essex Skipper

Desmond Hogan

Traveller's Joy on the hedges becomes Old Man's Beard in the autumn.

When I was a boy my father gave me a collection of art books, loose reproductions going with them. One of the reproductions was *The Nakedness of Noah* by Michelangelo – a naked, wreathed youth, whose own genitals are showing, covering the nakedness of Noah who has a wine jug alongside him, the youth's head turned back to a naked young woman who is gloating over Noah's embarrassment.

Men known as breeches-makers were employed by the Vatican I tell the two boys who are visiting me, one of whom looks like a Cyclops or a myopic pine martin, to cover the nakedness of Michelangelo youths (*ignudi*) with ribbons, drapery, entire garments.

But this one escaped.

I tell them the story as they look at the painting: As an old man Michelangelo was walking through the snow to the Coliseum when Cardinal Farnese accosted him and asked him why a man of his age was out in the snow.

'To learn something new,' was the famous reply.

Giovanni Bellini, from whose mastery of light the hour of the day can be deduced, gave a version of old age in those loose reproductions: Noah with beard of ermine and baby-nakedness.

The boys also look at Mary Cassatt's *Mother and Child*: naked American he-child who looks as if he's destined for a career in the navy. Mary Cassatt took her influence from Correggio I tell the boys.

In chapter fourteen of Mark, Christ is deserted by all except a boy wearing nothing but a linen cloth who follows him as he's being taken away, gives him the cloth and runs away naked. Correggio painted this scene but the painting is lost. There's a copy of it in Parma; boy with vermilion cloak on his shoulder being pursued by a soldier in an indigo cuirass.

The following Monday the Guards investigate.

A young detective in black jobber – half-boots – pays attention to *The Rape of Ganymede*, thought to have been by Titian, by Damiano Mazza, in which the rapist eagle has a decurved beak and wings with ctenoid edges – like the teeth of a comb, Ganymede's buttocks resolved for penetration while coral-pink drapery liberates itself from his body.

François Boucher's *Cupid* with his love-arrows in a gold-topped scarlet pouch is examined.

Even a child with golden hair and painted cheeks in biscuit (marble-like) unglazed porcelain by the eighteenth-century Düsseldorf sculptor Johann Peter Melchior is scrutinised. Sent by the girlfriend of a boy dying of Aids, for many years I'd thought it to have been a depiction of Melchior, one of the Three Wise Men, his name meaning King of Light.

An older detective seems unsettled by Franz von Lenbach's *The Little Shepherd*: boy in scarlet waistcoat, short trousers like the ones Hugo von Hofmannsthal wore in his prodigious Viennese boyhood, lying among poppies.

The young detective picks up the Penguin edition of Alain-Fournier's *Le Grand Meaulnes* with a black-and-white photograph of a boy's naked torso on the cover, an *ignudo* shadowed by leaves. Certain evidence of paedophilia and he consults with the clerkish older detective.

I had a copy of this book as a child with Sisley's *Small Meadows in Spring* on the cover... black-stockinged girl by poplars... blue ribbon around her hat... head dipped as if she's admiring a flower in her hand... Augustin Meaulnes used to gather the eggs of the red-headed moorhen in meadows such as these for his mother.

The great black-backed gull eats other gulls.

Earlier I was arrested on the strand by the young detective.

A half an hour beforehand the brother of one of the visiting boys had punched me in the face, splitting my lower lip open in two places. He was wearing a lavender school jersey.

A file of five Guards or detectives came into my chalet like Spanish inquisitors in their cone-hats.

A stout, rugby-playing *Ban Garda* (woman guard) looks through my album with images from the Narodni Gallery in Prague, the State Gallery in Stuttgart, collections in Arnheim, Cracow.

My shoes are confiscated and I am put in a cell with a ground-latrine and the name Dinny scrawled on the wall.

Mudlarks with bum-fluff moustaches and German shepherd dogs alongside them search for golf balls in the shallow river of this town.

I am interrogated under video camera. I make no comments.

On my return to my chalet, despite the fact that I'm next door to the Garda Station, I find the two windows broken. A gang of boys approaches the chalet four times, completely demolishing back-lane window glass so people can climb through. A heavy rock is thrown in at me.

'Come out here. But call the ambulance first.'

'That was only a crowd of young lads who did that,' a young ginger-haired Guard, who arrives on the scene, tells me.

After four nights of terror I abandon the chalet in haste.

The curtains of the bedroom I move into in Tralee have been rubbed with faeces. A drunken youth tries to break into my room one night, accusing me of stealing a Radiohead CD. One of the house residents served with Global Strategy Mercenaries in Iraq, saw the North Gate of Baghdad, and when I try to ask him about his experiences he threatens me with the IRA.

'What do you want to know that for?'

I stayed in the Salvation Army Hostel in Edinburgh once and this is just like it. There was a former professor from Saint Andrew's University who'd made the hostel his home.

I swim near a lighthouse. The ringed plover – *feadóg an fhainne* – lives in abundance here. When threatened it drags its body along the ground, tail spread, one wing extended and flapping as if it was injured

I recognise the black armpits of the grey plover – *feadóg ghlas* – which you can see in flight.

I move into a tiny room near the Lee River which flows into Trá Lí Mic Dedad (the beach of Lí, son of Dedad).

I frequently spot a heron by the river. Cinder-sifter boys search for discarded carbonators by this river which can be used for plumbing or heating. Girls sit on the crossbars of boys' bicycles like visiting aristocracy in the howdah on an elephant's back.

'I thought someone just left it there,' a boy tells me as I stop him stealing my bicycle.

A crowd of schoolchildren bang on my back-lane window. I look out.

'Queer,' one calls back.

A few evenings later, a Friday evening, there is a knock on the window. It is the same boy. A tall gander-like boy. An adolescent gorilla. His T-shirt says: 'I'm a workholic. Everytime I work I need a beer.' He asks if he can come in. 'I want to stay the night with you,' he says.

I bring him to the beach and give him my spare swimming briefs which he jogs in while I swim. In a corner of the beach he towels himself, naked. Gooseberry-velutinous chest – soft, fine hairs; moustachial hairs under his navel; genitals the salmon-red of the linnet's breast.

The geography of Essex with its many tidal rivers in its early body hair. He is the young warrior who after letting his beloved hawk fly into the Weald, advances towards his doom in battle with the Vikings as the causeway tide goes out.

Bricin – Bricin Pluckrose is his name. His father is from the wastes of Essex near Chelmsford.

Bricin brings a childhood snapshot of himself in rag hat with butterfly on it – Essex Skipper, orange with black rim.

He brings a photograph of his father standing against Union Jack in olive-green polo shirt with red-rimmed collar, black braces, black laced-up boots. His father used to sell fruit and vegetables in Chelmsford in scarlet work boots with white laces, jeans with rolled-up ends, scarlet braces and shaven head like William Pitt's niece and social hostess Lady Hester Stanhope who used to beat her servants in Phoenicia with a mace and employed an ex-general of Napoleon as soothsayer there.

Hs father's sister – his aunt – was a skinhead. 'No earring but a bald head. No jail record.'

She said then: 'I want to slow down and marry.' She married a heavy-weight boxer in Brentwood.

'He saved my bacon,' she said of him.

The boy who tells these stories has hair the black of the defensive liquid the ten-armed cuttlefish emits, pockmarks like the webbing between the sea otter's feet, Rudolf Valentino in mayhem good looks, mackerel-blue eyes. Eyes that suddenly liquefy into anguish at the remembrance of some insult or some uncertainty as to my expectations of him. They are different expectations, new expectations. Occasionally his eyes rivet dangerously.

Speech is frequently interrupted; a stammer, a caesura. The Queen's father, George VI, had a stammer, I tell him. His grandmother, who witnessed the Canvey Island disaster of February 1953, has a framed message from George VI on her encrusted-line pattern wallpaper. 'Help to make the world a better place and life a worthier thing.'

'She's with the fairies.' Bricin borrows an expression from his Irish mother who drinks an eggnog every night and occasionally a Club Dry Gin with it.

Bricin disappears from my life just as the Essex Skipper vanishes from a musk thistle.

She is the fairies' midwife…
Her wagon-spokes made of long spinners' legs;
The cover, of the wings of grasshoppers…
Her chariot is an empty hazelnut…

It is Saint Patrick's Night and the shelter from which I swim is invaded. A bin filled with glass from occasional winter drinkers has been emptied out. A small English boy with café crème baseball cap and a jailbird stride indicates he carries a flick knife. A girl in T-shirt with words 'Oopsy Tipsy! One Too Many' is walking around with jeans down to her knees. A flamingo bottom like François Boucher's toileting Venus. In the Boucher painting *putti* bearing chaplets administer to Venus.

Here the *putti* wear baseball caps.

I ask two of these *putti* – one with a T-shirt with the words 'So Wot Cha Say?' – to look after my bicycle while I'm swimming. They throw it to the ground, smashing the lamp to smithereens. A girl with 'Will Try Anything Twice' flaunted on her T-shirt, throws grit at me as I change. I ask her to stop whereupon the *putti* who threw my bicycle to the ground approach to beat me up. I manage to appease them and I make a getaway from this demonic theatre.

A boy with Fatty Arbuckle features, hair and freckle colouring of the red squirrel, eyes blue as hedge periwinkles, in tropical shirt and Dr Livingstone shorts reconciles me to Bricin. He delivers him to me.

The following Friday as he eats a forest berry Bavarian cream cake he tells me that his cousin Uinseann – Gaelic for Vincent – who has Adam Ant braids, eyes like the Japanese sika deer in Killarney National Park, has tennis star sisters Venus and Serena Williams on his mobile phone, used to make love to him in the shower of his home.

Bricin is wearing a J. Nistelrooy, Manchester United, black away shirt.

Uinseann has a girlfriend now who has beet-red dye in her hair, wears Mickey Mouse knickers, and said to Bricin: 'If you were a product you'd be mustard.'

They went together to a night club in Tralee where the boys danced with the boys and the girls danced with the girls and a boy and a girl had oral sex on the floor.

When Bricin is distressed he can make his jaws look like the Aristotle's lantern – the spherical jaws of a sea urchin. Alternatively he diverts to his father's Essex Polari – a mixture of pig Latin, Romany, criminal argot. Money he calls dosh.

In the casinos some boys sell themselves for sex for twenty euros. My father, donor of Michelangelos and Bellinis – from the books he gave me I learned that Leonardo wrote in mirror writing (reversed writing) – referred to my girlfriends as Mary Annes. Also known as Mary Annes were the London telegraph boys of the 1880s in their light-blue uniforms and sideaways caps whom speculation said satisfied the desires of the Heir Presumptive with spiv's moustache and frogged Hussar's tunic who on his early death was mourned each day by his mother with fresh flowers laid on his death bed. One of those London Mary Annes was found to have connections with Golden Lane Boy Brothel near the Liffey in Dublin, frequented by Dublin fusiliers and Grenadier Guards, which the Home Rulers used as propaganda against the British rulers.

Sometimes Bricin comes into my place from the casinos like a ruffled young barn owl with its kitten head and protuberant eyes. A man in a denim cowboy hat in the casino told him: 'I put ads in the paper and get couples. I only go with couples.'

His mouth is smeared with the Mississipi Mud Pie he's been eating. Dalta – foster child; Bricin in my life.

Late August he visits Essex with his father.

'I love this country,' his father declares when the Tube reaches Epping. 'In my childhood a mug cost a penny and very big ones too.'

They feast on Jumbo sausages, curry, chips and gravy, and Memory Lane Madeira cake in Colchester.

This is a conversation Bricin hears on a bus in Colchester: 'And the cat got into the fridge.'

'How did the cat get in the fridge?'

'Don't ask me. And it was so smelly.'

In a supermarket he witnesses a youth, accosted by store detectives, pulling down his trousers in front of the delicatessen, showing his Ginch Gonch underwear. 'I haven't got anything!'

Bricin's family knows the Roman roads of Essex, the ploughman's spikenard, same fragrance as the ointment Mary anointed the feet of Jesus with. 'Goodbye Bud,' his uncle who wears a silver lurex shirt and who has a bull terrier called Daniela says to him when he's leaving.

He has returned from Essex wearing a black and white baseball cap with rabbit ears and a belt with a monkey-motif buckle – three monkey cameos.

There are male strippers in Galway Bricin has heard. For hen parties: some of them appear on stage in nothing but Stetsons from Euro Saver shops. Perhaps he'll go there, wear Union Jack kit, bill himself as the Essex stripper or British kit stripper.

In September he turns up in the shelter in the evenings while I'm swimming as a black-headed gull – chocolate-brown head – drawn to sports fields does.

Body like a wounded gull. Joins hands, prays for his dead Irish grandfather. 'If he was alive he'd give me fifty euros.' Often he lights candles in church for his grandfather before coming to meet me. Here he may spend a votive ten minutes.

His mother got a portrait tattoo of his grandfather in Limerick on her right arm. His grandfather used to wear a hat with a scarlet cockade and pheasant feather on the brim.

I have to ban Bricin from my place. Coming too often, danger.

He bangs on my window for admittance, like the busty Caroline of Brunswick, in spite of her affair with Italian courtier Bartolomeo

Pergami, banging on the doors of Westminster Abbey during the corona-
tion of her husband George IV, the doors barred against her.

The Polish boy who fixes my bicycle is from Katowice, Henryk Górecki's
town, composer of *Symphony of Sorrowful Songs*, a tape lost in my flight.

The bicycle man with handlebar moustache frequently passes me in a
Toyota truck and honks at me. He's just out of jail, I think, and I'm going in.

I arrived on the first of November, a Friday – *Samhain* – to have my
bicycle chain fixed. He was in jail for not paying his taxes, an old lady told
me, who reprimanded me for wearing shorts in November.

I called at the buff bungalow of a boy who wore a lemon baseball cap
with the words The Doctor who'd pledged to help me if I was in trouble
with my bicycle.

He ambushed a girl with tricolour hair – hazel on front, fuschia on top,
ebony ponytail – on a madder rose junior bicycle which featured the
bobbed-haired Dora the Explorer in lemon ankle socks, and forcibly took
a link from her chain. She threatened the Demon Man on him.

The link didn't fit.

I was led to a greensward where boys in a flea market of baseball caps
stood around a *Samhain* bonfire. Between the first of November and the
first of May the *Filí* – poets – would tell a story for each night.

A Raleigh racing bicycle which wobbled like jelly was produced from
a shed. I was asked twenty-five euros for it. I only had twenty-two euros.
I was given it for that and I walked the two bicycles the ten miles back
against the night traffic and met a man with greyhounds, pink and white
electric fence twine attached to them.

The hermit crab crawls into the mollusc abandoned by the mussel of the
oyster.

A nosegay of snowdrops – *pluíríní sneachta* – comes to my door.

A child is a graph; he measures the year.

I see him again in a scarlet and navy-banded blue striped Tommy
Hilfiger jersey and pointy shoes, eyes the blue of the hyacinths the
rubbish-dump-frequenting herring gull decorates his nest with; white
polo shirt with vertically blue striped torso, listening to Rihanna's 'Good
Girl Gone Bad' on his mobile phone: I see him crying: 'They say I'm
retarded. I'm slow'; I see him crunching a Malteser – small round choco-

late with honeycombed centre, sucking a strawberry Fun Gum or biting on a raspberry and pineapple Fruit Salad Bar; I see his eyes again, blue as the blue pimpernel flower of Essex.

There was a honey-haired and honey-browed young drug dealer who ultimately used to reside in the shelter in the evenings. His mother's people were from The Island in Limerick where swans colonise the *turloughs* (winter lakes) with a view of council houses beyond. On his motorbike, with yellow back pack, he'd travel over rivers like the Oolagh and the Allaghaun, to places like Rooskagh, to sell marijuana and hashish to boys waiting on summer evenings in diamond pattern shorts.

The Lueneberg Manuscript of the Middle of the Fifteenth Century tells how in the year 1824, on the twenty-sixth of June, Feast of Saints Jon and Saint Paul, one hundred and thirty children from Hamelin, Germany, were led from the town by a piper dressed in divers colours to a place of execution behind the hills. A stained-glass window in Marktkirche, Hamelin, depicted the colours; Jacob Ludwig Carl and William Carl Grimm, known to embellish, retold the story.

Were the children drowned in the Weser? Did they depart on a Children's Crusade? Were they murdered in the forest by the piper?

Did they anticipate Theresienstadt where children were allowed to paint in divers colours before being gassed? Did they anticipate the children pulled out from the rubble of Dresden, on a night a Vermeer was burned, in Harlequin and Pierrot costumes because the bombing of Dresden took place at Fasching – Shrovetide Carnival?

Divers colours: the paintings of Michelangelo, Leonardo, Giovanni Bellini, Damiano Mazza – two boys look at them and then, like the two children of Hamelin who didn't follow the piper, debouch to the Garda Station to report this montage of pornography.

The Germans Have Landed

Alan James

I live on a tourist island; we have plenty of clean sandy beaches, and pleasant downs and woodlands. We also have an annual summer influx of young students from overseas, who come for an English-learning seaside holiday.

Thousands of these kids and teenagers descend on us every year, and have to be found rooms in homes in the small coastal towns, or in the villages that are scattered the length and breadth of the island. From France, Germany, Italy and Russia they come; from Spain, Portugal, Greece and Turkey. They even come from as far afield as Indonesia and Hong Kong. So every spring, the plea goes out via the local papers. Who would like to take a student in for three weeks or so? A bed, breakfast, an evening meal and a packed lunch; and at the weekends, a taste of local family life.

Well, I'm not a local family; I'm a single man. I live in a small town house with a spare attic bedroom. I had thought about taking students before, but for the small amount the organisers were offering it didn't really seem worth the hassle. Then last year the rates increased – more students were expected than ever before, and so of course more beds were needed, too. I decided to offer my room, and after a very cursory inspection, it was quickly accepted.

I knew there could be pitfalls ahead – friends of mine had given beds to students who had indulged in petty thieving, not only from their hosts' house, but from shops on the promenade… and I had seen some of these kids in action. Some years back, having a few spare weeks on my hands, I had joined the locally-recruited group charged with teaching the students English in the morning, and supervising them for 'activities', both on and off the island, during the afternoons and evenings. It had been billed as a fun time for all, and indeed it had provided its moments, but the time put in by us, the tutors and leaders, was in no way compensated for by the meagre sums paid out, usually after a weekly struggle with the head office located somewhere in the Netherlands.

So it could be said that I knew what I might be getting myself into; that summer, I had taught two groups – a delightful bunch of Hong Kong Chinese, and an unruly mob of mafiosi-brat Russians. When my room had been approved, I asked if I could have one of the accompanying foreign leaders to stay with me. But by the time I decided to join the scheme, these perhaps more desirable of the aliens had all been snapped up, so I was offered a German boy for three weeks. Not without trepidation, I accepted, and began to make preparations.

The main bedroom – my room – on the first floor leads into its own, and the only, bathroom. At first I had thought of giving the boy this room, and decamping to the attic; but then I thought he might be happier up there in his own little domain. There is in any case another lavatory on the ground floor, and as I am an early riser and would after all have to be up and about preparing some kind of breakfast, I imagined that I would have vacated the bathroom well before the lad would want to use it.

So I borrowed a small colour TV for the attic, made up the bed, screwed a couple of hooks into the back of the door, and cleaned the windows. I went to the supermarket and bought one of those plastic bottles of Coke, some eggs, bacon and milk, and a very cheap loaf of sliced white bread. In fact it was two for the price of one, and I had some difficulty in squeezing the extra 'freebie' into the small freezer compartment of my fridge.

Dawned the next day, when we were bidden to assemble at the ferry pontoon to welcome our charges. Off they trooped – wired up to iPods, and whatever the latest Walkman equivalent is, and chatting into metallic-blue mobiles. Girls from eight to eighteen, regardless of size – and there were some hefty Helgas – carried before them their bronzed bellies, tattooed and pierced, while the bullish, sporty-looking blond boys came skateboarding down the gangplank, or kicking footballs into the bay. My heart began to sink, along with the discarded banana peels.

With a pale shadow of the once-renowned German efficiency, order slowly came from chaos as the overseas leaders started to divide the shouting mass, herding them into singles and pairs. Clipboards with lists were brought into play, and the host families located and introduced to their (just about) paying guests. Still yelling at their friends, the kids were pushed by their leaders into the appropriate cars, and gradually peace again descended on to the quiet little port.

My boy was one of the last off the ferry, and kept such a distance from his party, that I thought I might have been spared having anyone to stay with me at all; my boy looked very different from his peers, too. As the crowd was thinning out, the leaders looked around, and eventually one of them beckoned to a tall, gangly-looking youth, very pale-skinned by comparison with the others, and without the sun-bleached Beckham crop, the mobile phone, the ludicrous neon-trimmed trainers. This boy, as he was led to me, glanced at his watch; it was a trifle after midday.

'Good afternoon. My name is Axel.' The boy held out his hand; I took it. Although the grip was slight, more a touch than a clasp, it was, it seemed to me, prolonged a trifle longer than might have been considered necessary. The palm felt cool, and dry.

'Axel. I see.'

I introduced myself, and made some trite statement of welcome. Axel smiled slightly, and nodded. I had an impression of dark, or chestnut, wavy hair, grown to some length, of spectacles, and of dark-coloured, probably even black, clothes. Further scrutiny was postponed, as we were sitting side by side as I drove to my house; Axel commented that the farmland was very green, and that some of the cottages were very old. His English sounded well-nigh perfect (I cannot imagine that there are many German teenagers familiar with the word 'thatch'), but despite this, by the end of the short journey, I felt that we had neither of us done much to put each other at ease.

'Oh. Pumpernickel.'

I had prepared what I hoped would not be too frightening a lunch; dark rye bread, ham off the bone from Sainsbury's, cheese, tomatoes. Would Axel like some Coca-Cola? No, Axel did not take soft drinks, thank you. I wondered where I was going to offload the family-sized [in the curious jargon of the supermarket] bottle I had bought. Did I by any chance have any green tea? As a matter of fact, I did. Would Axel like some biscuits with his tea? Axel stared for a few moments at the bright pink wafers from the bumper bargain packet of Peak Frean's Family Assorted. No, Axel would not like any biscuits, but if by any chance there were any apples… I placed the bowl of fruit on the table; Axel took an apple, and held it in mid-air. I produced a small plate, and placed it on the table in front of the boy; Axel positioned the glowing Orange Pippin centrally on the plate, and sat before it with his hands in his lap. After a few moments, I found the old steak knife, with a serrated blade, that I use for cutting fruit, and slid it over towards the boy. Axel quartered the apple, sliced out the seeds and core, and ate the four segments, one by one. Would Axel like another apple? No, thank you, one apple is generally sufficient. Thank you very much.

This first meal set a pattern followed by those to come; at the first breakfast, Axel turned the toasted slice of white bread delicately in his fingers, as if investigating a newly-discovered genus.

'Do you like toast?'

'Ah, so this is toast.'

But I grimly persisted in using up the pappy white slices for his lunchtime sandwiches, conscious that they could well have been fastidiously and neatly dispatched into the municipal litter bins scattered around the town.

From across the table, I had every opportunity to observe my charge at some length. His complexion was of the kind often described as flawless, a pale creaminess dotted faintly with freckles over the bridge of his finely-shaped nose, which in turn supported his narrow oblong glasses, with their frames of blonde tortoiseshell. He was thin: bony even; his clavicle showed clearly through his simple cotton T-shirts, which, like his jeans, were invariably either black or white, and unadorned with street-cred logos. As I had occasion to observe, when putting his clothes through the washing machine, his things rarely showed any signs of soiling, and the white T-shirts were never stained at the underarm.

The first few days settled into an easy rhythm; Axel was by and large an undemanding house guest, and, although he discouraged small-talk over meals ('What did we do today? I will tell you afterwards. If I may.') he was neither sullen nor uncommunicative. Then, one evening towards the end of the first week, Axel failed to return to the house. The hours kept were subject to the timetable of activities, and so I didn't worry until just after ten, when I thought to glance through the schedule. Beach barbecue at Whitecliff Bay, from six-thirty to eight-thirty.

I called the chief organiser, and was explaining my concerns, when Axel opened the front door and walked through into the kitchen; the organiser asked to speak to the boy, so I handed over the receiver.

'Oh. I'm so sorry to have caused any problems. I became separated from the rest of the group, and so I walked for a while and then I, what, took a hitch of a lift. Again, apologies.'

The organiser must have delivered some kind of a short lecture, judging by Axel's expressionless affirmatives and negatives. The call over, I smiled at him, said never mind, and asked him if he would have some supper with me. For perhaps the first time, he gave me quite a friendly look, and asked if first, he could change; as he glanced down at his white jeans, I noticed that they were indeed streaked with mud.

'Perhaps I could leave these here? I think there is no need to wear them upstairs, as they are… so dirty.'

'Of course.'

Axel, standing by the kitchen table, slipped out of his sandals, flipped open the studs of his fly, eased the jeans down over his narrow hips, stooped to push them to the floor, and stepped out of them. As he did so, I suddenly realised that the boy had never given me a pair of undershorts to wash; he stood before me now, in his tight white T-shirt, naked from the waist down. He was, as I have said, tall; and, in elegant proportion, his long penis hung before him, neatly circumcised, and framed by an inverted horseshoe of pale-brown frizz. He bent again to pick up the jeans, which he loosely folded, and placed in my grandmother's old wicker linen-basket, under the white porcelain sink.

'Thank you.'

He stood and smiled at me again, and with his left hand lightly flicked – as it might have been, by chance – his penis, which I thought was no longer as flaccid as before.

'Oh,' he twisted round, his hands on his hips, throwing his swelling self momentarily into profile, 'I think my T-shirt is also not so clean?'

'No – there is some mud, right across your back.'

'Ah.'

With his back now fully to me, he removed his shirt, and cast it down into the basket with the jeans. He stood for a moment, flexing his shoulder blades, and then threw his arms up and out into a full, luxurious stretch. His vertebrae cast a string-of-beads shadow the length of his elongated spine, and his pale buttocks – across which I fancied I could also distinguish streaks of dried mud – dimpled into shaded hollows. Without turning back to me, he strolled from the room, carrying his sandals.

I had never expressly told Axel that he could not enter my bedroom whilst I was actually in bed, so I suppose it should have come as no particular surprise when, at around six the following morning, he did exactly that. He quietly opened the door, walked, naked, lightly across the bare wooden boards, and into the bathroom. I sat up in bed, and by moving only very slightly, I could see him as he stood by the pan, urinating. After some moments, as he continued to stand there, I realised that he was masturbating. I watched him – and afterwards, I imagined that he was always aware of this – until completion, when he turned, out of my view, to the basin. The sound of hands being washed was followed by a quieter moment, during which I wondered vaguely what towel he was using (although all was always in pristine order when I checked a little later); then he walked back, without glancing in my direction, or closing the bathroom door behind him. I listened to him climbing the attic stairs; and we next met across the breakfast table.

This performance was repeated, sometimes on a daily basis, sometimes with a day's gap, but never more than that, during the second week of Axel's stay with me; so that I had every opportunity to study the boy in his natural state, which I grew to consider rather beautiful. His hair was long enough to tie back into a short ponytail, and this showed off his high cheekbones and finely made, somewhat aristocratic profile, borne on a long and graceful neck. His long slender arms ended in slender hands with long slender fingers, with the nails always clean, well-shaped and cuticle-free. I noticed that, although his body was generally hairless, a fine down of pale umber clothed his calves, and showed as a tuft on each of his big toes, which, like their neighbours, were, as his fingers, long and well-groomed, and also somewhat prehensile. The flatness of his chest and abdomen served only to accentuate his fine penis, protuberant over his neat scrotum, and often in any case semi-swollen.

Towards the end of the second week, Axel caught me by surprise; as usual, I was lying half-awake watching the boy urinating; but after this, instead of masturbating, he came straight back to my bedroom, and sat on my bed, before I had any chance to feign sleep. My room is whitewashed, and the early morning light falls through uncurtained windows, so there was no mistaking the aroused state of the young pale-skinned boy sprawled, not without elegance, across my great-aunt's faded old patchwork quilt.

'Could you please tell me the time?'

I took from the bedside table my watch, and passed it to the boy.

'Oh. A little after twelve minutes past six. Thank you.'

In passing me back the watch, Axel contrived to brush against my thigh, as it lay beneath the bedclothes.

'You're welcome.'

'May I come into your bed?'

'Of course you may. I was just about to leave it, as I believe you have an earlier start today, and I shall soon need to prepare breakfast.'

'Oh. An earlier start, yes. I see. Then perhaps…'

Axel rose – he had been, slowly, masturbating – and left my room.

That evening, I saw from the schedule that another barbecue – a weekly event, there was to be another the following week – was planned at Whitecliff Bay. I had been thinking during the previous few days, and so had a pretty good idea of what might lie ahead. I didn't worry that night when nine, nine-thirty came and went, and no Axel; he finally arrived at the house a little before ten. I heard the front door being quietly opened; and footsteps in the hall. I opened the kitchen door.

'Ah, Axel. Just in time to join me for supper.'

But Axel was not alone; tiptoeing behind him, as they both headed for the stairs, was a man – I didn't have a clear view of him, as the hall light hadn't been switched on, but I had the impression of someone middle-aged.

'Oh. I have with me a friend.'

'So I see. How nice. Shall I set an extra place at the table?'

But the friend was already shuffling towards the front door, where he seemed to mumble something, before letting himself out. Axel walked slowly into the kitchen.

'One of your fellow students, Axel?'

'No. Another person. As you could see.'

'Yes. Oh well, maybe he can join us next time. Goodness, you seem to be rather muddy again.'

'Oh.'

'On your jeans, just around the ankles.'

'The – oh, ankles, yes.'

Axel looked down.

'Then maybe –'

He began to undo the studs of his fly.

'I think it can wait until after we've eaten, Axel, don't you?'

The boy stopped what he was doing, and stared at me for a few moments, before sitting down in silence.

I didn't see so much of Axel, so to speak, during the week that followed, as various trips to off-the-island 'attractions' – Chessington World of Adventures, The London Dungeons – necessitated early starts and late returns. But the weekly evening barbecue was to take place as usual.

A short distance from Whitecliff, if one doesn't mind a scramble over the green-stained chalk boulders of the beach at low tide, lies another bay, a sweep of russet shingle under cliffs that shoot dramatically high. During the winter months, the place is all but deserted, for no houses can be built near. The strata of the chalk cliffs can quite clearly be seen, the soft white rock shot with horizontal streaks of slate grey – the treacherous substance known locally as Blue Slipper. Essentially a dried-out, solidified mud, after spring rains and heavy summer showers the Slipper can live up to its name and, liquefied again, spurt without warning from between its sandwich of chalk, causing the heavier layers above it to tumble down onto the beach.

This phenomenon has kept the place from being developed and, due to this and its slight inaccessibility, the bay has become an unofficial haunt of naturists. Some are genuine sun-seekers, the hearty families with their embarrassed-looking teenagers playing rounders, setting Mum's tits a-wobble like raspberry blancmanges and Dad's dong swinging like a pendulum, but further along, amongst the fallen white boulders, single men lurk, hoping to lure others into their rocky nests. Springs, thick and viscous with Blue Slipper, trickle down the beach at intervals, towards the sea, leaving pale meandering dehydrated tracks, that occasionally widen, under a dried-out surface crust, into deceptively-deep pools of the stuff, a cloying, grey-lavender clay, quick enough to suck sandals and trainers from unwary feet. It was this distinctive mud that Axel had brought into my house, dried on his jeans, his T-shirt, on his naked person.

On the evening of the barbecue, I approached Slipper Bay from the opposite end to Whitecliff, walked up and down the extensive crescent of fine shingle a few times, as it was a glorious summer's evening, paddled in the always surprisingly chill surf, and waited, keeping an occasional eye on the heaped-boulder barrier at the Whitecliff end that divided the two beaches. Sure enough, eventually, Axel appeared, this easily-distinguished, long-limbed boy, walking at the water's edge, past the few people at the family end who were packing to go, heading purposefully towards the rockier area where I was sitting. I climbed a low ridge of tumbled cliff, and lay in the coarse long grass that had colonised the dune. There were few other men around that evening, as it was a weekday, just two or three, displaying their soft, unattractive bellies.

When Axel came closer, within the men's line of vision, the boy stood for a while, facing the sea, as if in contemplation of the waves, and slowly, sensually even, removed his white T-shirt. When he turned, I could see that he had also flicked open the top few studs of his fly, so that his jeans could slip low on his hipbone as he walked, easily revealing his pubic mound. He walked in turn towards, and then away from, each of the men seated amongst the rocks, flirting, I suppose, taking his pick. Well, in my judgmental opinion, slim pickings indeed – if one could use such a phrase about the lardy flesh on offer. Axel walked on towards where I lay. I shrunk back into the shelter of the reeds, and he passed by. Cautiously I raised myself, enough to be able to see the stretch of beach along which I had walked.

I saw Axel heading up towards the foot of the cliff, where he disappeared from my view amongst the fallen boulders of white chalk that lay there; as he did not emerge, I imagined that he had found himself somewhere to lie, a little sheltered *al fresco* boudoir. Well, I was to be the fly to enter that particular parlour. I began to walk along the beach... I'm not out of shape; I took off my T-shirt. The sun was still warm, and pleasant on my shoulders. I suppose I must admit to a mounting sense of excitement as I approached the place where Axel was lying; due to the camber of the strand, I could see him before he could see me – see, at any rate, his long white feet, his calves, his thighs. There the boy lay, naked, floating pale-skinned on the orange of the shingle, but his flesh given soft, warm tones against the starkness of the white chalk boulders. His long, slender body was displayed to perfection on the gentle slope of the beach;

his eyes were closed, his arms stretched back and bent at the elbows, his head cradled in the hands folded behind his nape. I could see the pale tufts on the taut skin of his underarms. He had brought no towel to lie on; his jeans and T-shirt lay, folded neatly, nearby. I did not think he was sleeping – I thought that, as I approached, he would hear my footsteps on the shingle. A few paces from him, I stopped. After some moments, Axel opened his eyes… he focused on me, slowly, unclasped his hands, and raised himself up on his elbows. He gazed at me for another moment or two.

'Oh. So you have come to found me.'

'I have come to find you.'

'Ah, yes, to find me. And now, you have found me.'

'Correct. How did you know about this place?'

'This so-called naturist beach… compared to the ones we have at home, please excuse me if I tell you that… it is pathetic. But it was on a website, and so I came. You have taken off your T-shirt.'

'Yes.'

'Please also take off your jeans.'

'Because?'

'Because you know so well that I want to see your body. Your naked body.'

I gazed down at Axel. His penis was filling, stiffening, rising slightly from the pale shallows of his groin. I took off my jeans; no mean feat to perform this everyday – or every night – task with some dignity, whilst balancing on such an unstable surface, but I fancy that I managed. I had removed my cotton boxer shorts at the same time, so Axel had his wish. For some moments he stared at me; what he saw must have met with his approval, for eventually he nodded, and turned over, cushioning his head on his folded hands, and slightly spreading his legs. His buttocks and shoulder blades and the pale backs of his thighs were reddened and dimpled from having rested on their bed of shingle. I knelt beside him, and gently brushed off the two or three remaining tiny pellets of orange stone. The only time I had touched the flesh of the boy, since first we had shaken hands. From this, these two slight, physical encounters, I entered him, thus all at once bonding us together in a union of the utmost intimacy. I lay on him still, afterwards, my lips to his nape. I remember noticing that the skin was a little darker, there.

Axel began to speak, his head turned sideways.

'I hope that was enjoyable for you.'

As a matter of fact, it had been.

'I wonder if it was enjoyable enough for you to offer me... oh, some small *pourboire*.'

'Why, Axel, I didn't realise that you spoke French.'

'*Pas trop, mais ça suffit*... but... please do not be upset. I was not thinking of money.'

'Then?'

'In your house you have some interesting things. I would like to have... a souvenir, or souvenirs, maybe.'

'Oh.'

'Yes. In Germany, such things are not so easy to find.'

'I see.'

'For instance, there is a clock in the room at the front of your house.'

No room had been actually out of bounds to Axel, but I had not used the front sitting room during his visit, and I wondered when he had found the opportunity of casing its contents.

'That clock belonged to my grandmother.'

'Maybe she would like to think that it would be one day in Germany.'

'I doubt it – she was bombed out twice. That clock was about all she managed to save from the Blitz.'

'From the – oh. But nevertheless... you see, I have been texting my mother.'

'Oh. That's nice. Please send her my regards.'

I didn't even realise that the boy had a mobile phone.

'Yes. But I think she may not be happy to have your regards. Because I have been sending some messages in a little series, to say that I am a little worried that the man with whom I am staying is very interested in watching me if I am taking off my shirt, or... those kind of things.'

'So it seems I have been harbouring a viper in my bosom.'

For once Axel's impeccable English let him down. A note of puzzlement crept into his voice.

'A viper? Vindscreen viper?'

I put my hands around Axel's neck, caressingly, trying it for size, as it were; it was a perfect fit... what an easy matter it would have been to have crushed the life from the little tart, and to have left his pale, svelte mortal self for the tide... this seemed like a rather good idea. I started softly, with a few gentle massage pressures to his nape and shoulders, guaranteed to relax. And indeed, I felt the tension begin to ease from the frame of the serpent beneath me. He gave a quiet grunt or two of pleasure.

But another sound had caught my ear; a sound I had heard before, but from afar. I glanced up at the white chalk cliff that rose above us, and I intensified the massage, pressing deeper. I began to hum, the first thing that came into my head – as it happened, a German piece – Brahms' lullaby... Near the top of the cliff, a puff of smoke erupted; in reality, a breath of powdered chalk. A mini-avalanche of snowy debris trickled down, almost soundlessly; I hummed louder, keeping Axel pinioned beneath me. Without more warning, the cliff exploded, and I leapt from the boy, grabbing my clothes, and then running for the water. Pure-white boulders fell, like giant hail, and ricocheted around the beach – and then came their disturber, the great gush of liquid clay, the infamous Blue Slipper. Axel stood no chance; within seconds he was immersed deep in the flow of the stuff, as it poured like a dam-burst from its swollen strata on the cliff face, and covered everything in its path on its blind surge towards the sea.

At home, I put the clothes I had been wearing into the washing machine, I bathed, I dressed, I ate my supper – ate both our suppers, in fact; it must be true, that the sea air gives one an appetite. At ten-thirty, I telephoned the students' organiser, and said that once again, my charge had not returned – I was sorry to bother him, but since it was getting rather late...

I am certain of the time I made that telephone call; a few minutes earlier, I had gone into the front sitting room – just to see that all was well... the room had been peaceful, and quiet, the only sound coming from the pretty little French ormolu clock on the mantelpiece. It was about to strike the half-hour; it is a charming little piece, and an excellent time-keeper, and I am very fond of it.

The Violence of the Gardener

Cliff James

Somewhere in the garden stood Charlie. A soft frost settled on the grass and crept towards his feet. It climbed his jeans and coat, glittering on his stubble when it reached his face. Not thinking where he was or how long he had been there, he watched a star between the branches of the poplar trees. A breeze passed through the bushes and sent the leaves rattling. For a while he felt bodiless, earthless, flying with that star above the perfect borders of his paradise.

'Fucking arseholes.'

Charlie took his eyes off the sky and came back to the lawn. The sounds of the surrounding city returned, as did the throbbing pain in his cheek. He glanced at Jon, still sitting on the doorstep, still hugging his knees.

'Fucking arseholes,' Jon said again, his breath a cloud in the chilly air. 'What a perfect anniversary. I guess that's pissed all over our plans tonight, hasn't it?'

'Did you notice, Jonny, they didn't say anything – not a word, barely a grunt,' said Charlie, coming to sit beside his lover. 'It won't change anything about tonight; the show must go on.'

He put his arm around Jon's shoulder, but it was instantly shrugged off. Jon left the doorstep and paced around the lawn, his fists clenched deep in his pockets. He glared in every direction, but refused to meet Charlie's eyes. Sometimes you look so young, thought Charlie: sometimes you're just as angry and unpolished as when I first picked you up, negotiating prices under the railway arches. I forget how much I needed you back then, that pang of instant love when I saw you.

'What did the fuckers need to say? "Oh, excuse me, do you mind if I give your head a pounding? Can I trouble you for a quick bashing?" – I don't fucking think so.' Jon kicked hard at the trunk of the poplar, twice, and sent the tree into a fit. A cat panicked in the undergrowth and disappeared through the fence. 'How can we go out tonight? Have you seen your face? You look fucking older than ever.'

'I am older than ever,' Charlie smiled. He fingered the aching bump on the back of his head. He felt older than the hills, a body preserved in peat, a remnant from the last ice age. 'Was that a fox?'

'Just a cat, I think,' Jon sighed, now tilting his head so his wet eyes shone beneath the blonde fringe. They looked at each other for the first time since the beating. 'They got you bad, didn't they?'

Charlie nodded. 'Happy anniversary, Jonny.'

The first blow had come as a surprise. Walking home from the supermarket, it wasn't late but the midwinter streets were deserted. The Christmas lights hung motionless over the road, and Charlie lagged behind with the shopping. Jon walked ahead, always in a hurry, never wanting to walk two-by-two, and never holding hands. He had muttered something under his breath, but Charlie didn't catch it.

'What was that?' Charlie asked. 'I can't hear you when you're so determined not to walk with me.'

Jon hissed something again – perhaps 'Shut the fuck up'. Charlie stopped walking and stared at Jon's disappearing back. He was wondering what bee had got into Jon's bonnet when it happened. The first strike was a beer can thrown hard against the back of Charlie's head. It didn't hurt immediately but came as an explosive shock. The shopping bags dropped slowly to the pavement as his knees went weak and he slipped on the ice. Three oranges and a tin of beans tumbled out of the plastic bag and rolled into the gutter. The first pain came as Charlie's cheek slid against the tarmac; he heard himself make a ridiculous noise, a surprised 'woops!', embarrassed that he'd slipped up in front of strangers.

He looked up at their faces with an apologetic half-smile. One boy, barely sixteen, still clutched the Heineken can in his fist, ready to use it again should Charlie rise. The other two or three were background figures, moving everywhere at once, filling the periphery like the darkness. Charlie knelt in the road and felt the boot in his spine. A second and a third took away his breath, but the agony was in their unexpectedness not their force. A fourth kick, carefully aimed between his legs, shattered Charlie's consciousness.

He heard Jon's voice shouting over the chaos. 'Fuck it, Paul, fuck it,' and then footsteps racing away up the hill. Had he heard the name Paul? Had he heard Jon's voice at all?

There were more blows, more surprises, a rough hand digging into his pockets in search of a wallet – but Jon had the wallet on him. He had taken it as they'd left the supermarket to stop for fags on the way home. Charlie smiled knowing that his money was safe, though the rough hand still rummaged in his jeans. He knew Jon had run away, was out of danger.

'OK, boys, that's enough now,' Charlie tried to shout, his voice cracking as he gasped for air. 'Boys, that's enough.'

The kicking grew lighter and less furious. Charlie clutched his ribs and waited for a last blow to fall – the silence before the executioner's final cut. He opened his eyes and saw one of the oranges sitting in the drain. The street was empty and calm, but for the Christmas lights swaying above his head. He reached for the orange and clambered to his feet.

'The police asked if I heard them say anything,' said Charlie. A cloud of steam rose from the kettle and he unscrewed the coffee jar. He glanced through the window at the garden, floodlit with the glare from the kitchen, and paused. 'I thought I heard them say a name. Didn't you?'

'Like you said, the bastards didn't say anything,' Jon said, sitting on the kitchen work surface, banging his heels against the cupboard. 'I don't want to go out now.'

'Didn't you hear someone say "Paul"? I did, I'm sure. "Fuck it, Paul. Fuck it." That's what I heard.' Charlie poured the boiling water into the mugs and thoughtfully stirred the coffee. 'Jonny, I know you don't want to go, but we have to. It's a big day; two years, twenty-four months, one-hundred and four weeks.'

'Seven-hundred and thirty days, I know; I've been counting too.' Jon jumped to the floor and lit a cigarette. The flame from the match almost touched the tips of his fringe; sulphur hung in the air. 'Anyway, I didn't hang around long enough to hear what they had to say.'

'No, of course, you didn't,' Charlie nodded and passed the mug to Jon.

'I can't believe the garden now, I honestly can't. You've transfigured it in two years; our very own Eden. How clever you are.'

'There's still stuff to do,' said Jon. He avoided Charlie's gaze and went to the window. Staring, unblinking, into the night, he spoke to fill the hateful silence, to deflect the inevitable moment when they would leave. 'That ivy needs cutting back, and I haven't planted the daffodil bulbs yet. But, yeah, it does look good, even in winter, doesn't it? It was nothing when I came, do you remember? Don't know what you'd been doing before I arrived – stupid fucking old man – looked like a bomb hit it, didn't it? A right old mess. But the lawn looks great now, and the rosemary and the lavender and the rest of it down in the rockery. And there'll be fruit on the pear trees next year, I'll bet.'

'It's far too late in the year to plant daffodil bulbs, Jonny.'

They both jumped at the sudden burst of knocking on the front door. Standing with his back to the kitchen, Jon tried to keep his voice steady. 'Charlie, man. I don't want to go through with this.'

'That'll be the taxi,' said Charlie, turning to assess himself in the mirror above the kitchen table. He smiled at the red graze on his cheek and wondered if he should cover it with a bandage.

'Charlie, I don't want to go.'

'I know,' said Charlie. 'I'll go get our coats, shall I?'

The noise of the crowds in the bar area meant Charlie had to raise his voice for the waiter to hear him order crème brûlée. He hated having to repeat himself, and fidgeted with his napkin as he stumbled over the words for the third time. Jon just shook his head when the waiter turned to him.

'Nothing, really? That's unlike you,' said Charlie when they were left alone. 'I despise this racket, all those dreadful people. Why can't they just speak normally to one another. And that awful woman with the laugh – why don't they just shut up?'

'Because it's a fucking bar and they're out having a fucking good time,' said Jon. 'It's Christmas, hadn't you noticed?'

'Can't hear myself think,' Charlie sighed, tapping the table with his spoon. Another burst of laughter split the air and made him wince. Shaking his head, he stared out the window at the icy street. The sky glowed pink with frozen clouds, waiting to crack and shower the town with snow.

'I see that all the stars have gone,' Charlie said when the laughter had died down. He waited a moment, measuring the likelihood of another interruption. He didn't want there to be any uncertainty when he struck his blow. 'So, Jonny, was it good to see Paul again?'

Jon didn't move. He stared at the table and waited for the words to sink in, played them back to himself so there could be no mistake. Then he reached for the champagne and poured himself another glass. Turning the flute between his fingers, he watched the bubbles settle.

'You knew, didn't you?' Jon said at last. 'When did you realise?'

'When I saw his face; when he stood holding the can over my head, ready to hit me again. He looks just like you, doesn't he? Same dark eyes, same heavy frown, same sharp nose, same mixture of anger and fear in his face. I can see you in him, a much younger version, of course, but obviously your brother. What I don't understand is why you didn't let him take my wallet. That was why you orchestrated it, wasn't it?'

'It's not about the fucking money,' said Jon, leaning forward so quickly that their faces almost collided. They locked eyes, and Charlie smelled the sweet trace of alcohol on his breath. 'Do you really think all this is about money? Charlie, do you? Do you reckon I would have hung around you for two years, dug up your fucking jungle of a garden, kissed your eyes each fucking morning, missed the taste of your tongue when you weren't there and held your body against me every fucking night if it was all about the money? I longed for you, Charlie; each day you were at work and I was digging in the bloody garden, I longed for the evening when you would come home.'

'You were always a skilled negotiator,' said Charlie, smiling uncomfortably around the room to see if anyone was listening. He nodded meekly at the couple on the next table. 'From the very beginning, under those railway arches, that story about your life on the streets, and then when you demanded an extra five grand on top of an already generous deal, you were an excellent salesman. Is all this talk of tongues and longing an attempt to raise the stakes?'

'Fuck off,' said Jon, thumping the table and spilling his cutlery onto the floor. The waiter came running from the kitchen, and knelt down to collect the spoons. He apologised for the delay with the desserts, and Charlie ordered another bottle of champagne.

'Did they really hurt you?' Jon asked when they were alone again. He shook his head and wiped his eyes. 'What a fucking stupid question. I'm so sorry. I didn't know what else to do, how else to keep you.'

'And you thought you'd keep me by beating me up?' Charlie laughed. 'Or by getting your family to do it?'

'I didn't touch you, Charlie. I thought… I just wanted you to be helpless for a while.'

'So I'd need you if I was crippled?'

'Just for you to need me – until after tonight was out of the way.'

'Well, I'm sorry that my legs still work.'

The waiter returned with the champagne and Charlie's dessert. They waited in silence as he opened the bottle and refilled their glasses. Charlie tapped gently at the crust of his crème brûlée. Outside, the first faint snowflakes began to fall.

'You were always going to stick to the deal, weren't you?' said Jon. 'After two fucking years, no matter what happened, no matter how much I wanted you, you would always dump me back on the streets.'

Charlie pulled an envelope from his pocket and laid it between them on the table. He ate his dessert in small mouthfuls, the crust cracking dryly between his teeth.

'You can check it if you like, but the full amount is there,' he said. 'As per our agreement two years ago. Happy anniversary, Jonny.'

'I don't want the money,' Jon said quietly, the tears flowing down his cheek. Each droplet fell to the tablecloth and soaked into the cotton, ticking the seconds of their last moments together. He swept his fringe back and stared full into Charlie's face for one final assault. 'I love you.'

Charlie caught the heavy scent of tears – the smell that he devoured, that was perfectly different in every boy that he had ever bought, the essence that he always extracted as his own sweet triumph.

'And that's precisely why I don't want you anymore,' he said, licking the last of the cream from his spoon.

Long after Charlie had walked out of the restaurant, as the last stragglers were asked for the final time to leave the bar, Jon stroked the edge of the envelope. The waiter returned again to the table and removed the ice bucket with the empty bottles.

'I'm sorry, sir. We're closing now,' he said. 'Are you sure you're all right?'

'Cheers, I'll be gone in a minute,' Jon said, standing up and pulling on his jacket. He took one last look at the envelope on the table, and then turned his back on it. One by one, the waiter flicked the lights off above him, as he staggered across the floor and out into the snow.

Charlie stood alone in his garden, the snow settling on his eyelashes as he gazed up at a sky full of flakes. Everything around him – the poplars, the pear trees, the herbs in the rockery – waited for him to act. The wooden handle of the spade was cold in his hands, and his fingers began to feel numb.

Closing his eyes, Charlie lifted the spade behind his shoulder and brought it smashing against the trunk of the young poplar. He heaved the blade down again and again, cutting into the white flesh of the tree. When the trunk was demolished, he turned on the rosemary and lavender, crushing the twigs beneath each wild blow. As he split the branches from the pear trees, he lost all feeling in his face.

By morning, there would be nothing left of this place, no lawn, no climbing ivy, no living stalk or stem. By the spring, the garden would be a wasteland of thistles and stinging nettles. Come the summer, another gardener would be found to bring order to the wilderness, and another paradise would be planted. But for one pure night – tonight – the power belonged to Charlie.

A Bathhouse in Bordeaux

José Luis de Juan

Translated from the Spanish
by Martin Schifino and Selina Packard

The wine guys looked very macho, whereas he had always seen himself as a damsel, though he was a tall, robust man without ever having run to fat. At thirty-nine, he still had some of his adolescent, even boyish, features: his blush, his weak voice, his nervous gaze. He spoke seldom and was incapable of telling a joke in public; in fact, I doubt he was capable of telling a joke at all. He wasn't that kind of guy. In Oviedo, where he had grown up among four brothers and three sisters, he went unnoticed: first in the bosom of his noisy family (he was the fifth, an ordinal number that followed him like his own shadow, the discordant fifth), then at school and at university (where he started out as a lecturer in microeconomics after graduating in economics) and finally in his own family, as a father of two.

If he hadn't decided to take the course in advanced oenology in Bordeaux, his life would have followed the same roughly straight line, despite its ever-present knots, tight and tense. What might have happened? Nothing he wouldn't have been able to accommodate, even if it didn't seem so in retrospect; everything, even the most unexpected change, was rooted in a particular past. Back then he didn't know his wife had fleeting affairs; he would find out much later. His two boys were beginning to ignore him, to regard him as a piece of furniture, a comfortable, solid piece of furniture that sometimes spoke up, only to be corrected and overruled by their mother.

It was the death of his father that altered his career plans, uprooting him from the University of Oviedo, where he was professor of international commerce. His father was a vineyard-owner who had created a prestige label using vinestock transplanted into a stony soil with deep natural drainage. It was a delicate wine, different from the others in the region, though it remained what the inhabitants of Bordeaux somewhat patron-isingly called '*un vin classic*'. No one in his family wanted to take over the business when his father suddenly died of a heart attack at sixty-seven. His brothers were in engineering, medicine or law, and his sisters had other concerns. That left him.

His mother made him. He'd always heard the others say, with a mixture of sarcasm and envy, that he was his mother's favourite. But he never got that impression. On the contrary: he thought he'd been on the receiving end of more of her smacks than his siblings; he thought that as he was incapable of deception, or at least of practising it as casually and shame-lessly as they did, he always got the blame for their pranks, and their punishment too. To which his brothers and sisters replied: complete nonsense; he'd been a silly cry-baby, always hiding in his mother's skirts.

Now he tried to imagine his sisters' expressions if they could see him in this dimly lit room, bent over this light-skinned guy, giving him a vigorous hand-job. He was a little surprised by the girth and texture of the guy's cock, which was so different from his own, and which he didn't *feel*. He had masturbated since puberty, but he'd never done it to others (it was as if his cock had been grafted onto the guy). It was nice enough. The guy was now trying to suck him, to take *his* cock into his mouth, which he would not allow without first slipping on a condom. His sisters were wearing those expressions of disgust and censure he'd sometimes seen – directed first at him and later at their husbands. Thinking of his sisters at this moment was a way of settling scores.

Yes, these wine guys seemed very macho. They were different from the guys at home. A cloying, tactile, and yet distant courtesy towards women. It reminded him of the old-fashioned gallantry of his father's generation. And that reserve, dressed up in distinction and elegance and directed at members of the same sex, became violent, brutal, competitive. He'd noticed it playing tennis with two of his fellow wine students.

Over the past six months as a student – which might turn into eight, as he was planning to spend some time at the Saint Emilion and Bergerac vineyards – he had started seeing a divorcée. Christine Delmas appeared one day with a Bordeaux wine guru. He liked her smile, one of the most open and carefree he'd ever seen in a woman. It was an invitation to anything – everything and nothing at the same time. Brunette and elegant, with something slightly wicked in the contrast between the colour of her hair and the red of her lips and her pointed earrings, she was an intense, wounded woman. (All the women in Bordeaux looked wounded to him, however hard they tried to hide it.) Of course, she waited for him to make the first move, and he – slow to react as he was, this being his first affair – did so a few days later, in a café at the centre of town. The flat he rented, on Place des Martyrs de la Résistance, was ten minutes away, and as they walked there he wondered why he was taking her to bed. He didn't feel aroused. He simply needed female company, the kind of tenderness he'd been used to in the last years and now missed. Perhaps his sisters were right after all.

Christine had a scar on her thigh. She told him it was from a horse-riding accident. That first evening she tactfully excused his difficulties. It was normal the first time, she said. But the second time it was the same, and the third – they were in her office, on the Allée de Tourny – he only managed to masturbate over her stomach. Nevertheless, despite his poor amatory skills in a country where, at least it was said in Spain, men were good lovers who knew how to give a woman pleasure, Christine seemed more and more taken with him. It was on their fifth encounter (fifth, his number) that he felt the need to slow down. A little after eight in the evening, when they were both talking naked in bed, his wife called, and that brought about a crisis. He realised Christine didn't just want *that*; she wanted *him*. She spent the night, but left early for her work as a financial consultant. On the bathroom mirror she scrawled a message in fuschia lipstick. '*Je t'aime, mais tu ne veux pas m'aimer. C'est dommage.*'

A few lonely days followed. He didn't call Christine, and she remained silent. He realised he had become accustomed to her face and her soft accent. The social life in Bordeaux was a little slow. And in truth he wasn't a sociable man. The weather was fine, and in the mornings he walked by the quayside of the Garona River. In one of the streets parallel to the quayside, on the same block as a Gothic church he had visited out of pure boredom, was the bathhouse. He had called the previous day to find out what he should expect, and he had been told that most clients were men, but that sometimes couples ventured in, free of charge. In any case, the guy on the phone had advised him not to visit if he wasn't into men, because he would 'find it boring'. Once there he'd asked the doorman, behind the glass of a little ticket office like the ones in old cinemas, if there were many people in. The man answered that there were only men, but as it was Sunday maybe some couples would turn up later. Maybe not. *Je ne sais pas.*

The little changing room was poorly lit. He undressed, put his clothes in a locker, and wrapped a white towel round his waist. The place smelled of eucalyptus, like a Finnish sauna. The guy at the entrance was talking to some customers, some dressed and some in towels. He went into a room with low chairs and a coffee table laid with plates holding condoms and longish sachets labelled 'glisse'. He took one of each. He walked on along the corridors, feeling the damp wood against the soles of his feet. He thought he should have brought a pair of flip-flops with him. Just in case, he walked on the sides of his feet, until, laughing at himself, he realised that a bit of athlete's foot wasn't the worst thing he might catch there.

He passed serious-looking men wearing absentminded expressions, as if they were there by mistake, on their way somewhere else. Some seemed to be looking for someone they'd lost, and peered into the small rooms, searching; then they went on their way, unfazed, sometimes with a slight shrug of the shoulders. They did this with the sad, resigned air of men who know they won't find what they're looking for but have nothing better to do. As he inspected the place, which at first seemed vast and labyrinthine, and then, as time went on, cramped and claustrophobic, he started to mimic these men. He too wandered tirelessly from one spot to the next, his impatience increasing. His sole desire now was for something to happen at last, or to find someone he hadn't already seen.

Every now and again he slumped into one of the uncomfortable red vinyl armchairs and watched the videos playing in the rooms. Close-ups of cocks, of guys jerking or sucking them. Women easing dildos into men's arses. A woman wearing high boots and a spiked choker fucked by a guy who was fucked in turn by another guy. Four or five men tangled naked in an orgiastic rugby scrum. Fast talk between a woman at the door and two buff men in blue overalls, talk suddenly interrupted, their masks of housewife and plumbers shed even quicker than their clothes. He noted the expressions, or the lack of expression, in the customers who lingered by the door, as if they expected the buff guys or the woman to step out of the screen (what would they have done then?), or of those who remained seated beside him on the red armchairs, pointlessly covered by their towels.

No one said a word, except the doorman's acquaintances. No sign of erections under the towels. He, however, was aroused. His wanderings from the Jacuzzi to the Finnish sauna (where the steam blurred the faces, and even turned the white towels grey), and from there to the regular sauna and the showers, became more and more tense, and in time he noticed that an hour had gone by without anything happening. He started touching himself under his towel, more and more blatantly, in front of the screens; the others ignored him as if what he was doing were forbidden and shameful but something that they, like good mates, would not mention. Later he lay on the bed of a small room decorated with fake cowhide. For some reason the kitsch decor aroused him. He removed his towel. With a good hard-on, which had been reheated already a few times, he started masturbating. Some guys peered in and watched for a few seconds, but went on their way. After a while, realising that he was not going to bring about anything that he might not bring about at home on his own, he stood up and put his towel back on a little carelessly.

A woman's voice was coming from the Jacuzzi. He went over. She was a blonde in her mid-forties, accompanied by an older man who had silver-grey hair and looked like a Roman senator. Their elbows resting on the edge of the round pool, they were chatting with two young men. He got into the pool, his cock semi-erect. He couldn't make out what they were saying, but it was obviously some kind of courtship, and he felt excluded. He was not interested in the blonde anyway; let the others fuck her if they wanted. Sure enough, a little later he saw her and the Roman senator walk into the cowhide room with one of the young men – the more muscular one – and close the door behind them. Two others, who had smelled pleasure in the air, stood whispering by the door, as if standing guard or waiting their turn. There was also some activity in a smaller room fitted with a gynaecological chair. The door was not closed. He went in. A woman was spreadeagled on the chair and a guy was frantically trying to fuck her, but the sweat made him slip up on the leather straps, the stainless-steel bars and the linoleum floor. Three other men buzzed around the woman, licking her nipples, touching her or just looking. When she saw him come in, the woman blurted out a marital reproach to the man who was watching and seemed to be orchestrating the others' movements: '*Tu veux ici tout le monde, hein?*'

He left the room. One of the nipple-lickers, whom he'd been bumping into along the corridors since he'd arrived, closed the door in his face, growling like a dog unwilling to share his bone. He thought he must have arrived too early, as now there were new people. A black man, more expansive and talkative than the others, strutted by and smiled at him.

He saw a guy in the room where he had lain on the bed a few moments before. He was tall and sinewy, his muscles trained in a swimming pool rather than in a gym. His pubis was shaved, and he was gently, playfully, tugging at his half-erect cock, his eyes half-closed, as if the dim light that bathed the room in black and white shades was too bright for him. Seeing the guy's swollen pecs, he suddenly remembered standing in front of the bathroom mirror with one of his mother's bras on, pretending he had breasts. He'd tried filling the cups with oranges or apples, but the best fit were the big peaches they had in the summer. In front of the mirror, he would hide his cock between his thighs, and the vision of his black pubis without a phallus gave him intense pleasure, even more intense if he turned to the side and his cock and balls were visible on the other side. Balls, cock, absurdly pointed breasts, hairy arms and legs (he'd tried shaving them until the cuts started showing and he stopped), it all created a deeply alluring image. He would fall in love with himself then, with his own androgynous fancy dress. With a cock and without a cock, male and female. He would have fucked himself, but he'd have broken the mirror.

The guy let himself be touched and opened his half-closed eyes. He grasped the guy's cock, which felt very rubbery, more so than his own. He exposed the glans sharply and the guy uttered a muffled guttural sound of pain or pleasure. His own towel fell and his cock was nearly horizontal. When he started jerking the other's off, the guy stretched his legs, sat up, grabbed him and tried to take him in his mouth. He drew back instinctively, leaving his prey, and made to open a condom, but the guy, with a gesture of contempt for his absurd scruples, put his cock straight into his mouth. It was at that moment that he felt a change within his body. Without thinking, he lay down over the guy's body and swallowed his dick in return.

The man was roughly his height and of similar weight, although his build was different. He opened his eyes and saw above him, on the ceiling, their image doubled in a mirror he hadn't noticed before. Symmetrical and opposed, heads, mouths, cocks, arses and feet, and toes moving as if playing an invisible harp.

The only time he'd ever had a cock in his mouth it had been his own. Back when he practised yoga and his tendons and spine were more flexible, he'd managed to reach his glans with his lips and come on his mouth. Later the vertebrae of his neck ached, but the pain was nothing compared to the erotic excitement he'd experienced trying to reach himself. Now he had the strange feeling of reaching himself through this silent guy who felt like a phallic extension of his own body. And at the same time he felt mentally blocked, incapable of recognising himself in this new sexual situation, as if he were witnessing it from the outside, through a thick pane of glass.

The guy alternated powerful sucking and swallowing with soft licking of the frenulum. He was clearly an expert. He, on the other hand, found it difficult to take the glans into his mouth, and recalled that dentists always impatiently asked him to open wider. Nor did he know what to do with his tongue, or how to accommodate the bell of the cock in the small space between his teeth and palate. He tried to compensate for his lack of skill by tugging and squeezing violently on the member, which seemed to be at his mercy.

He was thus occupied when he heard a familiar, authoritarian voice a few steps away from the bed. He raised his head and took the spit-covered cock out of his mouth. Standing there without a towel, with the biggest penis he'd ever seen, was Benoît Ricade, one of the oenology experts who'd given him wine-tasting lessons during his first two months in Bordeaux. He was a heavily-built man with a tawny mane of hair and bulging blue eyes. Benoît clearly knew the guy, who looked weedy beside him; he called him '*merde foutu*'. Then, visibly angry, Benoît kicked him in the chest. He pounced on the guy and grabbed his neck. Benoît had enormous hands (he would later think of the correlation between big hands and big cock), which easily covered the white, sinewy neck. He threw the guy face down on the bed, his head hanging off the side of it, nearly touching the floor. The poor guy whimpered but did not attempt to defend himself. The oenologist went on insulting him and squeezing his neck, which was starting to bruise. Benoît squeezed and squeezed, and no pleading or sign of suffocation came out of the mouth that only moments before had been sucking and licking his cock.

The guy was now completely still. And at that point Benoît, straddling him, a hundred-odd angry kilos, started to loosen his grip, as if he was letting out a fishing line, and then pulled the guy's buttocks apart.

Ignoring the *glisse*, he brutally penetrated the guy, who at that moment released his breath in a deep, almost inhuman groan. Treating him like a puppet, moving his hips back and forth, Benoît fucked him with his darkly-coloured cock that had grown even bigger and went in and out like a club. The guy now seemed to be enjoying himself hugely. Frothing at the mouth, he murmured words touched with an incomprehensible tenderness.

Having witnessed the scene from the wings, without knowing what to do or say, he realised the two guys were or perhaps had been a couple. Without asking permission, as was the norm in the bathhouse, he simply stuck his cock in the guy's mouth, while the oenologist fucked him – now slowly, now frenziedly – and gave no indication of coming soon. It took *him* less than a minute to ejaculate into the depths of that abused throat. He had some difficulty taking his cock out. The guy refused to let it go until he'd swallowed the last drop. Then he wrapped the towel round his waist, and left the room, his legs shaking. He reached the blue room with the Jacuzzi. He hung up his towel and sank up to his chin in the turbulent water. He thought of Christine Delmas.

Maybe he'd call her tonight.

A Very Special Customer

Francis King

Luigi, the elderly Italian proprietor with the cracked patent-leather shoes and the dinner jacket dusted with dandruff as though with talcum powder, surveyed with weary disgust the tray that I was carrying back to the kitchen, a full soup bowl on it.

'What's up?'

'First she said it wasn't hot enough. Now she says it's too salty.'

He sighed. 'She's a very special customer. Been coming here for years. Don't talk to me about very special customers. They're always very special nuisances. Take it into the kitchen, wait two minutes, then bring it back. OK?'

I did as he said. The very special customer was a tiny little woman, with bony legs and arms and a lot of large rings on fingers gnarled with arthritis. Her hair, worn in tight ringlets to her shoulders, was a shiny black.

'I hope that will now be all right, madam.' Then I suddenly realised that I was serving her from the wrong side. Luigi had reprimanded me for this solecism only the day before. I darted round the table, one of the few that faced out into the street, slopping some of the soup onto the tray as I did so.

'I'm sure it will.' When she smiled, only her heavily made-up lips moved in her extraordinarily smooth, triangular, still pretty face. 'Bless you! And please forgive me for being such a wearisome old bat. But I like hot things really hot, and my doctor doesn't like me to swallow anything too salty.' At that, spoon raised over the bowl, she once more looked down at the *Times* crossword half-completed before her.

When, for her next course, I arrived with her usual Sole Meunière, she once again smiled up at me. 'Oh, lovely! But what a lot of butter! Far too

181

much for me. So do please be careful that I have only the fish. And bone it for me, there's a dear.'

My boning was clumsy. But when I set down the plate before her, she cried out: 'Oh, I can see that you're an expert!'

Two evenings later she was back at what, I learned later, she regarded as 'her' table. 'I like to watch the world go by,' she said as I pulled back the chair facing the window and she carefully lowered herself into it. 'Are you here only in the evenings?'

'Yes, that's right.' I shook out her linen napkin.

'What are you doing the rest of the time?'

'I'm at school.'

'At school? What are you studying?'

'Acting.'

'Snap!' she cried out. Then, seeing my bewilderment, she explained: 'I'm an actress.' She tilted her head on one side as, soup spoon in hand, she gazed up at me. I think that she expected me to recognise her. 'What's your accent?'

'My accent? Oh, do I have an accent?'

'Others wouldn't notice it. But I have this amazing ear for an accent. For a time, when good parts weren't coming my way, I was a dialect coach – donkey's years ago. Where are you from?'

'My family comes from Goa.'

'Goa! I once had a holiday in Goa. They told us that all the best cooks in India came from Goa. I could only assume, from the ghastly food served up to us, that the cook at our hotel was not Goan.'

'None of my family has ever been a cook, I'm afraid.'

She laughed and gulped at the soup. 'No, I'm sure not!' Then she raised her head to scrutinise me. 'You don't look Indian.'

'Well, I'm partly Portuguese.'

'Who is she?' I asked Luigi at the end of a long and exhausting evening.

'Mrs Grace. Netta Grace. Never heard of her? Most people haven't today. But she was famous once. So they tell me.'

On the next occasion that I served her, she asked me my name.

'Harry. Harry Da Costa.'

'*Harry*! Oh, I thought it would be something far more exotic. I once had an Indian lover whose first name was Ram. It seemed terribly appropriate. I used to call him the Battering Ram.'

Having now learned my name, she rarely used it. When referring to me, it was usually as 'My favourite waiter'. If I had been assigned to an area of the restaurant different from that to which her table belonged, she would demand that nonetheless I must still wait on her. If the restaurant was empty – and sometimes, inconveniently and embarrassingly, even when it was full – she would carry on lengthy conversations with me. It turned out that she had herself been at RADA, just as I was now.

A few days later, having answered the telephone, Luigi held out the receiver to me: 'She wants her favourite waiter.'

'Who wants him?' But I did not really have to ask. Clumsy and forgetful, I was no one else's favourite waiter.

'Is that my favourite waiter?' Her voice was husky and faint. 'Oh, darling, you must, must help me. I've got this flu that started with chickens in China. You've probably read about it in the papers. At least I think it must be that. I've got a terrific temperature and, as you can hear, I'm croaking. What I wonder is this. Do you think you could come over with some food? You know, I live just round the corner, only a hop, skip and a jump away. For you, since you're so young and strong, only a hop. What I'd love is a plate of pasta, any pasta, and some *tiramisu*. As I'm sure you know, *tiramisu* means "pull me up" in Italian – or so I've been told – and I need to be pulled up, I'm feeling so low.'

'I don't get off until eleven o'clock at the earliest,' I said, having no wish to carry food round to her when all I wanted was to see my boyfriend before he became too sleepy for sex.

'Oh, that's all right. Channel Five has a film with me in it, black and white, just a small part, but I'd like to watch it, depressing though that will probably be. So I can have a midnight feast after that.'

'How shall I get in? I don't want to drag you out of bed.'

'Oh, I can just about stagger to the thingummy that unlocks the door. Take the lift. Fourth floor.'

The door of her flat, occupying what had once been the attic of a single-family mansion, was open. 'Come in, come in!' she called. I entered a low-ceilinged sitting room, made to look even more cramped by a vast, sagging sofa and two vast armchairs, all upholstered in a startlingly vivid cretonne, bunches of pink roses on a turquoise ground. 'I'm here, in here!' she called. I set down the two carrier bags in which one of the sous chefs had placed the food in its plastic containers. Then I moved across to the open door that led to the bedroom. It too was low-ceilinged, with little space for anything but a dressing table and a brass double-bedstead. She was propped up on a pile of pillows, looking, bony and beaky, like some ailing sparrow. The first thing that I noticed about her was that she was wearing a grey beret at a jaunty angle. Then I realised that that beret could not possibly have contained all that shiny black hair. The shiny black hair could only have been a wig.

Perhaps she guessed that I had reached this conclusion. 'I hate to have you see me like this. I mean, in this crumpled nightdress, no make-up. I've no right to inflict it on you, you poor boy.'

Embarrassed I asked: 'Where's the kitchen? I'd better serve the food before it gets cold.'

'Oh, you are good!' she exclaimed as I placed the tray across her knees. 'Don't bend too close! I'd hate to give you my bug.' She picked up a square of ravioli in her fingers and popped it into her mouth. 'I feel better already.' She began to eat with gusto, now using not her fingers but the fork and spoon that I had found in one of the kitchen drawers. 'That film was *ghastly*. I had forgotten that Margaret Lockwood could be so utterly putrid. We never got on, you know. She was an absolute bitch to me during those weeks at Pinewood. Chalk and cheese, oil and water.' She continued to reminisce. Exhausted from racing around the restaurant and realising that by now my boyfriend would certainly be asleep, I longed only to leave and to crawl into the bed beside his humped, inert body. If it was quick enough, he might even allow me to give him a blowjob. At last she had finished eating. But she had far from finished talking. Eventually I got to my feet: 'I must go, I really must go. I don't want to miss my last bus.'

'Must you? Must you really? You've made me feel so much better already.'

'Yes, I'm afraid I must.'

'Oh, all right.' For a moment she sounded displeased. Then that mood vanished. 'Oh, you have been such a darling! As soon as I met you that first time in the restaurant, I knew you were the sort of person on whom one can rely. You're my *tiramisu* – you've pulled me up. In fact, I might even surprise you by being in the restaurant tomorrow evening. Who knows! Anyway, before you go, I want you to give me my bag.' She pointed, her nightdress sleeve falling away to reveal an arm on which the skin looked like grey, sagging crêpe. 'It's in the corner over there.'

I handed the bag to her. She opened it and began to count out coins with her right hand into the palm of her left. Then she passed over the pile. 'I *think* that's five quid. I hope it is. I do wish I could make it more but that's all I can find at the moment – apart from a twenty note.'

'Oh, no, no!' I protested. But she was so insistent that eventually I put the coins into my trouser pocket.

As I was leaving, she cried out: 'Oh, what a kind, kind boy you've been! I only wish I wasn't looking such a *hag* for you. Try to forget how I'm looking. *Please!*'

Soon after that, having discovered a shared interest, she began to invite me to weekend excursions to museums and art galleries. Since on Saturdays and sometimes even on a Sunday my boyfriend had to be behind his desk at Trailfinders, I was happy to accept. I particularly remember a visit to a Bonnard exhibition at the Royal Academy. Netta refused to take the lift ('Oh, no, the exercise is good for me!') but then clung to my arm and from time to time paused to gulp for air as we mounted the stairs. Like a small child, arms raised and palms pressed against each other, she went into a state of mounting excitement from picture to picture. 'Oh, Paris, Paris, pre-war Paris! How happy I was there! I was only a child, of course,' she added quickly, 'but how these pictures all bring it back to me! I'm bilingual, you know. I've acted in French. Some fluffy boulevard nonsense by Sacha Guitry, when I was barely sixteen. Now he *was* a card!'

After two rooms she began to flag. She once more linked her arm in mine for support; all at once she fell silent. 'I think I'll sit down here for a moment. I want to – to *contemplate* that picture over there for a moment.' The picture, a large one, showed Madame Bonnard in the bath. 'That woman seems to have spent most of her time having baths. Apparently he insisted on it. A kind of perversion, I suppose. Unless she was one of those poor people who cannot help their body odour. You go on. I'll catch you up.'

Eventually I went back to look for her. Chin on chest, shiny black ringlets covering her shoulders, she was asleep. She had kicked off her absurdly high-heeled court shoes and one of her tiny, misshapen feet, was resting over the other. There was a hole in one of her stockings over the crumpled big toe. For a while I sat down beside her, listening to her heavy breathing and an occasional grunt. Then I touched her arm. At once she jerked up. 'Oh, dear, I fell asleep. I had a late night last night. I suddenly decided to deal with weeks and weeks of smalls. Smalls are always a big thing in the life of a working woman.'

We ended up in the downstairs café. It was then that she asked me, for the first time, 'Tell me, Harry, is there anyone special in your life?'

'Special?'

'A little girlfriend?'

I shook my head.

'A big boyfriend?'

'Oh, no, no!' I forced a laugh, to convince her of the absurdity of such a suggestion.

'Oh, good-o! Then I can have you entirely to myself.'

Her enquiry had emboldened me. 'Is your husband still alive?'

'My husband? I've no idea at all. He was an Austrian refugee, a homeopath. A friend sent me to him when I was in a state of desperation over one of those inconvenient woman's things. Well, an abortion to be exact. I married him to give him British nationality. As soon as the war was over he skedaddled to Canada with his Welsh receptionist and a lot of money belonging to his partner. And a good thing, too! His breath was terrible.'

I asked nothing further.

When the summer vacation came and I was free at daytimes, Netta suggested that I have lunch with her in her club. I had often wondered where she ate her lunches – since Luigi had told me that she never ate them in the restaurant. 'It's small and it's secret,' she said. 'Passing it, you'd never guess what it was. Just an ordinary house, with a front door always closed and a television thingy and a phone to check you before anyone opens up.' She made it sound more like a discreet brothel than a club. I was fascinated.

I picked her up from her flat and we walked over. 'It's a club for the sort of people who did secret jobs in the war,' she explained. 'But since so many of those are dead or dying, we now also have a number of members – or former members – of the SAS.'

'What exactly was your wartime job?'

'Oh, it's too boring to talk about it. My real job has always been acting. Just as that will always be your real job, not waiting at tables.'

We entered the small hall. The burly, bald man seated before the CCTV screen greeted her with enthusiasm: 'Mrs Grace! Long time, no see! What became of you?'

'Filming,' she said. 'A lot of work's been coming in.'

'That's good.'

'Oh, yes! Even if it does mean getting up at five and sitting around for most of the day with a lot of boring people.'

We began to mount the narrow staircase up to the bar and dining room. The wall on the left was lined with black-and-white or sepia photographs of young men and women, usually in uniform.

'Who are all these people?'

'The ones I told you about. They worked in – or with – the Resistance. SOE. That sort of thing.' At first she was offhand. Then she halted in our ascent and stared first at one photograph of a girl with high cheekbones and a smile disclosing crooked, discoloured teeth, and then at another of a long-faced man with a crisp, handlebar moustache and bushy eyebrows. 'I knew those two. Dead. Captured and killed. When I think of them, one word comes to my mind. Valour.' She repeated it, with more emphasis: 'Valour.' The word, so little used today, seemed somehow appropriate for heroes and heroines of a by now remote past. Then she sighed and resumed her ascent.

We entered the bar. 'Hello, Barry!' she greeted the barman.

'Good afternoon, Mrs Grace.' He was as welcoming as the porter had been. 'Is it going to be the usual today?' Clearly she was as much a very special customer to these people as to Luigi and me.

'First I must find out what my young friend wants.'

When we were seated at a table, each with a glass of Chardonnay and a croque-monsieur, I glanced around me. I had an immediate impression of a lot of old men in grey suits, with close-cut, thinning grey hair and grey faces, and women with large bosoms, strong mouths and melancholy eyes. From time to time someone would greet Netta or even come over, having collected a drink or some food from the bar, to ask: 'How's things?' or 'What's up with you?' or to tell her something flattering like 'You're looking terrific, Netta, not a day older.' Everyone seemed to be on intimate terms with everybody.

As, on our departure, we were descending the stairs, my eye was suddenly caught by an Angus McBean photograph high up on the wall.

It was the head and shoulders of a blonde woman, in her early twenties at a guess, with a wide, full mouth, a slightly over-large nose, and a humorous, resolute, challenging expression as she stared into the invisible camera. I halted; and, since I was supporting Netta with a hand to her elbow, she also had to halt. 'Netta! Isn't that you? That girl…' I pointed.

'*That*? Yes, I suppose I must plead guilty. Yes, she's me. Or rather – she *was* me She's dead. I'm someone different.'

'So you were also one of those women you were telling me about just now. The ones who were parachuted…'

'Oh, don't let's talk about all that. I've already said – it's such a bore! Please!'

'But, Netta, I want to know. I really want to know…'

'No, sweetie. You see, I just want to forget. *Forget.*'

Once or twice later I tried to raise the subject. But I never got anywhere.

I had never known if Netta had any relatives, until she invited me to a birthday party being given for her by a niece. The niece, a gaunt, middle-aged radiographer, and her husband, a constantly beaming judge, lived in a sprawling Georgian house, with a large garden, near Hampstead parish church. Since it was a fine summer evening, it was in the garden that the guests were assembled on my arrival. Feeling self-conscious and nervous, I cursed myself for not having made some excuse and refused the invitation. I also cursed myself for not having put on my one dark suit and a tie. There were far more people than I had ever expected, and most of those were far nearer Netta's age than mine. At first I could not identify either my hostess or host and I could nowhere see Netta. A waiter brought me a glass of champagne. I then examined a bed of roses with feigned interest, the bulky present of a run of old numbers of *Plays and Players,* bought at an Oxfam shop, tucked under one arm.

An elderly man, in a dove grey suit and mauve tie, wandered up to me. 'Magnificent,' he said. I did not at first realise that he was referring to the roses. 'Isn't that a Bella Somerset?'

'I don't know. I'm not all that good at roses.'

'Neither am I, to tell the truth. What are you good at?'

'I'm an actor.' I thought that sounded better than 'drama student' did.

'Like our dear Netta.'

Fortunately at that moment I heard Netta calling: 'Harry! Harry! What are you up to over there?' She bore down on us, with a plump, plain girl in a dirndl skirt in tow. 'I want you to meet Gretel. You can be her Hansel. She's my niece's au pair. The poor dear's feeling rather lost.'

'I'm also feeling rather lost.'

'Then you can feel less lost together.'

The elderly man, whistling under his breath, had begun to move off.

'Gretel's such an obliging girl. She adores the children and she makes the most wonderful *knödl*.' I had no idea what *knödl* was – or were. I have no idea even now.

'I never imagined that there would be so many people here.'

'Well, in the existence of a strolling player, a rolling stone – or strolling stone – gathers a lot of moss. Half these old friends I hardly remember – and the other half I hardly want to remember. At all events, my niece keeps telling me that this is a very special occasion.'

'May I ask how old you are?'

'You may. But you won't get an answer. But if you're terribly inquisitive, you can tot up the candles on the four cakes.'

Later, with some difficulty because of the crowds surging around the still uncut cakes, I totted up the candles. I made the number twenty to a cake, eighty in all.

I was boning her usual Sole Meunière.

'The soles seem to be getting smaller and smaller here. This one is little more than a sprat,' she complained.

A few minutes later, I heard an anguished cry of 'Harry! Harry!' By the time that I had set down a tray loaded with plates and had hurried over to her table, Luigi was already there. A hand to her throat, as though in an attempt to strangle herself, she was coughing and gagging. 'Do something, do something about this bloody bone!' she got out, her eyes swivelling frantically between Luigi and me. 'I'm choking to death!'

Luigi lifted her glass of the house white. 'Maybe a sip!'

She lowered her head and sipped. She pondered for a moment, head on one side. Nervously swallowed. Frowned. Swallowed again, with greater resolution. Then she shook her head. 'Still there,' she said in a husky voice. At once she began again to cough and gag, her hands gripping the table. 'Oh, God!' At that, she looked up and glared at me. 'Why, why, why didn't you bone that bloody sole properly?'

By now everyone in the restaurant was staring at us.

'Would you like to go upstairs, madam? We have our private dining room there. Or the ladies room?'

'No, I would not! I must get to the hospital. A and E. Now! Pronto! Before this thing chokes me to death. It's *agony*. You've no idea.' She cleared her throat repeatedly and then gave a piteous mew. Lurching to her feet, she swivelled round to face me. 'You'll have to come with me. You can spare him, can't you, Luigi, dear? I must have someone to accompany me. I might pass out in the street.'

The waiting room was crowded with people. A long line snaked back from the reception desk, where two harassed women in white coats, their faces blotched with sweat, were at that moment arguing with a group of five or six foreigners, none of whom appeared to be able to speak more than a dozen words of English. After a few minutes, during which she kept coughing, gasping and gagging, Netta jumped to her feet and marched to the front of the line. 'Now look here! Excuse me! What's going on? I've been here for hours, hours! I'm an emergency. I could die before anyone saw me.'

The receptionist was steely. 'I'm sorry, madam. Everyone here is an emergency. After all, this *is* an accident and emergency department.'

Eventually Netta was summoned.

'You don't want me to stay, do you?'

'Of course I do, darling. Anything could happen.'

'But I'm terribly squeamish.'

'Oh, don't be silly! There won't be any blood.'

A youth, who looked no more than sixteen or seventeen, rushed into the room. 'Oh, there you are!' he greeted us. He peered at a sheet of paper in his hand. 'You're Netta, aren't you?'

'Mrs Grace,' she corrected.

Paying no attention, he turned to me: 'Sit down, do sit down. Move that overcoat.' His oddly sparse, greasy hair reached to the collar of a far from white jacket. The jacket was too long, his jeans were too short.

'Now, Netta, let's see.' He leaned over towards his computer. For two or three minutes there was a silence. 'We've got you here. You're an old friend.' He continued to read. Then he jerked up his head. 'You don't look your age, I must say. Remarkably well preserved. It says you're ninety, exactly ninety. Is that right, Netta?'

A panicky look passed over Netta's face. Her eyes veered sideways to see if I had taken this in. I at once turned my head to look out of a window, beyond which I could see a yard full of refuse bags, their swollen black shiny with the rain that was spattering down on them.

She did not answer the question. Instead she asked one of her own: 'What's *your* name?'

'Mr Wilson.'

'*Mr* Wilson. Does that mean you're not a doctor?'

He hesitated. 'I'm a surgeon.' I did not believe him. Neither did Netta. Later we decided that he must be a student or a nurse.

What followed was painful even for me to watch. Clumsily he pushed a variety of instruments down Netta's throat. From time to time, muttering unintelligibly to himself, he would remove one of these instruments and then examine it closely, holding it up to the light of a powerful lamp. 'Damn!' he would then exclaim. 'Oh, hell! Oh, shit!'

After all the fuss that she had made before, Netta was now amazingly stoical. He told her to keep her head steady and she kept it steady. He told her to open her mouth wider and she opened it wider. He told her not to swallow and she did not swallow. 'Good girl,' he said from time to time. Once he said: 'Well done, Netta.'

'I wish I had the right sort of speculum. This is no good at all.'

'Couldn't you get one?' I suggested boldly.

'Too late, I'm afraid.' Why it was too late, he did not explain and I did not dare to ask.

Eventually he emitted a yelp of triumph. 'I've got it, I really think I've got it.' He extended what looked like a large pair of tweezers. Netta and I peered. 'Yes, I've got it.'

The bone was so small that it might have been a length of yellowish-brown thread.

'Oh, the brute!' Netta exclaimed. 'Thank you so much, Dr – sorry, *Mr* – Wilson. You've really saved my life.'

In the taxi she was buoyant. She moved closer and closer to me, slipped an arm into mine and then, no doubt sensing a lack of adequate response, said: 'Oh, I'm feeling so cold. Do give me a nice little cuddle, darling. Please!'

I did the best I could.

When we got out of the taxi, she clutched my arm. 'Now that we've survived all that, let's celebrate with a drink.

'Oh, but…' Once again I was thinking of my boyfriend. By now he was seeing far too much of a bald dwarf from the Korean embassy in a pub generally known to its elderly clientele as 'The Elephants' Graveyard'.

'But me no buts!' She jerked my arm and meekly I gave way.

Once we were in the sitting room, she hurried over to the crowded drinks cabinet. 'The usual?' She did not wait for an answer. 'I can't be bothered to get any ice.' Clearly she was in a hurry. 'There you are, darling!' She held out a tumbler that she had first half-filled with gin and had then filled up with tonic that turned out to be flat. I had a terrible foreboding of what was going to happen next.

Having flopped down on the sofa, without bothering to pour herself a drink, she nestled against me, sighed, sighed again. 'Can't you be *kind* to me?'

'I'm always kind to you. Aren't I?'

'You know what I mean.' She raised a hand and tousled my hair. Then she lowered it.

Two or three minutes later, she asked, 'What's wrong with you?'

'Sorry.' I began to jerk up the zip that she had pulled down. Even thinking of my boyfriend had been no good.

She turned her head and stared at me with obvious concern. 'Darling – you're not *one of those*, are you?

I nodded. 'I'm afraid I am.'

'Oh, don't say it in that ashamed, embarrassed voice! When I was in Rennes – in the war – I was crazy about the French radio operator who worked with us. He was one of those too. Brave! I think he was the bravest man I've ever known. And yet – like you – he was terrified of me.' She jumped off the sofa with remarkable agility. 'Well – as so often in the past – I'll just have to make do with a stiff drink in a world in which nothing else is ever stiff for me these days.'

As she was eventually seeing me out, she turned at the front door. 'Oh, darling… One thing… May I ask a *great* favour of you? Please don't tell anyone what you heard! You know, what that Dr – Mr –What's-it said. About my age. "Remarkably well-preserved" – as though I were Stonehenge! If I weren't a working actress, it wouldn't matter – not a jot. But as it is…'

I put out a hand and touched hers as it rested on the door handle. 'Not a word. Promise.'

'After all, one's really only as old as one looks.'

'And you look not a day over sixty.'

'Liar!' But I could see that she was delighted.

A few weeks later, she and I were standing on a corner by the V & A, after having just visited an exhibition, when she suddenly saw a woman friend in a taxi stationary before a red light. 'Oh, it's Beryl!' she cried out. 'I must have a word with her.' As she rushed out into the road, a messenger on a motorbike zoomed round the corner and hit her. Many of those bird-bones were broken. So was the copy of a hideous art nouveau vase that I had tried to dissuade her from buying in the museum shop. So, too, was her neck.

Whereas there had been so many people at her birthday party, there were only a dozen or so in the chapel of the Putney Vale crematorium. Her niece told me that there would be a memorial service in due course – 'so that everyone can come and pay tribute' – but so far none has taken place.

As the few of us left the chapel, we followed the niece and her husband in the now accepted ritual of inspecting the wreaths. I found myself next to the old man in the grey suit and mauve tie with whom, not so long ago, I had inspected the rose bushes at Netta's ninetieth birthday.

We nodded mournfully to each other and then I said, for want of anything else: 'Sad.'

'Aren't all funerals sad?' He made it sound like a reproach. Then he said: 'She was a gallant old bird. I had a lot to do with her during the war. But I never had to go through what she went through. Mine was a cushy job back here in London. I had to send those poor girls out to God knows what.' He stooped and touched a wreath. 'Yes, that's the one I ordered. Unfortunately just a little wilted.' Creakily he straightened, one hand pressing into the small of his back. 'She had guts, had our Netta. They all had. They tortured her, you know.' He nodded his head, bluish lips pursed and turned down at the corners. 'Yes. Tortured her. But she never said a word. Not a bloody word. That's what I call guts. The brutes never got her to talk. And after that nothing could ever stop her talking. Until now,' he added.

'Valour,' I said. Mysteriously, the word, once used by Netta at that small, secret club of hers, had come into my mind unbidden, out of the lowering sky, the chill, misty air, and the insistent smell of the flowers at our feet.

Juba

Simon Lovat

At first, Luther was only aware of the heat. There was no sound, no feeling, not even any thought, just the crushing, oppressive heat. It was like waking from a general anaesthetic – all that existed was the present moment. Somehow, a radical separation from the past had been effected. For a long time he lay with his eyes shut as the glaring sun pinned him to the ground. It was impossible to move, his body seemed to weigh tons. Later, he opened his eyes and saw a vast, unobstructed canopy of blue floating above him. As he focused his eyes, two small black dots appeared, shimmering in the brightness. They drifted in two lazy circles high above him. His mind tried to grasp the word, but it darted away before he could catch it. Then it came: Bird. The two dots were birds. He closed his eyes again.

After a time, he became aware of a noise, a dull buzzing. He looked upward and saw a sweaty, blue-black face peering down at him. There was something wrong with it – it was covered in… something sticky, and the man's eyes were red-rimmed and hollow-looking. The man was saying something to him, but Luther couldn't make it out. Dimly, he thought the man seemed vaguely familiar, but his mind slid away again. It was too hot to think. He would have to rouse himself soon, and plunge into the sea to cool down and clear his head. The sea. Yes. Get into the sea. Luther felt a drop of rain fall on his check as the man stared down at him, and became confused. How could it rain out of a blue sky? He didn't understand. Luther closed his eyes again.

Luther had desperately needed to get away. He worked in Rome, for an international foreign aid organisation, and the past three months had been absurdly hectic. Arturo, his boss, was a manic, paranoid little Italian who

197

believed that his job was on the line if his subordinates did not manage to generate fifty per cent more work than everybody else. Consequently, Arturo's staff wandered through the air-conditioned corridors of their opulent marble office block like hollow-eyed ghosts for most of the year, and then disappeared altogether as the financial year drew to a close and the deadlines for the implementation of their foreign aid programmes loomed. Millions of US dollars were at stake. All that had kept Luther going through those long days and late nights was the thought that his contract was up at the end of July, and he would be able to walk away. He wasn't planning to renew, even thought he was paid handsomely for the work that he did. He wasn't in it for the money, he never had been. He wanted to help others. Sadly, he had soon discovered that the organisation was less interested in actually delivering the foreign aid projects it developed than in being seen to develop them. As far as Luther was concerned, the organisation had become a functionless, self-perpetuating behemoth, and he wanted out.

So he had planned a complete life-change.

At the end of his current contract, overseeing an aid package which was to supply treadle pumps to rural farmers in southern Sudan, he planned to go back home to Bonn and pick up the threads of his life again there, after six years based in Rome. His old friends Ernst and Geert had asked him if he was interested in playing guitar with them again, and it was this more than anything that had decided him. He had played with his two old university friends for twenty years on and off, between engineering contracts, but in the last two years their low-key jazz outfit, which they called Reduction, had begun to attract a small but appreciative following. Unfortunately their regular guitarist, who had grown tired of waiting for success to come, had joined another band in the meantime. So when Luther had told them he was thinking of coming home again, they had put the proposition to him.

Luther's three great loves – mathematics, engineering and music – all found expression in the form of the electric guitar. For Luther, a guitar was both a thing of beauty and a superb feat of engineering, each part specifically designed to fulfil a precise function in a most aesthetically pleasing manner. These parts, when arranged in a particular relationship, formed a whole like a beautiful equation. Furthermore, the whole was a working machine which produced music. He found this wonderful. He loved to play series after series of open sevenths and minor sevenths, sliding his left hand down the neck of the instrument like a lover to produce the sounds that gave jazz guitar its soul. He thought life as a semi-professional jazz guitarist would be the perfect antidote to the disillusionment he felt over the delivery of foreign aid. Once he had seen out his present contract, he would take a short holiday – he currently favoured Cape Town as a destination – and then return to his homeland. It would not exactly be retirement, fifty-one was a little too early for that, but he would choose future jobs with extreme care, and only accept short contracts of three months or less.

Sometimes Luther worried about this. To return home was to face the past, was to face the absence of Thomas. It was true, one never got over the death of a lover. One might learn to cope with it, but the gap still remained. Ten years after the fact, Luther had not completely reconciled himself to the loss of Thomas, his partner of seventeen years. Lying in bed at night he sometimes thought of people who had lost their entire family in a war, as so many of his parents' generation had done, yet still managed to carry on. Frankly, it staggered and humbled him that they could do so. Was it because their grief was shared, witnessed, valued, whereas his had not been? What made it worse was that poor Thomas had missed the advent of the new chemical therapies – the ones that actually worked – by only a matter of months.

It was Olu. The face belonged to Olu. But what was he doing here? Luther couldn't figure it out. And he was also puzzled by the silence. Where were the gulls, where were the hawkers who plied their trade up and down the beach, selling trinkets, towels, and cheap jewellery? And where were the relentless, crashing breakers? Had he gone deaf?

Olu, if it really was Olu, bent down and stretched out his left arm to retrieve something from above Luther's head, while covering his mouth with his other hand. His eyes were shining, and his nostrils flared as if in fear. Then he stood, and moved out of Luther's field of vision.

The first session had gone well. They had begun with some standards, and then cautiously slipped in a couple of their own compositions towards the end, which had been greeted with enthusiasm by the small crowd in the cellar bar. They were relieved at this, as it was their first performance outside of their home town of Bonn, and they had been worried that they might sound amateurish to the more cosmopolitan and discerning populace of Cologne. As Luther moved across the room to buy drinks for the band, he noticed a young man staring at him in admiration. He nodded to the man, who quickly left his table and joined Luther at the bar.

'Please. May I get these?' he said.

'OK, thanks,' Luther shrugged, taking the man in. 'Three Kölsch, please.'

The man was wearing a floral shirt open at the neck, a pair of green flares and baseball boots. He wore his hair shoulder length and parted in the middle, which nicely complemented his bearded chin. He slid three beers towards Luther and smiled.

'You're not from the university, are you? I would have seen you around, I'm sure.'

Luther smiled. 'No, we're from Bonn. We're all studying there. Natural Sciences. You?'

'Oh, I'm at the grand old University of Cologne, studying Arts. Specifically, literature – but *not* German literature!' He threw back his head and laughed gaily. 'I'm Thomas, by the way.'

'Luther,' said Luther, studying Thomas closely. 'So, you're into jazz?'

Thomas swung his head from side to side equivocally. 'Maybe *psychedelic* jazz.'

'What's psychedelic jazz?'

'I don't know, it hasn't been invented yet.' Thomas laughed again.

Luther stared at him, intrigued and amused. 'Are you *high*, man?'

Thomas nodded. 'A little. You want some?'

'God, no. I have to play. But maybe later?'

'I just wanted to say that you're good. All three of you, but especially you. I've been watching your fingers. They move so *fast*.'

'No, no. *Hendrix* was fast. I'm just average.'

Thomas looked straight into his eyes. 'I wonder what else those hands of yours can do?'

Luther stared back at him in amazement. 'What?' he stammered incredulously. 'Is this a pick-up, man?'

Thomas backed away. 'No, of course not. Sorry. I'm just high, you know.'

Luther grabbed him by the shoulder and looked at him. 'I'm cool, OK? I'm cool with it,' he said.

Thomas returned to his seat and Luther joined his friends on the tiny stage at the far end of the room.

'Who was *that*?' asked Geert as he took his beer.

Luther shrugged. 'Just a student from the university. He thinks we're very cool. His name is Thomas.'

'*Thomas*?' said Geert, exchanging a look with Ernst. 'What kind of name is that?'

'Meaning what?'

'Meaning nothing, man. Anyway, we have to play again now.'

Luther's mind was only half on the music during the second session. Thomas had unsettled him, engendering in him a response that he was too frightened to call desire. When the performance was over he bought himself another beer and drank it quickly. He looked up and found Thomas at his elbow.

'You're back,' he said flatly.

Thomas spread his hands out on the bar and stared at them as if they would reveal some secret. 'Sorry I came on to you, man. Don't tell, OK?'

'It's 1978,' Luther told him. 'These things don't matter.' He was talking more to himself than to Thomas.

'You think so?'

'Well actually, no.'

Thomas let out a burst of raucous laughter. 'Excellent!' he cried, smiling at Luther. Then, 'By the way, have you ever seen the cathedral at night?'

Luther thought for a moment. 'Actually, I've never seen the cathedral at all.'

'What? That's impossible.'

Luther shrugged apologetically. 'What can I say? I'm from Bonn, man. I've seen Bonn cathedral, of course,' he added by way of vindication. He didn't want Thomas to think he was a complete philistine. 'It's in the middle of this massive square.'

'OK, come on.'

Thomas leaped up and grabbed Luther by the left hand, almost dragging him out of the bar as Luther hurriedly slung his guitar over his shoulder with his free hand. They headed towards the new shopping centre.

'Now, you must trust me completely,' Thomas told him. 'I want you to look down. I'll lead you so you don't need to look where you're going.'

Luther laughed. 'What's going on, man?'

'Just do it, OK? This is the initiation practice for all Arts students at the

University of Cologne. As a rare honour, and in view of your status as a visiting guitarist, which qualifies you as an ersatz Arts student, I hereby confer upon you the initiation. Now, don't look up. Just concentrate on your hand.'

'OK, man, but this is insane.'

Luther let his gaze fall to his left hand, which Thomas gripped firmly as he guided him through the narrow streets of the paved shopping centre. Luther's fingers were strong, sensitive and supple. He felt the warmth of Thomas's hand in his own, felt the vibrancy, the life coursing through his body as they walked. Luther felt genuinely *connected* to someone for the first time in his life.

All this in the touch of a hand, he thought.

'But where are we going?' said Luther as he half jogged through the empty streets lined with shops.

'Just look down and trust me,' said Thomas.

After some minutes, they came to a stop.

'All right, you can look now,' Thomas told him.

Luther raised his head and was confronted by the vast bulk of the cathedral rising inexplicably before him. Its blackened stone glowed somehow in the night.

'That's wild,' said Luther, staring up at the ornately carved frontage which seemed to lean over him threateningly. 'I mean, it's impossible. How can it be *here*, in the middle of a shopping centre?'

Thomas gave a little bow. 'That's why you mustn't look up. This way it comes as a surprise.'

'Like this?' said Luther as he pulled Thomas towards him and kissed him on the mouth.

'Yes. Like that,' smiled Thomas.

The man he had thought was Olu had gone. Luther had the distinct impression that something was missing, but he had no idea what it could be. There was a space, an emptiness, a lack. It was difficult to grasp. It was like a chord with a note missing, a sense of incompleteness.

Luther's mind filled with a series of descending arpeggios as played on the original Gibson guitar that he had always wanted but had never been able to afford. It was a series of mournful, sliding notes that echoed in his mind like silvery ghosts. Magically, the series was endless, a musical equivalent of Escher's ever descending staircase. Round and round the arpeggios went, always descending yet always beginning from a higher pitch. Luther began to feel frustrated. There was a meaning here, if only he could grasp it. If only he could get the sequence of notes correct, they would equal ten treadle pumps.

And then he detected a smell. Someone was cooking somewhere nearby. It did not seem appetising to Luther. In fact, he felt a wave of nausea sweep over him as his lungs filled with the aroma. Perhaps it wasn't cooking after all. Perhaps it was a fire on the hill, or a riot in town somewhere. Africa was always burning. Yes. There was a definite metallic quality to the smell, and something else as well, something organic but elusive.

Luther opened his eyes and stared up at the sky. There were more dots circling now, endlessly spiralling downward like the music in his head. Luther blinked, and remembered that they were birds. Either they were small birds very near to the ground, or they were very big birds. They swooped majestically in the huge bright silence of the afternoon…

Luther stared down at Thomas. His whole body had shrunk, and his skin had acquired the texture of dry paper. There was a waxy yellow, jaundiced tinge to his face. Thomas lay motionless in the bed, seeming hardly to make an impression on the pillows that supported his head. His arms lay by his sides, resting on top of the covers like two sticks. He looked dead already. Luther sat down beside the bed, and gently held Thomas's hand, being careful not to apply too much pressure. He stroked the back of Thomas's hand with his thumb, and carefully studied the face he had loved for so long for signs of recognition. But there was nothing. Not so much as the flicker of an eyelid. The nurse had warned him of this.

'He's very weak now, and we've given him lots of morphine,' she had told Luther when he arrived, 'so he might not wake. In fact, he probably won't. I'm sorry.'

Luther sat in mournful silence beside Thomas, staring at the intravenous drip affixed to his left arm. Luther had been travelling non-stop for more than forty-eight hours and a wave of exhaustion swept over him as he stared down at his lover. First, there had been a garbled phone message from Ernst, taken by the foreman of the workshop at which Luther was stationed. Luther didn't get the message for several days, because he was out in the field in Soroti meeting with local Ugandan steel suppliers. On his return to Kampala, his mild-mannered and softly-spoken foreman had tried to relay the message, but his English was relatively poor and he was not at all sure if he had understood the message correctly.

'He say he come here wiv Mr Thomas,' the foreman declared uncertainly.

'Ernst is coming to Kampala?'

The foreman looked at the ground. 'Yis, sir.'

'Did he say why?'

'Don't know, sir,' said the foreman. His balding head was beaded with sweat. 'He is very German!' he added stolidly, in his own defence.

Luther smiled. Ernst's English was indeed rather distorted. Luther had teased him about it often. 'Are you sure he said he was coming *here*?'

The foreman pursed his lips together, looked at the ground and slowly shook his head. 'Not sure, sir.'

Luther knew that a message from Ernst could only mean one thing. Thomas must be ill. There followed a hasty, nightmare Land Rover journey through the ruined roads of southern Uganda in the middle of the night, against all UN safety recommendations, followed by two plane trips, the second of which was delayed by four hours because of a hijack alert. Dishevelled and exhausted, he had arrived, finally, at the bedside of Thomas, but clearly it was too late for goodbyes. Luther couldn't help but feel guilty. He laid Thomas's hand down and rubbed his face, trying to exorcise the dry tiredness in his eyes. His skin had the texture of sandpaper, and his stubble rasped against his palms as he massaged his cheeks.

He stared at the wall and felt a familiar ghost rising within him, the voice of accusation that perennially questioned his motives. What drove him to take work in far-flung countries, helping war-torn populations too apathetic, it seemed, to help themselves, when Thomas was sick at home, and needed him? It was because he was German, he decided. He felt the weight of obligation resting on his shoulders. They all did, all the children of the warmongering generation before them. He felt a desperate need to make it right, to pay the world back, somehow – but no matter what he did it would never be enough. How could it be?

Luther stood, and looked down at Thomas. Then he stretched out his arm and placed his brown left hand over Thomas's heart. Luther's nails were long, the new growth shockingly white against his tanned skin. Usually he kept them short, for guitar playing, but he hadn't taken a guitar with him to Uganda and so he had let them grow. He closed his eyes and tried to tune into the sensations in his hand, but he could barely feel the movement of Thomas's shallow breathing. He removed his hand and bent to kiss Thomas on the forehead. His skin felt dry as a drum. Then he folded himself into the chair by the bedside and fell asleep.

When he woke, Thomas was dead.

'Mister Jaeger, Mister Jaeger…'

A voice seemed to be calling for him, a rasping voice that kept catching in his mind like a saw blade. His mouth felt hot and dry, so dry that his tongue could barely move. It felt like a piece of old wood, and it hurt his throat to swallow.

Luther couldn't remember where he was. Had he fallen asleep? He squinted up at the sun but could not see the owner of the voice. Then he saw the blue-black face of Olu floating above him again. It was impassive, calm, almost the expression of a peaceful tribal mask. The doleful eyes regarded him carefully.

'Do you hear me?' Olu half whispered.

Luther smiled. He was not deaf after all.

'Mister Jaeger, do you hear me?'

Luther tried to speak, but he found it difficult to make his mouth work. 'What are you doing here, Olu?' he said at last. 'What are you doing in Cape Town?'

'They are coming for us now, Mister Jaeger. Mister Jaeger, do you hear me? They are coming.'

Luther closed his eyes as a new series of arpeggios fell like cool water into his mind.

And then there was Juba. The final three weeks of his contract would be spent in Juba, out in the field, liaising with government officials from north and south Sudan, as well as visiting local farmers, whom he would instruct in the assembly and maintenance of their water pumps. This was glorified intermediate technology – there had not been the will to provide the southern Sudanese people with the wherewithal to produce the pumps themselves. Indeed, his dealings with the Sudanese government had made it clear that the Arab Islamic majority actively discouraged any such project. It suited them to keep the black minority poor and hungry. Sudan was a country torn apart by civil war, the lines drawn up on the basis of race and religion. It was thus a double war, and doubly barbaric. The very nature of Luther's work meant that he was always finding himself in countries in crisis, but Sudan, somehow, was worse than anything he had seen before.

Luther was used to heat, but he was staggered by the temperatures in Juba on arrival. On the first day, it reached forty-nine degrees. He, and the rest of the official team, spent the whole day in their air-conditioned offices in the centre of town, and they continued to work until well after ten. This was not due to urgency or industry. It was quite simply the only place that was cool. Luther was underwhelmed to find that he had been allocated a tent instead of a hotel room to sleep in. This provided a further incentive to rise early and work late, rather than risk a roasting under canvas.

Nobody that he spoke to had a good word to say about Juba, neither visiting officials nor the locals. Luther's own ability to remain objective about the place rapidly left him as he thrashed around in his stifling tent, night after night, trying to get some sleep. To keep him going, he filled his mind with the thought that in less than a fortnight he would be gone. There was also the appealing prospect of a holiday in Cape Town to look forward to, and then home to Cologne.

During the second week, Luther had to travel south for talks with representatives from a farming collective on the Uganda–Sudan border.

'Lucky you,' said Clive, a ruddy Australian of about Luther's age, who was propping up the bar beside him the night before his departure. 'Juba's a hellhole. Actually, the whole stinking country is a hellhole.' He threw back the remains of his whisky, as if he had just made a toast. 'You been here before, mate?'

Luther shook his head.

'Well, you're in for a treat, then. You'll be driving several hundred miles down dirt roads in something like fifty degrees. You'd better pray the air-con still works. If you're lucky, you won't get ambushed. The rebels usually respect UN vehicles. Although I was once held up in Uganda by a Karamojan with an AK47, so who knows.' He laughed.

'What happened?'

'Actually it was bloody hilarious. This bloke, in full regalia, stops my vehicle in the middle of nowhere and just climbs in and demands to be driven several hundred miles in the other direction. My driver says nothing – he's scared shitless. *I* say nothing, for pretty much the same reason, I might add. But my fellow passenger, this tiny little woman from Wales, UK, just tells him to get out. She turns to him, and says that we aren't going anywhere until he gets out. She's very polite, but very insistent. At first he pretends he doesn't understand, but then she prods him in the thigh with her finger, and – I don't know, it was the strangest thing – he just gets out of the car. Bloody lucky we didn't get our heads blown off, I reckon.'

Luther nodded.

'But that was Uganda. You don't want to arse about like that in Sudan, mate. Keep your head down.' He ordered another drink, and bought one for Luther. Then, as an afterthought, he added, 'Of course, you know about the mines?'

'A little. The whole country is mined, apparently.'

Clive nodded sagely. 'More of them here than anywhere on the face of the planet, mate. The roads aren't mined, but it's not safe to go more than two metres from the roadside. Safety isn't guaranteed after that. And for God's sake make sure you're off the road by nightfall. All bets are off after dark.'

Luther nodded. He'd been briefed about all of this.

'Who's your driver, anyway?'

'Olu Watson.'

'Oh, I know him. The little guy? Good bloke. You'll be all right with Olu. He's got some stories, I can tell you.'

Just then, Clive's mobile phone chirruped in his pocket. 'Sorry mate, I'll have to take this,' he told Luther. 'Irrigation trouble.'

Luther took this as his cue for bed.

Next morning, he and Olu set off for the southern farmlands. They took water, food, and plenty of spare fuel with them in case of emergencies, but the drive was uneventful. Luther was presented with mile after mile of monotonously flat, barren scrubland, so different from the rich brown earth of Uganda and the more fertile countries to the south. The sun was relentless.

'How do you like Juba?' Olu asked him when they stopped for lunch, which they ate in the car, with the windows sealed to keep in the cool air.

Luther thought for a moment before answering. 'I can't really say, I've been here such a short time. What about you?'

'I am sad for Juba. I am sad for south Sudan. We are dying, but nobody remembers us. One day there will be no more black Sudanese people and that will be a bad day. We are – what is the phrase? – ah yes, we are an *endangered species*.' Despite the sadness of his words, Olu grinned at his own use of English, showing a set of remarkable white teeth. 'But there are good people. Good people like you, sir. And that gives me hope.' Olu placed a shiny black hand on his heart and smiled again.

Luther sighed at the futility of it all. Here he was, trying to help poor farmers water their lands, but really, what ultimate good would that do? It was like sticking a plaster over a severed artery. Did Olu realise that?

They drove on in silence, neither man in the mood for casual conversation, until Luther needed to urinate.

'Could we stop here, Olu? I need to, er…'

'Yes, yes. I understand,' said Olu as he brought the car to a stop. 'Here is a good place. I will also take the opportunity.'

Luther got out of the car and was immediately stunned by the scorching heat, which slammed into him like something solid. The countryside in front of him was vast, stretching away into the shimmering distance to the point where the infinite blue sky dipped down to meet it, and for just a moment Luther was touched by a sense of his place in the order of things.

Luther took a step away from the car, and the earth buckled.

He was floating. Definitely rising from the ground, as several faces peered at him from above. He didn't know them. His leg and shoulder felt unbelievably hot. Scorchingly hot. It was pain, he realised suddenly. A hot wordless shrieking that ran through his body. It might have been there for a long time. He thought it probably had.

Now he was being lifted into a vehicle, and laid down on a narrow bed. Beside him sat Olu, his clothes torn and blackened, his face a mask of horror. Then someone stuck a needle into his wrist as another person climbed into the vehicle, clutching a bundle of blankets to his chest. He put it on the floor near Olu, who flinched, and glanced nervously at Luther. The blankets fell open slightly to reveal something. Luther recognised it but couldn't make sense of it at first.

It was that missing something.

Yes.

He recognised the fingers.

Mariposo, Butterfly

Patrick Roscoe

Fernando was born in a house on the main street of town during the time when this road was still unpaved. His eyes opened on a world where the light seemed too glaring and the sun too strong. Fernando squinted. Recalling a dimmer place, the baby crawled into caves of shadow in the corners. Soon he was able to stand at the front window and watch passers-by whose footsteps were apt to raise large clouds of dust in the dry season, either because inhabitants of this town had a tendency to scuff wearily through their lives or because here the earth was especially eager to ascend. From the beginning, Fernando wouldn't play with other children. At the approach of older boys laden with buckets of oysters stolen from the sea, he flew to his mother in fear. 'Mariposo, butterfly,' dripping Juans and Josés would call after him, their voices floating like pools of colour through the air.

Fernando's mother looked at her son as though at something that she needed to forget. She pushed away the crying, clinging child until he learned to sit quietly for long periods of time in order to avoid her notice. In the corner, he played with scraps of cloth or any gaudy object to fall his way. The sensation of seeing and touching bright colours created a tingling in Fernando's mind; a shy memory almost moved from shadow into plain light. Before that ever happened, Fernando's mother would turn from the mirror and frown. 'Go away,' she said, sometimes gently, sometimes angrily. 'All the other children are playing in the plaza. They aren't underfoot night and day.' No matter how she pleaded or threatened, Fernando wouldn't willingly leave the house. His mother had to push him out the door and turn the key. Fernando sat on the step, trembling beneath each waft of breeze. He waited for the locked door to open.

His dreams were darker than the sky beneath which they occurred. Yet just beyond the blackness, he sensed, brilliant colours flashed and splashes of sound sang a musical language which on the day of awakening would tell him what he longed to know. When noise did rouse him, it was only his mother's voice carrying through the pitch dark. He couldn't make out what she was saying on the other side of the bedroom, in a voice as angry and biting as mosquitoes that buzz in your ear and won't go away. There was his father's voice, too, deeper and darker and sadder. Although he couldn't hear his name spoken, Fernando knew that his mother and father were discussing him.

One morning his father took Fernando by the hand. He led him from the town and up to the banana plantations scattered over the lower hills. While his father swung a machete along with other men, Fernando played with sticks and stones at the clearing's edge. He sang quietly to himself as God pulled a white ball of sun higher into the sky.

The jungle surrounding the clearing was dark and thick and green. Vines clung to trunks and limbs of trees from fear or from love. Through the tangled growth, snakes slipped with a secrecy that thwarted their being detected or pursued. Birds unknown to the lower world flapped wings that beat air against Fernando's face. He waited to be swooped down upon, snatched up in claws, carried through blue sky. The town would appear small as he waved to everyone below, as he signalled a farewell to his mother leaning on her broom in the doorway. Faces would lift and fingers point upward until Fernando was carried out of sight, high above the sea, away forever.

The boy opened his eyes. His father's glistening back no longer lay in sight. In the distance, machetes rang like the church bell calling a question. Fernando waited for an answer.

Above his head, through the murky green, just out of reach, fluttered a winged parade.

Each butterfly was large and beautiful and unlike the faded ones Fernando had seen in the town below. In and out of the jungle, through various degrees of shadow, they floated and fed from blossoms that shone like alert eyes. Fernando bit into a jungle flower and waited for a brilliant colour to spread across his dull, brown skin. His arms would widen and

212

thin; he would fly away on paper wings. But the flower tasted bitter, and only pain spread through the boy.

When the sun began to sink past the edge of the clearing and into the jungle beyond, the butterflies followed its light and warmth. One by one, they vanished through the wall of green; one by one, machetes fell silent in the distance. Shadows lengthened into darkness that crept up on Fernando from all sides, then swallowed him. He stayed very still in the black belly until his father suddenly appeared. When father and son returned hand in hand down the hills, the lights of the town spread a shining enigma before them. Approach dissolved the mystery for Fernando, and illuminated only familiar disappointment.

Fernando accompanied his father up into the hills every day for three years. The boy never disturbed his father's work or wandered into the jungle surrounding the clearing where he would be left to wait to be taken home at dusk. Time floated by on invisible wings. Fernando listened to the breathing jungle and watched it grow. He came to believe he knew each butterfly that inhabited the western slopes. His sleep was no longer black, but full of vivid, flickering dreams.

One day Fernando noticed a butterfly whose beauty exceeded any he had glimpsed before. He tried to avert his eyes to prevent his heart from swooping through his throat and up into cool green air. But he had to look. Fernando turned to see the butterfly float from the clearing and into the jungle. He longed to observe this vision clearly and closely. He yearned to touch it just once, just gently.

Fernando ran to follow the butterfly from the clearing. He stumbled over twisted roots, tripped beneath dangling vines. As he penetrated farther into the jungle, the light grew greener and darker. At the point where his vision became obscured by dimness and distance, the butterfly tantalised. It led Fernando deeper into the jungle. His desire to be enfolded within beating wings increased with the same strength as his wish to know for one moment the reason for his own heart's beating.

When Fernando became too tired to walk farther, the jungle opened up into a small clearing he had never been in before. The space wasn't created by machetes, but by a pool that in turn was formed by a stream falling into it. Both stream and pool were the same silver as the clearing's light.

The air above the pool was thick with butterflies. Rainbow colours danced, swirled, swarmed. Butterflies merged together and drew apart.

They drifted near the pool to view their beauty reflected in its mirror; they soared to the top of the jungle to escape this vision. They fed on jewelled blossoms, then slept.

Fernando gazed hungrily at the sight. From the stream emerged the voice he had been waiting so long to hear. It said that such a moment could not last and would never occur again, though longed for always.

The unseen moon spun high above the jungle ceiling when Fernando was found beside the stream. He had heard his father calling through the darkness, but hadn't answered. He knew his cried reply would murder more dreams of butterflies. As his father struck him, Fernando saw red and blue and purple flash against a black background. Then the colours were gone, and the darkness contained only the sobbing of the stream, and of the father beside it.

Now Fernando stayed down in the dry, faded town. The place seemed stranger to him than before. The white sun had grown more blistering. It bleached the colour from houses and streets, as well as from Fernando's memories. He began to attend the school across the street, but none of his classmates knew Fernando. During the days he had spent upon the western slopes, they had built walls of friendship around themselves which he could not climb over or break through. Fernando remained in the classroom after other boys left to work in the sea or on the hills. He grew used to the high, clear voices of girls; the scent of their freshly washed dresses and skin and hair.

After school ended in early afternoon, Fernando would return across the street into the dim rooms where his mother was caught in a trance cast by a gleam of pots and pans, the glow of fire, water splashing in the sink. Fernando's presence didn't waken her from this spell; from deep within it, she turned slowly to look at him with questions that remained unspoken in her eyes: Who was this boy? Where had he come from? What did he want?

Fernando sat with a book inside the doorway, partly obscured by shadow. He peered at the page before him, then at the street beyond. It would loom nearly empty during the hottest part of the afternoon. Now and then a single figure slowly approached down the baking road. A man was returning early from the banana fields, his machete glinting in the sun. A boy was coming up from the shore with a bucket of oysters hanging from one muscled arm. 'Mariposo, butterfly,' he might croon in passing. Fernando raised his eyes to the hills.

Sometimes a butterfly paler and smaller than those up in the jungle would tremble through the town. Above hot dust, through harsh sunlight, it fluttered in search of nectar. Fernando's eyes followed the butterfly until it moved out of sight; then they returned to the book resting in his lap. Words winged him far away from the town and carried him to places no one here had journeyed to before. A voice that spoke increasingly loudly and often inside Fernando warned he would never be able to remain in such exotic lands for long. The words always ended. The visions they evoked would drift away like clouds, leaving behind a white sun, the empty street, dogs sleeping in the shade.

An hour before dark, when the air softened, a butterfly would infrequently drift down from the hills to show off his beauty and to make the butterflies below look smaller and paler in comparison. When Fernando saw one of the winged visitors, he would chase it to the edge of town. There each jungle butterfly dipped, swirled, then vanished as if snatched up by a greedy God. These brief appearances of beauty left the town a drabber place. As he walked slowly back to his chair inside the doorway, Fernando would seem oblivious to calls of 'mariposo, butterfly'.

Fernando's father returned from working on the hills at dusk and with exhausted eyes walked unseeing past the boy in the doorway. He fell on the big bed in the back room; at once, snoring spread through the house. Fernando became convinced his father spoke to him through this wordless language. Though he listened intently, the boy was never able to decipher the sound.

The main street became crowded as evening cooled. Within spheres of street lamps, tacos sizzled and dogs yelped and salsa pulsed. Butterflies fled the clamour. Beyond the edge of town, they rested with folded wings on leaves that swayed in currents of air from the sea.

From behind the window, Fernando watched bands of boys and clusters of girls stream towards the plaza. The voice of his sleeping father addressed the dark corners of the other room while his mother stitched cloth foaming over her knees. When she pricked her finger, she remembered Fernando. 'Go out with the others,' she urged. Yet Fernando wouldn't often stir. In the distance, the groups of boys and girls began to join together. Soon couples would steal away to press against a stone wall at the dark end of the street.

On rare occasions, an unseen hand or an unheard voice pushed Fernando outside. He would find himself floating just above the street, trying and failing to touch the ground. He would never really know the portion of earth on which he lived; its textured surface didn't learn the unique weight of his step. Fernando and the town remained strangers. The sharp eyes of both boys and girls pierced him; in pain, fearing capture, he would beat his wings to attempt escape. Though his heart raced and leaped, he couldn't soar away; and with bruised, broken wings he fluttered weakly home. Cries of 'mariposo, butterfly' pinned him inside the window. He pressed against the glass.

Fernando's contemporaries began to marry, set up house and start a family. He remained at school until seventeen, when the teacher had nothing more to tell him. Fernando was already full of knowledge that served no useful purpose in the town.

His father died. A body worn and scratched as an old record was buried. Fernando realised he would never know what his sleeping father had tried to say to him. The house became a silent place through which mother and son moved in separate, widening orbits.

The widow was advised to turn the front room of her house into a store: on the main street, just across from the school and three doors down from the movie theatre, it was advantageously located. Since his mother felt indifferent about the business, Fernando ran it from the start. He stocked a little of everything in order to meet the daily needs of the neighbourhood.

The greatest part of the sales was in candy. The dim store shone with cases filled with bright colours. From the capital city, Fernando ordered varieties of sweets that had never been seen or tasted in the town before. His mother stirred pans of caramel and fudge in the kitchen behind. She gazed into richly scented steam that drifted to the school across the street. Students skipped over at recess to fill themselves with sweetness; they buzzed like flies around the sugary space. The store was usually crowded with children clutching flat, dull pesos that could be exchanged for rainbow-coloured flavour. Customers tended to stand with open-mouthed awe at the possibilities before them; they became lost in long moments of undiluted desire. 'I want,' they would finally say. Fernando moved quietly to satisfy the greedy clamour. He watched red and blue and purple candies being placed like wafers on tongues of children who flew out into the afternoon, soared away on sugar wings. At night, adults stopped in and bought treats to savour secretly in the darkness of the movie house. The store did good business, and Fernando and his mother prospered.

One afternoon Fernando was drowsing before the store when he heard the approach of clopping hooves down the main street, which had been paved at last. Both horse and rider looked hot and tired. The mount's coat was matted and stiff, showing it had sweated then dried repeatedly, as in the course of a long, hard journey. The rider's hair was blonde, and seemed to render his face obscure. Fair colouring was unusual in the town; it was found more often in Jalisco, the next state to the south. According to widespread belief, God favoured such people with a smile that gilded their heads.

The rider dismounted in front of the store and asked for water. Fernando fetched a bucket, and horse and rider drank deeply. The stranger did not say where he had come from or what had brought him to the town. He was silent. As he moved away with the horse, Fernando stared after them. One hand reached to touch his own thick, dark hair.

That evening, in the store, Fernando did not appear his usual inexpressive self. Often he did not hear customer requests; several times, in what was a rare mistake for him, he gave back incorrect change. He sat up long after the movie ended and the street emptied. In the darkest hour, his mother woke to the sound of weeping. She touched her cheeks and found them dry. Stealing from her room, she discovered Fernando pressed against the front window. He turned once, then looked at the deserted street again. At the end of the block, yellow light clung to a lamp post. The mother returned to bed, and when she woke at morning her son was gone.

Fernando followed the path that he had climbed as a child with his father. He walked quickly and steadily up into the hills, not pausing to glance at jungle blossoms and birds which he had not seen for years. He brushed past vines hanging in his way. Snakes slid from the noise of his footsteps.

The air turned cooler and cleaner and greener as Fernando climbed higher. Like the slap of cold water that wakens a sleeper, colours suddenly splashed against his face. All at once, the thick, rich scent of the earth and vegetation became overwhelming. *Look! Look!* whistled birds until Fernando slowed. He studied his surroundings as if puzzled by where or when he might have seen them before, and what they had meant to him then. He began to breathe quickly, from more than exertion.

In the year of his absence, the jungle butterflies had grown more beautiful and large, and they seemed more numerous, too. Wings came to fill the air around Fernando. God was shaking a host of heavenly trees, sending blossoms to float and flutter downward, releasing red and purple and blue gifts. Three times butterflies brushed wings against Fernando's face. Each time, he gasped. Powder clung to his skin like the tattoo of a touch. Dazzled by the multi-coloured swirl, Fernando climbed onward, and he didn't notice when he left the trail.

A singing voice flowed on and on. When jungle gave way to clearing, Fernando halted. The silver song drew him forward until a louder sound filled his ears.

A multitude of new wings unfolded and stretched with sighs of pleasure, feeling for the first time their strength and grace. From all sides, they burst through cocoons and reached towards Fernando and merged into a whole that enfolded him. His clothes melted away at his touch; wings trembled with contained power against his bare skin. Fernando closed his eyes as the dull ache of long years sharpened into acute pain. The wings beat more powerfully, until they thrashed the young man's flesh with a force that had to rip and tear. Then they flapped harder. Caught within the butterfly embrace, Fernando could no longer breathe.

Gossamer arms dropped Fernando to the ground beside the silver pool. In the moment before he fell asleep, he glimpsed his reflection in the water. Behind his red and blue and purple image was mirrored one shining figure of gold.

Later, the air turned cold; then the light in the clearing quickly dimmed. Fernando roused his aching body, gathered his scattered clothes, and covered his vary-coloured bruises. A carpet of mangled butterfly wings rustled like dead leaves beneath him. Although the illumination of moon and stars couldn't penetrate the jungle ceiling, Fernando made his way surely down the hills. He was unaware that each of his heavy footsteps crushed worms that were imprisoned on the earth over which they crawled.

Years passed secretly, and Fernando was known as a steady young man, a hard worker, a good son. Increasingly, his mother remained in the rooms behind the store. She became so rarely seen that on her death Fernando didn't appear to be more alone.

After the funeral, he altered the front room that had housed the store. A long, low counter lined with stools was installed first. Behind this bar, Fernando built a small kitchen with a two-burner gas stove, an ice-box, a sink. Tables and chairs were scattered around the room; a jukebox sat in one corner. Fernando strung coloured lights along the ceiling, from which crêpe paper streamers listlessly drooped, waiting to be fluttered by some breeze.

The candy store was gone. From the start, for no articulated reason, neither small children nor adolescent girls nor any adults frequented the renovated place. It became a meeting spot for the town's teenaged boys. At the counter, they sprawled with *tortas* and *chocomilk* which Fernando sold them at lower than ordinary prices. Often the lounging boys wouldn't purchase anything. They told jokes and listened to the jukebox and smoked Partytime cigarettes. Leaning against the doorway, they would croon to passing girls.

The new business was not as profitable as the candy store had been. Although some wondered why he had made the change, they did not question the silent, solitary man. Maybe it was good for boys to have a place to go when they grew too restless to remain in their mothers' kitchens. Because they were accustomed to Fernando, townspeople didn't ask why he had never taken a wife, why he remained alone.

The man wasn't often the subject of speculation until the Sunday morning he locked his door and ventured through the streets with a wicker basket, a new sombrero and a sky-blue scarf. 'I'm going up into the hills,' was his response to curious neighbours.

'Fernando's meeting his lover up there,' people told one another to explain the expedition. After failing to envision who this object of affection might be, they recalled that voices drifted down from the western slopes on especially clear nights. 'Fernando's going to make contact with restless spirits who've chosen to haunt the hills instead of the graveyard. When he returns, he'll bring us news from them.'

By the time preparations were underway for evening mass and the Sunday dance to follow, Fernando had been forgotten. The church bell rang insistently at dusk. One peal after the next floated up the hills in yet another attempt to lure the missing down. Only Fernando eventually descended. As the band was tuning up in the Casino, he emerged from the darkness surrounding the town and passed through main-street throngs wearing their Sunday best. No one took sufficient notice of Fernando to ask him about any ghosts he might have seen on the hills.

In his room, Fernando opened the picnic basket and tenderly removed butterflies, as though in death they could still feel his touch. The next day, a truck arrived from the capital city with glass cases that were unloaded in Fernando's front room. Each Sunday, during the following months, Fernando ascended the western slopes to fetch more butterflies. The glass cases slowly filled with images of frozen light, while in the distance Sunday revels sounded louder, drunker, wilder. No matter how brilliant the specimens to have been captured, their collector looked at them with what seemed a deepening disappointment.

One Sunday Fernando failed to go up into the hills. Whether he had lost interest in his butterfly collection or whether he felt it was complete, no one asked. Fernando would not climb the western slopes again.

For a time, passers-by would invariably glance through Fernando's doorway at the neat arrangement of butterflies on the walls inside. It was thought curious that someone would trouble to catch insects, offer them death without flurried struggles of wings, then display each as if the Virgin. 'He has every butterfly in the world,' people would marvel. It was true that from this time all butterflies did seem to vanish from the air. Then passers-by no longer peered through Fernando's doorway. 'He's the butterfly man,' they shrugged, looking the other way.

Beneath the butterflies fidgeted boys whose bright beach shorts added further splashes of colour to the dim space. Their unlined skin glowed; their unstained teeth gleamed like moonlight. The boys told jokes and stories that carried only between themselves. They carved their initials into the tabletops, roughly scarring those surfaces. They took scant notice of the man whose features slowly blurred with something more than fat.

With time, the butterfly man left his place less frequently, finally venturing out only to buy food or other necessities. Days spent in dimness made his eyes narrow when sunlight confronted them. Through slitted lids, he glimpsed women he remembered as little girls standing entranced before his candies. Now they were pulled and pinched by their own sweet-starved babies.

'The butterfly man,' cried children, catching sight of Fernando. 'The butterfly man can fly,' they exalted, waiting for him to soar into the air and then to lead them to some bright, sweet place. 'Fly, fly,' the children pleaded, as Fernando walked quickly away, trying not to turn.

Every year the world turned more slowly. The jukebox records became outdated and scratched and played less often. Faded, wilted crêpe streamers hung like cobwebs from the ceiling. Now customers were sons of boys who had called 'mariposo, butterfly' down the street long ago. Fernando still tended his establishment day and night, though more and more he seemed to be dozing in his chair. The place was mostly empty during daytime, while boys dove for oysters. At night, too, there was little business after the town went to its early bed. After closing the door at midnight, however, Fernando still waited in his chair just inside the doorway.

Sometimes at three or four in the morning, when the streets were dark except for the light in his window, Fernando would be wakened by hammering. The wings of his heart beat wildly. He unlocked the door and let in a pair of boys who had been down at the shore. Their hair was sandy and damp, their eyes were glazed. They created a sphere scented by salt and sperm. While the boys dozed at a table, heads resting on pillows of arms, Fernando moved quickly over his stove. The lights strung overhead bathed him in changing colours. Now red, now purple, now blue.

Fernando placed *tortas* and Cokes on the table. The two boys wakened. Reaching for his snack, one boy's hand seemed to brush the aging man. Fernando blinked, as people do when a bright light is switched on in darkness. His body trembled almost imperceptibly, only for a moment. The boy detected this reaction to his touch. 'Mariposo, butterfly,' he whispered. Then, with his friend, he laughed.

Fernando stood still behind his counter, beneath his cages of glass. In the blinking of the coloured lights, the butterflies seemed to move, though pinned.

Isle of Women

Jeffrey Round

For John Davison

For his twenty-sixth birthday, Steven Patterson threw himself a will-writing party. He invited his closest friends over to 'give suggestions and stake your claims while you can', as he put it in the gold-embossed invitation.

'I don't want to be remembered as some cheap queen when I'm gone,' Steven blithely announced. 'So I'm giving you the chance to tell me what you want now.'

His oldest friend Frank was offended. He chastised Steven for being morbid and threatened to boycott the party.

'Loosen up,' Steven told him over the phone. 'I live for today. I don't have the luxury of waiting till tomorrow like the rest of you.'

Frank dutifully arrived on the appointed day with all the rest of us. We were thirteen in total, a proverbial last supper. For all intents and purposes it seemed to be no more than our usual boys' night out, as we covered our concern with something like hilarity.

Not long afterwards I received a handwritten copy of the will with my future inheritance outlined: *To the lovely and talented David Barnett, I bequeath my everlasting love, my collection of genuine Fornasetti ties which he always coveted, and my cashmere great coat, as he was always just a little cold.* I took the jibe for the affectionate tweak it was intended.

Two months later, at the beginning of December, Steven came down with pneumonia. A long, worrisome vigil ensued. By New Year's, however, he was much improved, complaining only that Toronto winters were too long and bleak for a dying man. On a whim, I suggested he and his boyfriend Terry accompany me to Mexico on a trip I'd been planning.

We met for a tête-à-tête in a coffee shop on Yonge Street. Snow fell lightly outside the window as Toronto assumed the dismal grey face it always wore between December and April. Gay life would be scarce where we were heading, I warned, over steaming bowls of cappuccino. And emergency medical facilities might be hard to find. Despite my warnings, they both seemed eager. We agreed on a date.

I hoped the trip would give me an opportunity to spend time with Steven and perhaps get to know Terry better. So far I'd known Terry only over hospital beds when Steven was ill, and at those bitchy Sunday brunches that are *de rigueur* in any gay man's social life, when he was well. In turn, Terry had shown me the equal parts respect and jealousy which every gay man shows his current lover's former boyfriends.

A design consultant, Terry was a rising star in the industry. This meant he made a lot of money for having a sense of taste and style. He was a frequent guest expert on television decorating shows. He struck me as just another vain, self-centred gay professional, but Steven said Terry cared devotedly for him when he was sick, and that meant a great deal.

My impetus for the trip had been to write a travel article, bypassing the usual Acapulco-Vallarta scene and aiming instead for a tiny island off the Yucatán Peninsula. Isla Mujeres – the Isle of Women – was a largely barren outcropping to the north-east of Cancún. Named by sixteenth-century Spanish explorers for the large number of statues of the moon goddess Ix Chel found there, the island was already deserted when the explorers arrived. Anthropologists speculated the Maya population had been vanquished by a stronger civilisation, but later concluded it had been decimated by a mysterious plague.

At the Cancún airport, we caught a bus to Puerto Juárez where a ramshackle wooden vessel sat low in the blue-green water. We scrambled aboard, quickly stowing our luggage for the hour-long crossing. I bought a round of beer and the three of us stretched out against the ship's railing to watch the island approach in the flat bright distance. Opposite us, the only other non-native, sat a man with carrot-coloured hair and white skin. The muscles on his forearms and biceps were covered in freckles. I thought he was American, though he eventually turned out to be German. Not once did he look in our direction.

When the ferry docked we stepped onto a long narrow wharf extending tenuously from a palm-clustered beach. Bright adobe walls traced a meandering route along the waterfront. Cars were plentiful, but the favoured means of transport were the two-seater mopeds weaving in and out of traffic in the midday sun.

We followed directions to a rose-coloured hotel where the proprietor greeted us cheerfully as we walked up the front steps. He showed us to a sparsely furnished but comfortable room with a shower and two double beds. Terry looked sulkily around, holding on to his bag as though he might change his mind and go elsewhere. Steven sprawled across a mattress with a loud groan. He shot Terry a look that said, 'I'm staying.' That settled it.

Half an hour later, armed with sunglasses, suntan lotion and my camera, we ventured out to explore. The town was small enough to be traversed in fifteen minutes. A shopping strip catering to tourists ran through the centre of it. Cafés and restaurants were plentiful.

Colourful displays of jewellery, native crafts and hand-woven blankets loomed in shop windows and on every street corner. Terry invariably disapproved of whatever we saw – whether for the quality of materials or their design or both – this despite the remarkable prices. I found his attitude grating.

We quickly passed through the centre of town and emerged in a residential neighbourhood. The buildings were starker here compared with the colourful boutiques and restaurants we'd just seen. Many had no exterior doors and were closed off from the afternoon sun by limply hanging blankets.

A short native woman stood hunched over a pot washing clothes by hand. Next to her, a young girl in a ragged purple dress stared at us through a white fence. She held her raised foot in one hand, an unexpected ballerina, as though offering us lessons in balance. The woman looked up and barked an order. The girl dropped her foot and went to a table propped against a tree. Her eyes never left us as she doled out a sticky brown concoction onto plates set on the rickety tabletop.

I held up my camera to indicate I wanted to take her picture. She nodded shyly. I took the shot, waved my thanks, and we went on.

'What did you take a picture of that for?' Terry asked in a disapproving tone.

I shrugged. 'One of life's beautiful moments,' I replied.

'David's an artist,' Steven said, pushing playfully at my shoulder. 'He does lots of weird things.'

I tried snapping pictures of the two of them, running ahead and turning towards them, but Terry kept putting his hands in front of his face. Eventually I gave up and took a few shots of Steven alone.

The white sand beach at the north end of town was largely deserted. A handful of men with beautiful physiques – our only clue they might be gay – braved the waves along with a family with two kids. The family spoke French. The men spoke German, when they spoke at all. There was little camaraderie among the men as there would have been on a gay beach at home.

Steven and I left Terry on the beach rubbing suntan lotion onto his muscles as we wandered over to a thatched cabaña and ordered beer, clinking bottles at the bar. I looked him over. He was still a bit under-weight, but he seemed to have recovered from his bout with pneumonia. Steven was good-looking in that boy-next-door kind of way. Kind and gentle, he was everything a gay man will tell you he's looking for in a lover. He was the friendly stranger you invite home for a night, and who stays the next night, and then the next.

When we first met, his boyishness brought out a tender side in me. It surprised me. I'd never had that sort of relationship before. Both my parents were strong and independent-minded, and encouraged similar qualities in me. After a few months, however, Steven's boyishness and enthusiasm began to crowd in on me until I felt smothered. He'd been so open and guileless that it was relatively easy to dampen his faith in me until he retreated to what I considered a reasonable degree of comfort, if not outright safety.

Between leaving me and meeting Terry, Steven ended up HIV-positive in one of those silly desperate flings that end quickly but never quite go away. For what I considered my failure to love him, I proceeded to make up to him in friendship. In the years since I've often asked myself why I, or anyone, would turn away love offered so freely, so unselfishly. I still have no answer.

All this flashed through my mind as I sat over a beer with Steven in his red headband, blue Speedos and Keith Haring T-shirt. In the middle of our drink, Terry arrived dragging his towel. He glared suspiciously from Steven to me. I smiled and waved him over. He'd barely repressed his jealousy all morning and I didn't want to encourage it. He made a scathing comment about the Germans being such snobs they wouldn't look at him. I told Terry he was much sexier than them anyway and he warmed to the flattery.

I proposed an afternoon of fun for the three of us. Terry surprised me by accepting. Although our conversation never approached anything like genuine camaraderie that day, sometimes a superficial conviviality is really all you need. All those weekend tea dances weren't going for nothing, I told myself.

We drank beer and tequila and discussed our plans for the day ahead. There was a cliff said to be worthy of Heathcliff at the south end of the island. There was also a national park with a coral reef, if we wanted to go snorkelling. The more we drank the more our plans grew, but we sat there without moving all afternoon.

Back at the hotel that evening several straight couples assembled on the terrace directly outside our room to watch the sun set. Steven and I chatted freely with them. Terry boycotted the gathering, reading in the room alone.

Eventually we went off in search of supper. Over dessert, Terry got drunk and leered at an attractive young waiter. The boy blushed, aware he'd become the focus of our attention. Eventually he stopped coming over to the table.

'I think you scared him off,' I said.

Terry looked at me defiantly. 'Straight men look at our women like that,' he snapped.

I hadn't meant it as a reproof, simply as a comment.

'In the first place,' I said, 'what makes them "our" women? In the second place, isn't that exactly why women call men assholes? And in the third place, this isn't our culture, so you might learn to respect it for what it is.'

Terry glared but said nothing, as though he considered it beneath him to respond. Steven wisely stayed out of it. We paid the bill and left.

On the way back through town, the light from TV screens filtered eerily through open doorways. Blowing curtains revealed sparse interiors with dirt floors and meagre furnishings. I felt like a voyeur, ashamed to be glimpsing these views that suggested something far too intimate to be perceived by passing strangers.

That night I slept a laboured sleep that harboured dark secrets somewhere on the other side of consciousness. I woke before dawn to the sound of a rooster crowing nearby. Others joined in, one after another, like a relay race. I pulled a pillow over my head and eventually fell back to sleep.

When I woke again, it was full daylight. The other bed was empty. I showered and had a cigarette. I'd just finished dressing when Steven and Terry returned. I could tell they'd been arguing.

'We're waiting for you,' Steven said. 'We've already eaten.'

'I'm ready,' I said, grabbing my bag and stuffing a towel and a tube of suntan lotion into it.

Terry had wandered back onto the terrace without saying a word.

'What's the matter with him?' I said.

'He says the day's wasted.'

'It's only nine-thirty!'

'Terry likes to get an early start,' Steven said apologetically.

'Well, next time wake me earlier or the two of you go your merry little way without me,' I retorted.

Steven looked chastised. 'I'm sorry, Dave. I wanted you to come with us. Besides, you're our tour guide, remember?'

I felt bad for snapping. 'There's nothing to be sorry for. Let's go.'

We explored the south end of the island that day. The sun beat on our heads as we trudged through the dry scrub that dotted the rocky terrain. Small grey lizards darted away at our footsteps. We soon found the cliff and stood on a ledge jutting out over the ocean. The spray rose like giant fingers reaching up to us from below. With the wind in my hair, I felt that if I raised my arms I would instantly be carried off.

We rented snorkelling equipment at the park and scrambled around in the water, getting used to the awkwardness of the fins and breathing apparatus. Out on the reef, schools of colourful fish swept past my vision like bursts of light. I kept reaching out to touch them, only to find they were beyond my grasp.

That evening the three of us ate on an outdoor patio where cheery chefs manned sizzling grills, keeping up a steady supply of fresh fish and steaks. It was crowded and smoky and we stayed drinking cold beer until late. Since my outburst the previous day Terry had hardly spoken to me. I, in turn, had stopped worrying about whether he was enjoying himself, and tried to make the most of my time with Steven.

I asked our waiter if he knew of any discos or late night bars, thinking there had to be some gay people around. He said there was one small disco on the island and pointed vaguely towards the far end of town. We found the nondescript club with a dance floor that boasted a show of five red lights and two blue ones. The place seemed like a time warp where old pop songs came to rest after leaving the 'burbs. There was nothing gay about it. A handful of curious tourists huddled at one end of the bar across from a crowd of Mexicans. We settled in and amused ourselves by watching the tourists awkwardly imitate the natives, who danced up a storm around them.

The next morning we all had the trots. No one wanted to eat. No one spoke much either. I pulled out my book and sat on the terrace most of the afternoon to be near the bathroom. Terry and I watched for further signs of illness from Steven, knowing how sudden weight loss can be dangerous for someone in his condition, but he never worsened. In fact, he pulled out of it faster than either of us.

'When the immune system is constantly being attacked,' he explained, 'it's also constantly vigilant.'

Later, feeling a bit better, I walked through town alone. Just before dusk I passed a dirt yard where a long-limbed monkey sat chained to a tree, spinning a wooden wheel with a stick. As I approached, the monkey bared its teeth and shrieked loudly while tugging threateningly at its collar. I crouched to watch, but it never abandoned its aggressive posturing towards me, the intruder in its mound of dust. Eventually I moved on, leaving it to its random turnings.

That evening we decided it was safe to venture out again. We found a restaurant with a menu in five languages. We were all feeling expansive and relaxed.

'You know what I like best about this island?' Terry said. 'I like the pace.'

Up till then I hadn't thought he'd found anything to like about it.

'What pace? Nothing moves!' Steven exclaimed.

'That's what I mean,' Terry said. 'I love it! I could see myself living happily here someday.'

'You mean you'd give up your fabulous lifestyle, your new clothes and expense accounts for this?' Steven said, laughing.

'I could give those up in a second!' Terry retorted.

'You live in a dream world,' Steven said. 'You'd never do it.'

I was laughing too by then.

'You wait,' Terry told Steven. 'Next year, we'll be down here living together.'

'Well, count me in, boys,' I said. 'There's not much back home I'd miss in exchange for this.'

Our conversation that evening was a mixture of jousting and friendly banter. We were getting along at last – and none too soon. Another few days and we'd be home again. I wondered how long the feelings of camaraderie would last.

The sky above us was black and glossy, like the ocean at night. A falling star speared the horizon. I pointed out its descent before it vanished.

'What did you wish for?' Steven asked.

I shrugged. 'I wouldn't know what to wish for,' I replied truthfully.

'I'll wish for you then,' he said. He thought for a second and then said, 'I wish that this moment – right now – could last forever.'

Back at the hotel in the room next to us, a straight couple were breaking up, arguing in loud voices. It was hot and we tossed on the sheets. The arguing went on for half an hour. Terry pounded on the wall. The voices grew quieter but didn't stop.

'I'm going out to the terrace,' I said, eventually.

I lay in one of the deck chairs with a cool wind on my face. Palm trees swayed in black silhouettes and the water sparkled in the moonlight like a negative of the day that had just passed. Waves rolled onto the beach with a faint intake of breath as of someone grieving at a distance.

Unable to sleep, I crept down the stairs. Here and there, couples strolled along the silent streets. I wandered down to a pier jutting out into the ocean. By chance, I passed the redhead who'd come across with us on the ferry. He was wearing white cotton pants and a dark T-shirt and stood beneath a palm tree. I nodded and kept going.

I sat on the end of the pier looking over the liquorice-coloured water to the lights across the bay. Above me, the constellations looked completely unfamiliar till I spotted the Big Dipper and located the North Star. I stayed there half an hour. When I returned, the redhead was standing in the same spot. I caught a German accent when he asked the time. I tried to decipher my watch face in the darkness. Before I could answer, he put his hand on my shoulder.

Things happened quickly and we had dry, hard sex on the beach. He was big and dark in the moonlight spiralling off the water. Afterwards, we parted and I returned to the hotel alone.

The next morning, Steven and Terry were gone when I woke up. I wandered down to the beach and spent the afternoon in the sun, but I didn't see the German. Strangely, I missed him, though I hadn't even asked his name.

When I returned to the hotel, Steven and Terry were back. They'd been quarrelling again, but gave no clue what it was about. Terry had probably disapproved of the design of some knick-knack Steven wanted to buy. They lay, not quite touching, on opposite sides of the bed. I ignored them.

Eventually, Steven looked over and asked where I wanted to eat supper. I suggested going back to the place from the previous night where the food had been good and the service friendly. Terry mumbled something about not eating twice at the same restaurant while on vacation.

We got dressed and walked up and down the streets for more than half an hour, looking for a place to eat. Both Steven and Terry suggested places and tore each other's suggestions apart. Then we all began to argue. Somehow we ended up in a small café where a band of raggedly-dressed Chilean musicians stopped in to perform during the middle of our meal.

'Oh, that's pathetic!' Terry exclaimed, as the musicians took up a strident rhythm on their instruments.

Steven and I glanced at one another and smiled. We both enjoyed the simple, unaffected sound. It was music with life.

The food was good and the wine was cheap. And, surprisingly, the evening turned out to be pleasant. We all ended up enjoying the music, even Terry the snob. I thought about how much he'd complained during the trip. I knew he was unhappy because of Steven's health, and possibly for reasons I knew nothing of. Maybe he didn't even know how unhappy he was. It must be possible to be unhappy and not know it.

We flew home two days later to our respective lives and jobs. I turned my account of the trip into a feature article and sold it to a glossy travel magazine for the cover story of their premiere issue. It pleased me when they chose my photo of the young girl spooning food onto plates to introduce their publication.

Somehow, though, I'd hoped for more. I wanted to have connected better with both Steven and Terry. I'd like to have created something lasting – to have come away feeling that life is more than these temporary bridges we make between ourselves and other individuals when we need to share something apart from the weather or talk about something other than how our day has been. Perhaps I was asking too much.

At least I know it made Steven happy to go on that trip, escaping winter and his health concerns, if only for a while. On our return, he thanked me profusely for inviting him. The experience had been good and he'd been grateful to share it with me.

For a while afterwards I would pull out the pictures I snapped that first day on the island to remind me of his smile, though lately I do it less often. And of course, I still see Terry every now and then at brunch or the parties of some mutual friend or other. We wave to one another across the room as though we are friends, too. Sometimes we speak a word or two, but never more than that.

And I still recall the ferry trip back from the island. I remember the sense of loss I felt at not seeing the red-haired man on board with us that morning, as though I'd left something behind. As I watched the island recede, I wondered who he was and where he might be going next. I also wondered why our chance meeting had affected me so strongly. And for that, I have no answer either.

Eventually, I forgot him and turned my attention to the waves. The sun was shining even more brightly than it had on our arrival. The others on board might have been the same people as on the trip going over. Our return seemed as though it would be as uneventful as our arrival had been.

At one point during the crossing, however, a boarding gate on the side of the ferry swung slowly open like an invitation to walk out over the wide blue-green water. Someone had neglected to latch it properly. None of the crew or nearby passengers moved to close it. Perhaps no one noticed.

I watched a group of children race past. One of them, a small boy, stopped to look out. No one called or made a move to keep him away from the gate, though I kept him in sight until he stepped back and continued after his friends.

I felt a sudden surge of anger for the indolence and carelessness – the casualness of a disaster-in-the-making. Then, just as suddenly, the feeling vanished and my mind drifted back to the day I'd gone out alone and come across the monkey that had protested when I got too close. It struck me how the human heart is like that – a small animal tethered to the end of a leash, frightened by the approach of passing strangers.

Far ahead, mountains of pure white cloud piled high over the gleaming hotel strip where I could pick out tiny palm trees and umbrellas and the seemingly motionless figures on the beach. I had a sudden flash of a life fully fleshed out and intensely lived. And I understand now this is what you were trying to tell us with your wish, Steven: this moment that is now, that is forever.

And in that moment I relaxed and leaned into the railing, not wondering how far you had to travel to leave the past behind or obliterate it in the face of a future that waits like a gate opening on the edge of the sea. Wherever we were going, we would be there soon enough.

Kinder, Gentler

Steven Saylor

For Rick

I used to see him at the gym. We never spoke, but it wasn't hard to get an idea of his personality. He liked to talk, he talked loud, and he seemed to know everyone there except me. He would have been easy to meet, but he wasn't really my type. Clone-style cropped black hair and a moustache, an arch tone, slightly exaggerated genteel gestures – a queenly top. His eyes always seemed to be half-shut, as if he were too lazy to open them all the way, which gave him a shrewd, indolent look. One day I overheard him bragging to someone in his faintly regal Alabama accent, 'I'm a pitcher, Mary, not a catcher.' This was in the locker room. I'm sure I glanced down to check him out, and I'm sure he must have had a big one, though I can't really remember. Once I saw his name on his membership card and for some reason it stuck in my head: Andy Doogan.

It was a shock the first time I saw him on the street. I mean *living* on the street.

I'd missed him at the gym. When a regular stops coming I always notice. That happens a lot these days, but with Andy Doogan it was different. He was the first person in my little world, however slightly I knew him, to end up panhandling and homeless.

Once he started living on the street, I saw him almost every day. There was a recessed store entrance on Castro Street where he'd huddle at night, wrapped in a blanket with his heavy-lidded eyes peering out. During the day there was a sunny spot on the sidewalk near the gym where he'd hang out. Every time I'd see him a line would flash through my head, about ghosts returning to the places they had frequented in life. There was something about Andy Doogan that frightened me.

239

For a long time I never heard him ask for money. He never talked to anyone passing by, except an occasional old friend, usually another face I'd recognise from the gym, stopping to ask how he was. I'd watch from the corner of my eye as they slipped him a bill; Doogan would give them his wry, heavy-lidded smile and look away at the instant the money changed hands.

Eventually he started asking strangers for money. The first time I heard him do it I felt a twinge of embarrassment. He never asked me. I think he only asked strangers and friends, and I fell in-between. I never stopped to talk to him. I never gave him money. Whenever I spotted him ahead of me on the sidewalk I'd set my eyes elsewhere and move towards the curb, not a lot, just a little, just enough to put the minimum distance between us so that neither of us would feel an obligation to speak. I'd feel a little guilty, but that would quickly pass.

There must be at least a dozen other panhandlers around the neighbourhood at any given time, regulars like the white-haired lady with the little accordion and the crazy guy who walks around with his pants half-off. I've learned that I only have to ignore them long enough and eventually they become comfortably, painlessly invisible – except for Andy Doogan. He wouldn't fade away. Every time I passed him I felt the same flash of anxiety. I wasn't afraid of Andy Doogan himself. I was afraid of whatever it was that had thrown him out of the gym and onto the sidewalk.

I had nothing in common with those other panhandlers, never had, never would. But once upon a time a disinterested outsider peering into the gym probably wouldn't have been able to tell Andy and me apart. Not anymore. Something had picked up Andy Doogan and dropped him onto the other side of an invisible, impenetrable wall. In swift little glances I searched his face for signs of disease, craziness, alcoholism, and saw only lines of bitterness about his primly pursed lips and half-shut eyes.

One night, walking home from a late show at the Castro Theatre, I pointed him out to Dave and asked if he knew anything about him. Dave said no. It was a cold, foggy night. As soon as we got home we stripped and snuggled into bed. Basil was already settled on my pillow, purring louder than you'd expect from a ten-year-old cat. I left him where he was and let him mould himself against my head. Zoë slipped under the covers and pressed warm and furry against my stomach. Dave made a jealous grunt and spooned himself against my chest, squeezing her between us.

She made a pitiful little squeak of protest and then started purring furiously, vibrating against my belly and the small of his back. Dave and I both laughed. 'Dumb-ass cat,' he whispered. I reached up to stroke his cheek, slid my hand on to his shoulder and then around to hug his chest. I felt myself stiffening against his buttocks but fell asleep before I could do anything about it.

One Saturday a few weeks later we were sitting inside Cafe Flore, at the table in the inner crook of the L, with my back to the door. Dave looked up from his *Macworld* and kicked me under the table. 'Look who's coming in,' he said.

'Who?' I was busy staring over Dave's shoulder at a curly-haired boy lined up at the counter, who briefly stared back.

'Your friend.'

'What friend?' The curly-haired boy looked demurely away, turned to a friend behind him, laughed. I looked into my coffee and remembered the days before the plague. Hard stares, stony expressions of lust, instant come-ons, electrifying eye contact made without the least apprehension: *Will you or won't you? Now or later? This very instant, or can you give me fifteen minutes to douche?* Vanished now forever. Innocence replaced by chastity. The thrill of the instant spoiled by hesitation, suspicion, erotic apathy.

'Coming in the door,' Dave said again. 'You know, that guy. The homeless guy.'

I turned enough to catch a glimpse of him as he slipped behind me and queued up at the end of the line. 'Andy Doogan,' I said.

Dave nodded. 'Must have a job.'

'Maybe.'

Doogan was freshly shaved, his moustache neatly trimmed. His jeans were stained and dirty, but his coat looked brand new. When he sat down he took off his jacket. He was wearing an old I-Beam dance club T-shirt I remembered from the gym. He didn't fill it out the way he used to. He didn't look gaunt or unhealthy, but he'd lost a lot of mass. His skin was dark and weathered from the sun. He sat alone at a table against the wall, sipping his tea, surveying the room through heavy-lidded eyes.

'He doesn't look bad,' Dave said.

'No. Maybe something's happened.' I felt an odd sense of relief.

A few days later I saw Andy Doogan through the plate-glass window of a restaurant on Church Street, eating with another man and laughing, and for a while that was all I saw of him. His usual spots on the sidewalk were empty. He was off the streets. It was a small change in my world, and it gave me a small happiness. The situation had resolved itself, against all expectations, for the better. I had failed to do anything about it, but it had righted itself anyway. This was evidence that all was not wrong with the world, and it cheered me more than you might think.

The next time I saw him was on a Friday a few weeks later. I remember the day because every Friday I stay home from the office and work around the house. That morning I did what I do every Friday morning. I sorted the laundry, carried it to the back porch and started the washing machine. I vacuumed the living room and the bedroom and the dining room and mopped the kitchen. I scrubbed the toilet bowl and put off doing the bathtub for another week. Towards lunchtime I made a cup of coffee and spent a half-hour sitting on the sofa stroking the cats, who are always in a purring mood on Fridays because I let them stay inside all day.

Around noon I opened a can of tuna, fed some to the cats and ate the rest myself. Dave called from his office. I don't remember the call, but he always calls me at lunch on Friday. Probably we talked about seeing a movie that night, and haggled over whether to eat out or order a pizza. We always order a pizza.

Sometime in the afternoon I baked a dozen oat bran muffins. Dave makes fun of them by bouncing them like a ball on the table, but I try to make him eat two a day. It's because of the egg-lecithin he takes every morning since he got his positive HIV test. Supposedly it inhibits replication of the virus. The stuff is concentrated cholesterol, like an egg yolk injection; nobody in his right mind would take it if he wasn't worried about something worse than a heart attack fifteen years down the road. Supposedly the oat bran helps eliminate cholesterol. Dave will make a face at the muffins and say something like, 'If I live long enough to die from a heart attack I'll count myself lucky.' But I still make two or three batches a week. Somehow it makes me feel better when he eats them.

Afterwards I switched on the Mac and played half a dozen rounds of whatever arcade game was new on the disk. I used to be addicted to the things, but the thrill is wearing thin. Like Dave says, unless you're fourteen years old Crystal Quest can't really substitute for sex. Ten years ago, with a Friday afternoon off, I would have been doing something very different.

When the game started boring me I switched off the machine and went back to the kitchen. I made a salad to go with the pizza later and put it in the refrigerator, loaded up the dishwasher and turned it on. Around four I went to Café Flore. Dave had said he'd meet me there after work.

Andy Doogan was there, too, not inside but crouched against the newspaper boxes on Market Street wrapped up in a blanket. I bit my lip when he looked up at me. He needed a shave, his moustache was ragged, and he still couldn't seem to open his eyes all the way, giving him that shrewd look that had seemed to mean something in the gym but meant nothing now. I turned my eyes away.

Dave never showed up. I finally called his office; he was working late on a new account. Coming back from the phone I ran into Peggi. She was sitting alone at a table, poring over a batch of computer listings. She looked up, smiled and gestured at the empty chair.

'And what are you doing anywhere except at the Names Project?' I asked.

'Oh, somebody left the lock off my cage. I figure they'll be in here with the nets in a few minutes.' Her voice was hoarse from too many cigarettes.

We made small talk. Peggi kept one eye on her listings, flipping to a new page every now and then. I looked around the room, and wasn't surprised to see the curly-headed boy sitting at a table with some of his friends. He looked at me, stopped laughing for a moment, and looked away.

'You know, Peggi, I'm getting to be of an age that I feel I should start being, oh, I don't know, mentor to some younger guy.'

'I see. Is that code for saying you'd like to leave Dave for someone fresher?'

'Of course not. Not at all.' And I meant it, looking down into my cup, thinking of home. 'I don't know, I mean, when I was in my early twenties, it seems like I had something in common with older guys. Something to share. The hottest men I knew were all ten years older than me.'

'Sex,' she said.

'Not just sex. They had more than that to offer. Experience, security. They knew their way around. Like a tribe. But now that I'm older, I feel like there's this big wall that's come down between me and the younger guys. This generation gap that wasn't there when I was their age. It's not that they don't trust you if you're over thirty. They're afraid of men over thirty. Physically afraid. The virus. I feel cheated. There's something in me that's being wasted. This isn't where I should be right now in my life.'

'You know, Eric, you need to get out of yourself.'

'I'm boxed in. Like everybody else.'

'You're not trying. Look, Dave spends four, five hours a week down at the Names Project. Why don't you come with him? It would open you up. You're too insular, curling up at home with Dave and the cats. I know they're important to you, but you need a bigger family than that.'

'Do I?' She pressed too hard and I ended up resentful, as usual. 'I'm not the volunteer type.' I glanced over my shoulder. Through the windows I could just see the top of Andy Doogan's head.

'He's a sad case, isn't he?' Peggi said.

'You know him?' I shouldn't have been surprised. Peggi knows everyone.

'From when his lover died, about six months ago. He brought in a panel. A beautiful thing – you must have seen it, we had it hanging in the workshop window for a while. An airbrushed portrait. A blond guy with a moustache in a cowboy hat; his name was Freddy. Beautiful work. Andy's an artist.'

I shrugged. 'I probably saw it. I don't remember. So how did he end up on the street?'

'It happened after his lover died. They'd been together for years. It was really hard on him. And on top of that he didn't have a lot of money of his own. Freelance commercial work, not very steady. Most of the savings were gone because of the hospital bills, and then Freddy's family moved in and took everything else. I mean *everything*. One of those situations where the blood relations can't stand the lover.'

'No will?'

She shook her head. 'A bad scene. You and Dave have all that done, don't you? Will, power of attorney? I know it's Dave who makes most of the income. You have to plan ahead, Eric, and look out for yourself.'

Peggi was always blunt. I felt something like a shiver and nodded. 'So what about Andy Doogan?'

'He slipped through the cracks and just kept slipping. I think he still gets a little work every now and then. Friends put in his name when they see a job. I guess there must be some place he can clean up every now and then. But once you're out it takes a lot of money to get back in. First and last month rent deposit, all that. I guess he lives hand to mouth. The last time I saw him was when he came to see the quilt at Moscone Center. I don't know if he'll ever pull himself out of it.'

'No family?'

'I guess not. Or maybe just too far away.'

Peggi left after that. I took her seat and sat looking at the top of Andy Doogan's head. From the way he turned whenever people walked by I could tell he was asking for money. It was after five and there were lots of people on Market Street. No one stopped.

And then I had a fantasy. Amid the music and the murmur of the crowd my mind began to wander. I imagined getting up from the table and walking on to the street, sitting down beside Andy Doogan, talking to him, laughing, touching his hand, inviting him home with me. Why not? We never used the dining room for anything but paperwork; it could double just as well as a bedroom. Maybe all Andy needed was a place to stay for a couple of months while he got back on his feet. I saw him at the gym again, healthier, heavier, cracking jokes, calling other men Mary, casting his Alabama accent across the room and checking us all out with his half-shut eyes as if he knew a secret he would never tell.

There was something comforting about the daydream, and I kept replaying it, embellishing it with happy details, even though I knew it would never happen. I could hear Dave almost as if he were there at the table: *Eric, get real. Remember the last time we had a roommate? Remember what happened when your brother came to visit for three weeks?* And there was another voice I couldn't blame on anyone else: *Why me? Where are his friends, anyway? If all he needs is a little time and a place to sleep, why haven't they given him that much? What do they know that I don't? You can't just let a stranger into your house.*

Instead, as I was leaving, I stopped outside the gate and offered him the two muffins I had brought along for Dave, along with a ten-dollar bill. I told him my name, and said I remembered him from the gym. He told me his, and said thank you. 'You're from the South,' I said, just to make conversation, and he said, 'Mobile, Alabama. But I hated it there.' It was a start, but I still felt small and a little cowardly as I turned my back on him and walked towards Castro Street.

There was a message on the phone machine from Dave. He'd dropped by the Names Project on the way home. They were in the middle of their latest data entry crisis; he was going to stay and help for a few hours. Peggi slipped on at the end and said I should come down and join them.

I phoned for a pizza. When it came I ate half and put the rest away. I heard rain against the windows, and when I looked through the drapes I saw the street running with water and pricked all over with raindrops, orange and white in the car lights. I pulled on a sweatshirt and turned up the heater, and wondered what Andy Doogan did on nights like this, and where his family was.

I turned off all the lights except for a lamp in the living room and sat for a long time on the sofa, alone and quiet, no television, no magazine, listening to the rain. After a while I got up and walked through the house, leaving the lights off, not needing them to see every object from memory, all the things we had accumulated together over ten years: chairs, tables and desks, decorations for the walls, carpets and lamps, the telephones, the message machine, the computer, the microwave, dishwasher, typewriter, bicycles, shelves full of books, all the comforts of home. I felt a richness and an emptiness. These things seemed to me at the same time trivial and vulgar, absolutely necessary and sublime.

I pulled a photo album from the shelves beside the bed, turned on the bedside lamp and leafed through at random: photos of trips, festivals and street fairs, of once and would-have-been lovers, living and dead, the tribe of ten years ago dissipated, decimated, atomised into clean-living couples and half-couples, regrouped into committees on grieving and death.

Dave came in very late. I was half-asleep. I heard him move about the room in darkness, taking off his clothes, turning back the sheets. I could still hear rain against the window. I rolled over and pressed myself against him, disrupting the cats, who murmured in their sleep. I pressed my face into his hair and whispered in a voice so low I'm sure he didn't hear, 'Never leave me, David, never. Never change my world.'

Dead Man's Hand

Michael Wilcox

We buried Harry Sandling in a willow coffin on a bleak, Northumbrian hillside. What should have been a peaceful woodland burial seemed nothing of the sort in the cutting north wind of a freezing November afternoon. Harry was a hundred years old when he died. His mind was strong and clear to the end, but his body could stand it no longer. He was proud of his eight children, twenty-two grandchildren, and over fifty great-grandchildren. I lived with one of them for more than twenty years, until poor Mathew was snatched away, aged only fifty-seven, two years ago. No one could claim that Harry had not left his mark.

I was not expecting anything from Harry's estate with such a huge family ready to scrap over every damn thing. Most of them cold-shouldered Mathew and I if they possibly could. But a month after the funeral a large envelope arrived. The address was written in Harry's distinctive hand. Inside was a series of smaller envelopes, each carefully numbered, and a covering letter from the dead man himself.

Peter, my dear, you better have these. I've kept them all my life. You'll understand. I've numbered everything to help with the chronology. Start at the beginning. There's a puzzle you'll enjoy. What really happened? There are some secrets that should rightly die with a man. All my love, Harry

I opened the first envelope. Inside was a postcard from France dated Sunday, 4 June 1916. It was addressed to Harry's mother. 'I'm just off to join our front line – address' (this part was difficult to read) '4th attd (?) 2nd Bt Sherwood Foresters'. It was initialled 'SSD' and written in pencil. Across the top of the card, 'Carte Postale' had been scribbled out and replaced with 'S.S. Doyle – on active service'. There was a censor's red stamp, approving the contents. On the other side of the card were printed the words and music of a French patriotic song, 'Regiment de Sambre-et-Meuse'.

I'd never heard mention of S.S. Doyle before. I reached for the second envelope and opened it expectantly. Inside were three thin sheets of paper, torn out of a notebook. Once again, the writing was in pencil.

B.E.F. 2 July 1916

Dear Mrs Sandling,

I'm afraid you haven't had much news from me since I left. It seems only the other day that I came over but it's nearly five weeks now. Happily there is not very much to tell. I had a very busy time in London – a great deal of shopping which was tiring work in such warm weather. And I had to go very slow as my wife was none too well. However we had an enjoyable time together and I got away (for once in quite good time) early on the Monday morning. We had quite a pleasant time on the way but it was a very long journey!

We ended up at a camp in a very pleasant situation with fine views of sand dunes and sea. There we had a very strenuous time for just four days. Late on Sunday we were told to join our units. I've come up to the 2nd Btt Sherwood Foresters and am third senior in my (D) company, so really have much more position and responsibility than at home. But it helps a great deal in experience.

Since I joined this gallant little company I've been in half a dozen different huts, tents, dugouts – no more than that! But since the rainy fortnight has passed by we have had little to complain of. We are having really warm summer weather at last. But eight days ago, rain and mud described everything.

Our officers are a very jolly set and there's little room for favouritism or intrigue here. It's share and share alike. We seem very well provided for too and – no secret – the battalion has a splendid reputation.

There is little to write about beyond. Some of the country is finely picturesque – especially the little farmsteads generally surrounded by a moat and a belt of graceful, tall willows. Many are deserted and dilapidated however. We see few living things – soldiers, soldiers, soldiers – and comparatively few flowers. Just now saw some martins. Poppies are in season.

My love to you and young Harry. How I miss him! I loved staying with you and learned so much.

Yours very sincerely,
Stephen S. Doyle

P.S. My wife wishes to add her thanks for the colourful tray!

I tried to figure out how old 'young Harry' must have been in 1916. Fourteen years old, perhaps? And what was Stephen Doyle doing, staying with Harry and his mother? Harry's father had died famously in a railway accident. His scarf had been caught in the carriage door and he was dragged off the platform under the wheels. This provincial tragedy had made the national news. The widowed Mrs Sandling was a woman of wealth and property. Her estate gardens were renowned in the North of England and she employed a small army of gardeners. I reached for the third envelope.

B.E.F. 12 September 1916

Dear Mrs Sandling,

Our days have been so exciting, so busy and often so upside down that weeks and even months shoot past without more than the most necessary letters getting written. So it must be long indeed since I gave you any of my news. I have always been counting on something 'turning up' – some hours or (perhaps) days of peace and quiet, or some pressing, real news which could and should be chronicled. But my real news is practically no news at all. I'm fit and well after three months with the Battalion and now I am having something of a rest, learning all about trench mortars in a peaceful wee hamlet so far away from 'the line' that we hear the guns only when the wind wishes it. The rest is not all pleasure though. There's a certain amount of work to be done, but it's not that; it is the constant wonder what is happening to old 14 Platoon while I'm away from it. After three months with it – day and night – and only four odd days away, it was hard to leave it in just such uncertain days and hours as these.

I've seen lots of country and lots of war since I came out, but I've seen only one place that I knew before the war. The more one sees, the more one realises how impossible it is to depict it and – also – how much a blessing it is that the war never came to England.

But if it is not to be properly described, the war is not more awful than it is currently painted. It has its moments of gaiety and brightness. Within hours of the worst dangers and most uncomfortable conditions, the men will crack jokes as persistently and as optimistically as one ever hears at home. The spirit of the men is wonderful. They are wonderfully pleased and heartened by the great change that has come over the war. It is like champagne to hear some of the older ones when 'Fritz' gets a particularly warm time. They saw the days when the boot was on the other leg. But now the 'Boche' has generally a very, very thin time, and I think the newspapers at home exaggerate very little, if at all, about that side of the war. Meanwhile, the conditions for us have improved.

There doesn't seem to be any more that I can say – unless I try to cheat the censor, and I won't do that! But I'll beg of your news. How are you and Harry? And how is the estate planting coming on? I wish I was there to see it. How did my planting in the walled garden develop? Can you send me drawings? Or photographs, even? Harry! Perhaps this is a job for you! And can I have a photograph of Harry? I love the boy so much. It would give me extra courage to have his picture with me. I hope you are reading my letters to Harry. Heaven forbid that the war should drag on so long that he has to come out here. That thought is too distressing.

All my news from home seems good – but how I should enjoy a holiday! My wife has told me about your many kindnesses. I am profoundly grateful to you.

I am
Yours very sincerely,
Stephen S.Doyle

How curious to read such passionate messages to Harry. From today's perspective, all manner of alarm bells are set ringing. But here was a glimpse of a different age as though before the Fall of Man. And what other deductions should I make? Stephen Doyle is married and shops in London with his wife. Do they live in London? Mrs Sandling's estate was in Northumberland. If Stephen had travelled north to advise on planting and the design of the gardens, he must have been a special talent. How old was he? In my mind, I see a young man in his early twenties, but he might have been a lot older. I reached for the fourth envelope.

For the first time, Stephen Doyle is writing in ink. His hand is clear and steady.

B.E.F. 27 October 1916

Dear Mrs Sandling,

Have I thanked you for the Parkin yet? I'm afraid not. And it was so good! It came at just the best possible time as well. How grateful I was, I can scarcely say. As it was we were in a very tough corner and for several days I could not get a letter written, to say nothing of getting it sent off. Altogether we were ten days without shave, wash or change. It saves a lot of time, but all the same... Because it isn't very nice to use one's hand first to clean a dirty, greasy rifle, then to prop oneself up against a muddy sandbag, and – all in the same ten minutes – then to put butter and jam onto one's bread! But that's what it comes to. The parcel came just before our company had to go and do a little forward work, and as we could light no fires, I wanted all the food I could get. And Parkin is great food! At first I thought I'd be generous. I asked one fellow: 'Do you like Parkin?' – because I didn't wish to hear him say that he didn't like gingerbread made that way as I've heard others say it. 'Parkin? Don't know him. Who is he?' So I gave up – said it was very peculiar, and only an acquired taste or an absolute Yorkshire constitution could digest it. Indeed, I was (feignedly) very, very sorry, but so it was. So I ate nearly all myself and did well on it. All the same, I don't want another ten days like those – even with Parkin to solace me.

I don't suppose you and Harry want to hear much of either the drab or gory parts of campaigning. Mud, puddles in our sleeping bags, every rag of linen in the wash, or (as I had for three weeks) in the dirty clothes bag, or servant and kit all gone astray, or (horror of horrors, but unavoidable and common from colonel downwards) creepy-crawly creatures all alive-oh! They are all in my day's work. But at present, except for raw, wet autumn weather, we are (almost) in clover, being at 'rest', our tents pitched in a really beautiful part of the country among very pleasant people. I am even enjoying a bed – the fifth time in five months! And such a bed too – one which some big general slept in not long ago, at a château too. It reminds me of the one I slept in next to Harry's room at your splendid house.

(At this point, Stephen's pen runs out of ink. He continues in pencil)

But what pleases me most of all is finding some kiddies to play with. The French country children are such fun. But they don't help me forget the others at home. All the same, you would enjoy a glimpse of this part of our campaigning. The woods, the windmills, the tall, graceful (I was going to say Harry-like) trees on the roadside, the orchards and the low hillocks with their flocks of browsing sheep, and – above all – the splendid autumn colours, all fill with joy the heart of man. Though all the same, I am always wishing to be up and away with two good horses, and Harry for a friend, for a gallop.

And what else am I going to write about? It is always so difficult to find something to say. One gets so entirely enveloped in routine and military technics – and three parts of the jokes, even, are scarcely anything but military: it is hard to convey the sense of things to civilians. I am so much out of date with the news that I cannot even talk of the Balkans. There never was such a diplomatic (and absurd) tragi-comedy as that of Greece. Though I think the Germans delayed us there, and that this delay and the delay elsewhere on account of bad weather have gravely lengthened the campaign. All the same, I think there are signs every day – of all kind – that 'Fritz' now realises – dimly perhaps as yet – that he is beaten, or soon will be. I've seen enough at one time or another to be very thankful that I am this side of the lines and not the other.

I was glad to hear how Harry escaped diphtheria (or the worst of it) and I hope the garden is going well in spite of no camp labour. I have written to my wife, urging her to trade a photograph of your humble servant for one of Harry, so that she might know what a wonderful boy should look like. I presume you heard that she is expecting her first child?

And I must thank you for your provisional invitation to travel north and stay with you and Harry once again. If the war were to end (if, if, if!) how many visits of thanks should I love to pay!

So my love to you and dear Harry. And many thanks and many good wishes.

Yours very sincerely,
Stephen S. Doyle

There were three more, precisely numbered envelopes left. I quickly opened the next. But this was not from Stephen Doyle. It was from his wife.

1 December 1916

The Beeches
Ruskin Avenue
Kew Gardens
Surrey

Dear Mrs Sandling,

I seem to know you all so well – hearing my husband speak of you – so I hope you won't mind me writing to you in this most unceremonious manner – he asked me lately if I would write and beg you for a photograph of Harry. I was even to offer a bribe in the shape of his photograph, looking so smart in his uniform!

I am expecting him home on leave. When, is more than I can tell you – you must ask the Gods at the War Office – but if you would be so kind as to send me a photograph of Harry – so as to welcome him on his return, I know it would give us both great joy – and especially my husband – for he thinks him the most lovely boy he has ever seen – and I have heard all the stories he has to tell of Harry – and how he used to come into Stephen's bedroom each morning to plan out the day – and how you were all so good to Stephen when

255

he stayed with you. My husband is still only nineteen years old and his astonishing talents are sorely missed in Kew Gardens. I have got one of his photographs specially for you and Harry. Shall I send it at once or would you like him to autograph it when he comes home? He has had a very bad time, but keeps fit I am thankful to say.

With kind regards
I remain
Yours sincerely,
Mabel F. Doyle

Still only nineteen? I found this very surprising news. But Stephen's connection with Kew confirmed my opinion that he was a special authority on planting and horticulture, even at that very young age. I quickly opened the penultimate letter. Stephen was writing in pencil once more.

B.E.F. 3 January 1917

My dear Mrs Sandling,
Thank you ever so much for the cake, the drawing book and the letter. You can scarcely imagine with what joy and laughter they were received. Here we were, the dirtiest couple in the wettest dugout in the muddiest part of 'the Line'. And in came a parcel with good fun, good cake and good news in it. But what do you think caused most joy and laughter? The lovely piece of white damask! It looked so wonderfully out of place – like a lily growing in a pit heap – so white, so much the epitome of 'Blighty'. We would have framed it and hung it up in the dugout, but we shan't have the chance. But do as we can, it has scarcely a cat's chance of getting 'out' without being soiled with either French dust or French mud. Really, we're just as filthy as can be, but as it is not our fault at all we don't mind making (so to speak!) a clean breast of it. Anyhow, we've had some good fun this journey.

I don't suppose it's a military secret to say that one of the entrances to our dugout is a cross between a waterfall and a chimney flue, and that the dugout itself would make a good coal hole if it were dryer. We had no end of fun about the braziers. We live in a long tunnel-like place with the servants the other side of the first blanket (substitute for curtain), the Sergeant Major beyond the second, and the signallers just beyond the third. Everyone hears everyone else's conversation, and comment 'sotto voce' is always loud enough to be heard. 'Thomas Atkins' ' gift for impromptu is amazing. We both roared with laughter yesterday when a servant wandered down our waterfall to attend to our braziers, and picked up the tattered blanket-curtain saying, 'Lift up his skirts, O ye gates!' (The 'him' was the brazier!)

But now and then the servants were slack. Their brazier worked well so it just pulled the freezing air down the Niagara and froze us out! Three times we gave orders and made appeals and supplications, but all in vain. So we tried sterner measures. We had some horrid black powder under our table (one never thinks twice about what one sits on, sleeps on, or eats on) and so we let it off in doses, the draft carrying the fumes away to the servants who soon stampeded. As we showed that we meant it, we got our brazier properly attended to – but not before we made half a dozen of these gas attacks on the servants' quarters. After two shots at it we said no more but simply lighted up, listened to the coughing and cursing, and then expected our fire would mend. The game grew fashionable and (just as the wind happened to blow) the Sergeant Major and the signallers started smoking each other out. Finally, the servants retaliated on us and put us out of action twice with some terrible vapours – candle ends and bacon rind I think it was. Someday soon I may be able to get a shave, a wash, a haircut and a bath and a change, meanwhile we look like chimney sweeps who've been working in a flour mill. We get black from the brazier and white from the chalky mud.

At this point Stephen's letter breaks off. He continues some days later.

7 January 1917

And now I'm clean and I sleep (when the guns allow it) in a bed with real white linen sheets! I can shave every day and wash twice a day and prospects there are of a bath twice a week. It's softening in its influence perhaps, but it makes the war more enjoyable. At present, I am understudying the Brigade Intelligence Officer and should take over from him when he goes – as is probable – to a higher job. It is swank being on the Brigade staff... I shall not be wearing red tabs, indeed, there won't be much difference to notice. But I shall feed and live with a real, live General!

And at last! The photograph of Harry has arrived. I am so entirely delighted I can hardly speak of it. Harry, I shall carry you with me in my breast pocket wherever I go from now on. I won't let you down, dear boy.

Happy New Year to you all!

Yours very sincerely,
Stephen S. Doyle

I hardly dared open the final envelope, being sure of what it contained. Within I found a black-bordered envelope, stamped with a 'penny red' and an exhortation to 'Buy National War Bonds Now'. The last, black-bordered letter was from Mabel Doyle.

9 January 1917

Ruskin Avenue
Kew Gardens

Dear Mrs Sandling,

I am sure you were grieved to hear of my husband's death – it came as an overwhelming blow to me – tho' I had always tried to school myself to every emergency – and I cannot even now really believe that he will never come home to me again – yet there is already a blank that I don't receive any more letters. It's all so painful and cruel. I have just one photograph left and will send it to you – I have really kept it for you but I am sorry to say he only autographed one and that was for my sister. Did you send him young Harry's photograph? I would like to have one too, if that is possible. My husband loved him very much and always spoke of the time he spent with you as a loving memory. My own child is due in a month. If it is a boy, I shall name him after yours if you will allow me.

Yours sincerely,
Mabel F. Doyle

The dates of the last two letters suggest that poor Stephen died within hours of placing Harry's photograph in his breast pocket. I looked again at Harry's last letter to me. 'There are some secrets that should rightly die with a man.' Evidently, there were also some secrets that Harry wanted to share.

The Buggery Club

Ian Young

The Finsbury Park Men's & Boys' Boxing Club was housed in a crumbling brick warehouse off the Holloway Road. It has been a significant club as late as the 1960s. By the eighties it seemed perpetually on its last legs but stubbornly refused to go down for the count and provided a centre of social as well as athletic activity for a selection of local lads. Andy Boom and one or two of his pals had taken to sparring there and Tommy Noakes, a burly journeyman middleweight, made it his home base. I was standing outside the club with Andy and Tommy on an overcast Friday afternoon.

'I'm not sure I like the look of those eyebrows,' Tommy was complaining; he was talking about Andy's friend Paul Tyler. The two skinheads had taken up amateur boxing at the suggestion of the Old Sarge. It seemed to do them good, channelling a worrisome capacity for violence into what Tommy called 'good healthy pummelling'. I was grateful to Sarge, Tommy and the club manager Seamus Moore for giving Andy's penchant for brawling a legitimate outlet; I badly wanted him to stay out of jail.

My dad had done a bit of amateur boxing in his Air Force days and I'd picked up an interest from sitting with him as a kid in Canada, watching the *Gillette Friday Night Fights* on TV and listening to his commentary. For me though, boxing was strictly a spectator sport. I was tall and skinny and getting smashed in the face and ribs for recreation didn't appeal to me. I'm a runner, not a fighter.

'Young Paul can punch all right, that right hook – that right hook comes natural to him,' said Tommy. 'Fast too. Tall. Good reach. Nice left jab.' He darted little glances at Andy and me and was obviously brooding about something.

'*But…?*' I asked.

'Well, he's very strong, see.'

I looked surprised at Tommy seeming to see Paul's strength as a liability.

'He's not a very big boy. He's stronger than his frame can handle. Might be a bit prone to injury. And,' Tommy added, 'I'm not sure I like the look of those eyebrows. He might get cut a lot.'

Andy grinned. 'Wouldn't want him bleeding all over our nice clean ring, would we!'

'But he's a good boy, good amateur,' Tommy was quick to admit. 'He'll do himself credit… You got that *Gay News*?' Andy handed it over.

Before Andy and Paul started showing up at the club, Tommy and the irascible Seamus Moore were the only openly gay members, though we had our suspicions (or more than suspicions) about a few of the regulars. 'He may be on the straight and narrow now,' said Tommy about one handsome heavyweight, 'but I think he's been round the corner… Well, I *know* he's been round the corner. *And* he's had a look! He's had a *good* look!'

'Anything on tonight, Tommy?' asked Andy.

'I want to go to this new Buggery Club,' Tommy blurted out, causing me and Andy to chirp up, almost in unison, 'This *what*?'

'*The*. Listen to me. *Buggery*. Are you listening? *Club*. Didn't Andy tell you about it? Some skins have got a place in some back street in Camden. They're running booze and music there on the weekends. Some of the boys get a bit wild, I hear.'

'Is it licensed?' I asked stupidly.

'Shouldn't think so,' Tommy said. 'They've got beer though. Thought we'd have a look for it tonight. A mate of mine told me where it is more or less. Come with us, we'll all have a go.'

'It's not boneheads, is it?' I had no interest in getting involved with the neo-Nazi skins we called boneheads, but Tommy assured me these lads were strictly a gay or gay-friendly lot.

'I said buggery, darlin', not thuggery!'

The press tended to depict all skinheads as right-wing hooligans but while some more than fitted the bill, we dismissed the stereotype as just a way to sell newspapers; fads and fashions generally being more subtle than they seem. The Park skins I knew were far from the neo-Nazis of popular mythology. Most of them were non-political or vaguely Labourite, and Andy and Paul were part of our 'armchair anarchist' contingent headquartered around the big table at the back of Boris Mostoyenko's stamp shop.

In the early eighties, the Punk movement was in full swing with an array of bizarre, colourful hairstyles and ripped clothes held together with safety pins. The Punks around Finsbury Park were outrageous ragamuffins, mostly squatters, or on the dole – lifestyles the skins disdained, seeing themselves as clean, patriotic working-class blokes. Skins were proud, clean-shaven roundheads rather than tatty cavaliers; they cut their hair almost to the skull, wore Doc Martens work boots, tight jeans or Sta Press trousers held up with braces ('suspenders' in American translation), plain shirts or T-shirts and Crombie overcoats. They reminded me of Hutterites, minus the beards and hats. Their simple style was basically that of young manual workers, with a dash of Mod flair. I found it very sexy – and Andy and I agreed the Buggery Club sounded like an irresistible prospect for a Friday night out.

We all arranged to meet at the Black Cap pub in Camden at ten o'clock that night. I was the last to arrive and found the lads in conference with one of the locals – a regular customer at Boris's. Brian Bevis was an eccentric, good-natured gent of sixty or so, an ex-army intelligence officer who always introduced himself as 'Brian Bevis, Anarcho-Monarchist!' He had a calling card printed up bearing that inscription and an emblem he'd designed – the anarchist A in a circle – topped with a crown. Brian claimed to be a member of an obscure group founded in Spain – whose most prominent member (what am I saying – whose *only* prominent member) was the painter Salvador Dalí.

Brian Bevis himself was a tall, aristocratic-looking man with a thick mane of immaculately coiffed silver hair; he always wore a blazer and the old boys' tie of one of the more obscure public schools. He had (Sarge had assured me) served with distinction in the post-war Malayan campaign where he had lost his left arm and left eye in a munitions explosion. One blazer sleeve tucked into a pocket took care of the missing arm; the eye had been replaced by a glass one, over which he habitually wore a monocle. At Boris's once Brian explained that he did this on the premise that people would notice the monocle and overlook the staring glass eye. I couldn't decide whether this was logical or not, but as I said, Brian was eccentric. And he had, he readily confessed, 'an eye for the boys – *this* one!

I can't get the glass one to see a thing! Must get this monocle seen to!' He laughed at his own much-repeated joke.

By the time I came in the doors of the Black Cap, it had already been decided that Brian would be our guide to the night's destination, the so-called Buggery Club, located in a back street down by the canal, which after a cursory glance at Tommy's handmade map, Brian assured us he could find, no trouble at all. He was holding forth quite loudly as I sat down.

'I was just telling these chaps' – he lowered his voice a few decibels – 'about the parliamentary debates we had about legalising queers back in the sixties. I expect you were a bit young then, weren't you. What a frightful row that was! The bill was sponsored in the Lords by Boofy Arran, who kept a tame badger in his house. I met him once, smelled a bit – the badger not Boofy who was a very clean old man. And in the Commons our champion was a Mr Abse, a Welsh Jew I think, who wore op art waistcoats.'

'Did these things help,' asked Tommy, 'or put people off?'

'I don't think anyone paid much attention,' Brian ruminated. 'But some of the old fogeys were blue in the face over the prospect of making us legal. Monty – Lord Montgomery of Alamein Right, who did so well against Rommel – thundered that we were about to "condone the devil and all his works".'

Andy let out a whoop.

'"*We* are not *French!*" Monty shouted at the assembled House of Lords. "We are Englishmen, thank God!"' Andy and Paul thumped on the table at this.

'Another old fart warned that legalising us would result in "an immediate rush on the part of tutors and army officers" – I liked that one – "into acts of mass buggery"!'

Brian continued these fond reminiscences as we finished our drinks.

'The British people were warned, you see, that legalising us would mean the establishment of "buggery clubs" all over England, and in Wales too, I suppose. *Buggery clubs!* Well, as you can imagine, I could hardly wait. Alas! Well, apart from some very nice, rather well-mannered establishments, it never happened. *Until now!* All these years later!

'Of course,' he said with a shrug, 'legalisation hit the aristocracy very hard. At least one old country squire was convinced it meant the end of everything he held dear, or else he got frightened he could no longer resist temptation. Went up into his study, opened up the Game Book –

you know, big ledger where you write up whatever birds and animals you've shot that day on the estate – wrote his own name in it – and blew his head off. Now I'd say that was taking punctilio to an extreme!'

'Well, come on Brian, drink up,' urged Paul. 'Show us the way!' And the five of us headed out into Camden Town. The evening was getting cool and Tommy said he thought it might rain.

We ended up in a little lane beside the Camden Lock, bordered by warehouses and decaying old brick lockups. Tommy and Brian were scrutinising the map while Andy and Paul and I stood by the side of the canal gossiping about our friend Boris and the two teenaged brothers who lived with him.

'You ever been upstairs at Boris's?' Paul asked.

'Yes!' said I. 'It's like a museum up there, all sorts of old clutter. Mostly the Triplets' stuff, closets full of clothes, lots of costumes, cowboy and Indian gear and theatre props and old masks, some nice sex toys. Hat boxes full of feathers. What with them and Boris's candlesticks and religious bits and pieces and all the furniture, there's quite a horde.'

'The Triplets came home with me once,' Paul confided. 'Quite fun but they love to play all these odd games. I suppose that's why they like Boris so much. He acts out all their stories with them and hides under the blankets while they tickle each other with feathers and whisper word games. Boris doesn't mind it all, he quite gets into the spirit of it, I think. It's all a bit much for me but I did have fun. They tied me up at one point and painted their faces with shaving soap.'

'I wonder what either one of them would be like on his own,' said Andy.

'I think they're strictly a double act,' I said. 'If you're with one, the other's watching.'

'Am I the only one who hasn't had sex with Elliott and Lionel?' Andy asked.

'There's still time,' said Paul. 'Maybe we could double date.'

'I'm not much for theatrical performances,' admitted Andy. He thought for a moment, '*Although…*'

Suddenly we heard Tommy alerting us to a door opening some distance down the lane. A few likely lads were emerging from one of the warehouses.

'There it is, come on,' said Brian, and strode on ahead of us, swinging his single arm.

A pair of skinheads were horsing around as we got to the green metal door of the old building. The doorkeeper was a fellow about my age, mid-thirties.

'Squaddie!' Tommy knew him by name.

'Tommy! Lookin' for a fight?' Squaddie wore a peaked forage cap, American camouflage fatigues and polished boots. Lean, handsome and clean-shaven with a square jaw, he reminded me of the space pilot Dan Dare in the old *Eagle* comics I devoured as a boy.

'I'm off duty, darlin',' Tommy answered.

As the door opened, the heavy beat of a band leaked into the laneway.

'Who's playing?' Andy asked.

'TBH.' I'd heard this lot before. TBH was a Camden group – a juicy mix of black skinheads and white Rastas. Their music was a mix of reggae and old pub music-hall chestnuts delivered with a raw, punky sound and rudimentary instrumentals. Their signature tune was a raucous reggae version of the wartime Vera Lynn anthem 'We'll Meet Again'.

As Tommy and Squaddie bantered, I noticed Squaddie eyeing Brian Bevis. A sixty-year-old man with one arm and a monocle, wearing a blazer and highly polished oxfords was hardly an expected guest at the Camden boys' Buggery Club. But before Tommy could vouch for us all, Brian included, a nearby commotion caused Squaddie to leave his place at the door and march around the corner to see what was happening. He sent a couple of noisy lads on their way and rejoined us.

'Don't want to upset the neighbours!'

Brian's eye had fallen upon Squaddie. 'Brian Bevis, Anarcho-Monarchist!' he boomed, extending his one big hand in Squaddie's direction.

Squaddie took Brian's hand in his with a quizzical look.

'Green Jacket, were you?' Brian asked.

'I *was*!' said Squaddie, taken by surprise. 'How did you know?'

'Rifle Brigade!' Brian barked. 'Always recognise that quick march!'

Brian and Squaddie, it seems, had been in similar army units in different decades and now it was Old Soldiers' Night all over the place as the two of them stood about swapping stories and the rest of us were waved in.

I was never much of a clubber. I drink hardly at all and don't take chemicals or dance all night. But like every other gay fellow in London, I turned up at some of the clubs now and then. My favourite was the Catacombe Club in Earls Court (Seamus Moore called it the Catamite

Club). Always packed, it was a cozy underground hideaway with a bar, a dance floor and a series of alcoves with booths in them where you could sit quite comfortably with friends old and new. A beautiful, long-haired Hawaiian boy called Keoni used to dance there with his Canadian lover, and on occasion the MP Tom Driberg would show up with a small entourage.

Another rendezvous was the Carousel Club, hidden down one of the twisting lanes adjoining Soho. The Carousel, up two flights of stairs, had acquired several seats for two from old roundabouts and these were arranged around walls painted with fairground and circus images. An old *trompe l'œil* mural of the London skyline at night (said to be by Rex Whistler) surrounded French doors leading to a small roof garden with a few metal tables and chairs crammed on to it and benches around the outside – most welcome on hot nights.

The West End club Heaven and its new rival, Hell ('Going to Heaven tonight?' 'No, I'm going to Hell!') were more upscale, and more expensive, with admission fees which our crowd couldn't afford. But you could get into Heaven for nothing if you went on 'Uniform Nights'. The drill was to go before ten o'clock and say you were there for the Union Club. No actual uniform was required, and once in, you could stay as long as you wanted. But all these clubs were a long way from Finsbury Park and, London Transport being what it was, entailed a long trip home by bus and then on foot at the end of the night. The Buggery Club was closer to home.

The back door opened on to a big room with a high ceiling, probably once part of a warehouse. Raised platforms served as stage and DJ booth, round metal tables and plastic chairs were arrayed around the walls and bottles of cold beer were served out of oil drums. There was a cramped, fetid bathroom and a haze of pot and tobacco smoke.

The Buggery Club soon filled up with skinheads, punks and other lads. TBH filled the place with sound. Then came records from the turntable as the boys took a break and mixed with the mob. No actual buggery could be detected but the night was yet young. As the place grew hot and stifling, I fled for a while to the cool damp of the laneway. A breeze was springing up and it felt as though a storm was in the offing. I stood in the darkness by the canal; every time the door opened there was a blast of sound from the records – 'Don't Stand So Close to Me' by the Police, The Boomtown Rats' 'I Don't Like Mondays', The Clash's 'London Calling'.

After a while I plunged back into the fray, catching up with Andy having a drink with a curly-headed young fellow we'd noticed earlier. 'This is Mitch!' Hellos all round; Mitch seemed very friendly. Andy went off to get another beer and left me *and* Mitch in the crush discussing the relative merits of Blondie and Queen, shouted over the din, which meant we got up close and personal.

TBH started up again, bold and loud. Their lead singer was a skinny white lad with tattoos, dreadlocks and a fashionable sneer. They launched into their trademark shouted, spittle-flecked take on the hoary old urban folk songs of our cockney forefathers:

Mother Brown said Darlin'
You've got a nasty cough.
If I catch you bending,
I'll saw your legs right off!

O! Knees up Mother Brown,
Knees up Mother Brown,
Ee-eye ee-eye ee-eye O!
Under the table she must go!

Knees up! Knees up!
Never get the breeze up!
Knees up Mother Brown!
Oi!

The heat, the noise, the people – I was getting ready to flee when Andy and Mitch came up, arms around one another, suggesting we all go back to Turle Road for the night. Mitch was a freckle-faced lad with tight trousers, a ready smile and bright eyes behind thick, plastic-rimmed glasses. I was ready to go. TBH finished their spirited rendition of 'My Old Man's a Dustman! / He wears a dustman's hat! / He wears cor blimey trousers! / What do you think o' that?' And soon Tommy and Paul were in the middle of a line that was swaying drunkenly to 'The Lambeth Walk', Tommy with a beer bottle tucked in his belt. Could 'Hands, knees and *boomps*! a daisy' be far behind? The skins were sweating and jumping about and the decibel level was now approaching deafening.

'Where's the Beast with Five Fingers?' shouted Andy.

'Brian? He's over there!'

As we headed out the door, we passed Brian sitting with Squaddie at a table full of beer bottles, his one meaty hand on Squaddie's thigh, shouting in his ear, 'You're a fine figure of a man, Squaddie!'

'What?'

'A fine figure of a man!'

Squaddie had his eyes closed and a big grin on his face. Brian was as red as a radish. We signalled with hand gestures as we passed them, heading for the door. A chalkboard with a scrawled notice announced:

NEXT WEEK

ROMFORD

ROOD BOYS

Brian waved us through as he and Squaddie broke into a chorus of 'Sod 'em all! / The long and the short and the tall… / There'll be no *promotion* this side of the *ocean…*'

By this point, the cacophony, the smoke and the heat had become overwhelming and the damp night air outside was a welcome relief. The three of us walked a few yards to the canal. While the others mopped their faces with handkerchiefs, I leaned against a tree and stared at the black water. An extensive old canal and lock system had once wound through much of London. Now, only Camden Lock, a picturesque stretch by Regent's Park, and a few other fragments remained. As I was musing what it must have been like in its heyday, someone closed a nearby window with a loud bang and it occurred to me that the Buggery Club, even if it did try not to annoy the neighbours, might not be around for long.

A sudden gust of wind swept by and I turned up the collar of my coat. Andy came over to me and put his arm around my shoulder.

'Ready to go?'

Before I could answer, the heavens opened and the long-awaited deluge rained down with a vengeance.

As I huddled with Andy and Mitch in a nearby doorway, we quickly decided to head for Mitch's place only a couple of streets away, rather than make the long journey in the rain back to Finsbury Park.

The three of us hurried down the road with newspapers over our heads.

'Where do you live?' Andy asked?

'Up by Hawley Road,' Mitch answered. 'I live with Squaddie.'

'Squaddie won't mind you bringing two blokes home?'

'No,' Mitch laughed. 'He likes you!'

Andy and I shot each other a glance but we were in for a pound now and the rain was falling hard. We got to the corner and looked back towards the club, only to see Squaddie and Brian, holding each other up, singing 'The Rifles, the Skins and the Bold Fusiliers'. They were following (a bit unsteadily) in our footsteps, undoubtedly heading to the same place we were.

Suddenly, the sky lit up with a magnificent streak of lightning followed by a loud crack of nearby thunder. Everyone started to run, laughing and shouting.

'Oh well,' I thought, 'what the hell. Wet or dry, one way or another, I'd say we're in for a long night.'

A Dry Past

Richard Zimler

The island of playground vibrated with the disjointed popping sound of basketballs. Waves of traffic hugged close to the shore of fencing, their reassuring monotony giving the days inside a protected feel, as if the city itself were agreeing that it was much safer to play pick-up games than to venture into the outside world.

Tony Silva leapt upward towards the basket in his faded jeans and torn, black sneakers, the ball arched over his head, keys and coins and disposable lighter jangling in his pocket. He was seventeen years old and he didn't want to be taken for one of the Anglo punks who needed to change into special clothing to sink a running hook in the face of some lanky homeboy cultivating his first, tentative shadow of moustache.

My brothers and I noticed black dots of stubble peppering his upper lip when he was lying in the dark wooden casket at the back of the Fonseca Funeral Home. We tried not to peer over the lid, but his nose was poking out and didn't look human and everybody in line was looking at us with these great big marble eyes the Portuguese have. Tony's icy skin reflected the creamy, polished folds of blue satin lining. Big white lilies with sharp crests popped up all around, but he smelled like dust. And he looked like he was packaged for a long trip.

Not even in his nightmares would Tony have ever sported a suit like the one he had on then. It was charcoal grey with yellowish pinstripes. Like in a big-budget gangster movie musical. Looking at him on the basketball court, you'd have thought his muscular shoulders and arms would have ripped through the seams of any sport coat. But bodies are deceptive like that.

The game was argued over. While heads shook away curses, Tony grabbed the ball and positioned himself at the foul line, tossing in shot after shot. The players on the sidelines kept eating peanuts, were waiting for either J.K. or Harold to give in. And all the while the traffic drove by the island.

We wouldn't have admitted it, but we were jealous of Tony. We couldn't sink so many foul shots while everybody was arguing. And we couldn't dunk in one of the rebounds. He'd have been given a chance at the point guard spot on the school team if he weren't already an anarchic legend. Sometimes, after he made an impossibly off-balance fifteen-footer or driving reserve lay-up, he'd look at you with those green falcon eyes of his, just waiting to pounce on you if you couldn't censor some smart school-yard comment. Then all of a sudden his lips would twist into that loopy lopsided smile of his meant to charm everybody. At school, he'd grab your lunch with an inflamed threat about ripping your head away from your neck, and after he'd wolfed it down, buy you a replacement. He'd grin with his rubbery lips while he was patting you on the back. Like it was all a game. And you could either appreciate it or risk getting walloped.

Sometimes he'd open his mouth and stick out his tongue and there'd be your food all chewed into a brown ball.

Whenever Tony noticed a pretty girl walking by the playground, he sang Prince's 'Gotta Broken Heart Again'. His tenor was rough, scratchy, as if he retained sand in his vocal chords, but he could keep a tune. If he was waiting for a game, he'd sing the whole song and maybe J.K. or Big Ben would slap the bleachers for percussion. Tony knew all the words. He had a memory like that.

He confessed once that no matter how desperate he ever got, he'd never follow in his father's footsteps. Spitting through the fence and looking us up and down to make sure we believe him, nodding that he was planning on becoming a rock star. Or if things didn't work out, he'd be satisfied just being a cab driver or maybe a waiter. Didn't really matter.

His mother had made him swear on the Bible that he'd stay in school and live at home till his eighteenth birthday. My father said it was more for her own protection than anything else. At the time, I didn't understand and thought it was a bad English translation of whatever he was really thinking.

There were twenty-two rows in the funeral parlour. I counted them over and over. The air conditioning had given out and the Puerto Rican and

Portuguese women were wiping their foreheads with lacy handkerchiefs like the doilies the sparrowish ladies cover pastries with at the Lisbon Bakery on Jericho Turnpike. Rumour had it that Gregory Gill was out on bail by then, $50,000 paid for by an anonymous donor. But he'd never stand trial. There'd be a plea bargain and he'd get a suspended sentence.

Even after he was cleared, Gregory's parents treated him like he was tainted with a blood disease nobody ever dared name. So at age seventeen he stuffed his Flaubert and Victor Hugo novels into a canvas bag and grabbed the E subway train into some neighbourhood of Manhattan where either nobody noticed such illnesses or everybody had one or another of them. The West Village maybe. That was the rumour at least. We had never been there so we wouldn't have had any idea where to begin looking. Many years later, I ducked under the awning of an art gallery in Chelsea during an impossibly bright sun shower and there he was behind a desk in a fancy suit not so different from the one that held Tony at his funeral. They were coming back in style then.

In the casket, it looked as if whatever invisible ether had made Tony Tony had evaporated without a trace. For one thing, he wasn't glaring or smiling. His lips were sculpted into a kind of contented pucker, as if he had caught his breath before saying something angelic. His long eyelashes fluttered out like perfect cilia above crazy, pink, bulging eyesacks. His face was too long, like maybe they had trouble getting his mouth to close or certain parts of his jaw to fit just right. Apparently that's what happens when all your bodyweight crashes against a tile floor with your face in between. Thinking about that too much is why I started counting those pews.

Tony made pocket money by driving his Uncle Manuel's taxi for a couple of hours on Tuesday and Thursday evenings. A rich young stock-broker in Brooklyn Heights with a thing for barrel-chested Latin immigrants waited for Manuel under her black sheets on those nights. They screwed for an hour then watched *Seinfeld* reruns.

You couldn't see where the knife had made the opening which allowed life to swirl out of him, of course. But we guessed that below the green paisley tie the wound was patched and powdered and refrigerator-cold like the rest of him.

Gregory Gill was the only black kid in the French Club. I had the club's advisor, Monsieur Miller, in ninth grade. I overheard him saying to Mr

Coleman, the driver's ed teacher, that Gregory was a brilliant student, one of a kind. The only one who ever used the subjunctive correctly. Was going to sojourn in France one day, too. And the French liked black people, Josephine Baker, Miles Davis, Michael Jackson.

The way he said it made me think that nobody in our neighbourhood liked them even a little bit.

Gregory walking down the hall with a pile of monster textbooks and notebooks balanced on his hip, held back by the spindly buttress of his bowed arm. A tyranny of footsteps lurking behind. Solemn eyes bearing shame. Daring not to turn till books and papers explode forward. The triumphant laughter of manufactured amusement. Got him again! Back-patting boys disappearing into the crowd of shuffling students. A teacher stooping to help.

All those disjointed notes across the dirty restroom-yellow vinyl of the school floor made you wonder why he bothered.

Most of the basketball players called Tony, Tony-S. It was better for shouting across the playground. And the rusty-haired old man, Belden, who held court when he wasn't complaining about rent control at City Hall, could use it in his raps. Most nobody got in Tony-S's way, on or off the court. Kind of gangly and crazy even with all those muscles, like he was made for dancing some macho lambada all his own. With a jangly, bobbing walk. Always moving, jumping, twisting, like maybe there was some gyrating spark at his centre that would never be cooled. You couldn't imagine he'd turn up so perfectly confined in that casket. Falsely perfected by all that powder and make-up. I was tempted to smear my finger across his cheek or maybe poke his chin to see if some lingering nerve would make him twitch even a little, like those sliced frogs in biology class. But all those Portuguese eyes behind us...

Tony's floppy brown, music-video-messy hair always slapping over his forehead when he walked, of late greased around the sides with something smelling like caulking. His hands stank like that, too, from wiping his fingers through. You sniffed it in when he popped you on the chin, daring you to say that there was something you wanted from him.

His eyes would bug out when he ate, like he was asking himself some daring question or was just barely stifling a shout. He liked the school's spaghetti and grilled hot dogs and veal parmigiana. And the square hamburgers with grey dribblings of fat, which the posted menu had the nerve to call Salisbury steak. But if there was something he didn't want, he'd make you watch him while he gobbled yours down. Freshmen boys blanched till they grasped the idea of the game.

Maybe Tony could have become a model if he'd learned to walk with less energy and fit neatly inside a thirty-five mm grid. The Portuguese and Latino girls, some of the blacks, too, thought he was *louco* but handsome.

Teachers sent him into a trance. He'd slouch back into his chair and suck on his pen like the ink was honey. Boredom paled his face until he latched on to a daydream of basketball. The bell was the only way to get him back from that. When it rang, he'd kind of slither out of his chair, yawn and pretzel his arms behind his back to get his circulation going and to show us just how sick he was of daily incarceration. Once in history class he must have dreamed the period was over. He swirled up, wriggled around and cracked the vertebrae in his neck by cocking his head all the way forward, Egyptian-dancer-like. Mr Trainer snapped off his glasses and furrowed those white caterpillar eyebrows of his. Did Tony have a pressing problem he wanted to share with the class? When the bell rang for real that day, Tony sat up, gripped his chair and looked around till we had all popped up and he knew it was safe. It was the first and last time I saw him intimidated. Only gym gave him pleasure. But it was only three times a week.

How he passed through school each year without being left back was a mystery that could only be answered in the school boardrooms of large American cities.

The game never did get going again. Harold wouldn't give in and left with his ball. J.K. sat smoking on the bleachers.

Tony left the playground and started to walk home the long way, by Miller Avenue so he could buy some Camel Lights at the Italian deli. A pack with one cigarette missing slipped out of his pants pocket with some change when he fell to the kitchen floor. Getting them meant that he could cut back towards his house by the high school. Occasionally you know the right way to go, but most of the time you haven't got a clue.

Reading *L'Education Sentimentale* by Flaubert with the help of a tiny purple dictionary, Gregory was by himself, sitting cross-legged on the field behind the school gymnasium, down near the steps into his home street, Greenway Drive. Afterward, people all said they knew. Had that plaintive, cottony voice, was always turning away like you had the secret he needed to reach adulthood but was afraid to ask about. His parents should have tried some cure when he was little, before his habits were imprinted on his brain. The public school had had psychiatrists on staff, and maybe it's true that they weren't that good but they were free.

Mr and Mrs Gill claimed they didn't know. Sure he mumbled French idioms to himself during dinner, but was that any indication? Mr Gill stopped paying attention to him early. Not the kind of boy a father reaches without a long and lonely uphill climb. Early on, there were constant sideways looks exchanged between mother and father. Assurances held back, enthusiasms stifled. Frustrations ending in beatings when Gregory was little. Neighbours said he didn't scream, he screeched. Like a tropical bird. Nobody knew what it was he was trying to say in that avian language. Or who he thought might answer him.

Nights afterward my father could hardly look at me. I'd say goodnight and he'd sort of lift his night-time glass of hot milk and rum above the back of his *Newsday* like he was toasting an invisible guest. Or, if my mother had settled nearby with her crocheting, he'd make an extra effort to finally look me in the eye to show her he wasn't afraid of our connection at all. Before bed, my mother would hold my face in her cold hands and give me clinging kisses on both cheeks, like the ones she gave her orphaned nieces from Porto meant to watch over them when she wasn't there. You didn't need to hear her or understand Portuguese to know she was whispering to God to protect her strange little boy from all those things that could get him in New York. In 1981. Not like back in her mythical, whitewashed ivory crown of a village perched on that serene mountaintop overlooking the Spanish border.

Imprisoned by her hands, I'd close my eyes tight and make believe the darkness confirmed that none of this was happening. I knew that my parents were trying, but the words wouldn't form and I'd have to do the talking for all of us sooner or later.

Mrs Gill explained that Gregory had always been 'a little nervous and shy' to anyone who brought the subject up. She'd hesitate, fawnlike, before disclosing her description, then shrug like it wasn't of any use to speak. When pressed further she'd offer an awkward smile, like maybe if you looked at him from some upside-down angle you might see that Gregory possessed an incipient charm.

Gregory – thin, naturally coordinated, gifted with a streamlined, foal-like musculature, but compelled to hide himself below woollen sweaters even on the hottest days. Green almond-shaped eyes that led to questions about a possible Afro-Asian heritage.

He wore insect-eye tortoiseshell glasses and, even when you were talking to him, had a tendency to slip one or two carefully studied steps behind you. He never laughed or swore or ran, had had his overt enthusiasm trained out of him. He touched the backs of chairs before sitting down as if he had to constantly verify the presence of the real world. Strange fantasy secrets seemed to seal his forever pact with silence. Like when we all learned over the school intercom that Mrs Olivetti, the girls' gym teacher, had given birth to a boy and he started humming the Marseillaise real softly to himself while curling his lips toward a bemused smile.

Sometimes at night, reading in bed before sleep, when death is only a single page of darkness away, I wonder why his mother abandoned him after all those years of uphill struggle.

Just after I got my learner's permit, we were driving around near Jones Beach when the car next to us crushed a terrier of some sort. Gregory hid his eyes in his hands and sobbed.

He opened up once to me and said in his carefully moderated voice that he daydreamed about growing up in South Africa or Namibia and fighting for a country. On my fifteenth birthday, he gave me triangular stamps from Mozambique because they had brilliant pictures of iridescent honeybirds and he knew that I occasionally went birdwatching with my brothers. He spoke French to people who teased him. He knew they didn't understand. But that, I suppose, was the point.

In a corner of my basement I goaded him into looking at pornographic photos for the first time, men bowed back, hoisting up powerful erections. I was calculating and casual. He stared at me with a criminal look in his eyes, then dashed home for the safety of his familiar regrets. I felt the weight of our solidarity at the back of my throat. Affirming an identity to yourself can have unforeseen consequences for somebody like Gregory. We didn't talk much after that.

Tony's family lived in a big old clapboard house behind Vito's Restaurant on Mineola Avenue, and the baked ziti and pizza scents that had come to inhabit their walls and furniture would never be exorcised. Mr Silva hailed from the arid city of Beja in the southern interior of Portugal and Mrs Silva from Fajardo on Puerto Rico's north coast. It was the climatic differences that produced their arguments, even the bruises and burns on her arms, Mr Silva claimed. How could he be expected to get along with a woman born in a rainforest? They had four children, Tony the oldest. Their limbs were all too long, and the protruding, bug-eyed, questioning face that Tony made when he ate had solidified in varying degrees in each of the younger Silvas as their normal, resting expression. Mrs Silva's fidgety anxiety in her children's presence, her lowered eye, her yearning gentility all gave you the feeling that her family embarrassed her. A long depression following the birth of her youngest took her appetite and left her with skeletal arms and wrinkled, turkey skin. Waxy blue veins shone through on the undersides of her wrists and she often gazed around as if astonished to still be in this world.

Mr Silva was a plumber for the town of Hempstead. He went bare-chested in summer, the black hairs on his chest and shoulders matted and sweaty. He never learned any of our names and frightened us all. Tony used to say you could hear the Miller and Super Bock beer sloshing in his stomach whenever he came near. And that it was a good thing, a jungle drumbeat of warning.

Mr Silva didn't come to the funeral. Nobody knew why but we all tacitly acknowledged it was because he was drunk. Mrs Silva sat with her three youngest, clutching with those bony, shrunken hands onto her black leather bag like it was going to fly away at any moment, the kids' faces all asking those protruding questions. It scared me the way she gripped Tony's head and whispered conspiratorially to him. My mother stood at atten-tion behind her and led her away when the ceremony was about to begin.

Was it significant at all that the game had never really ended at the playground? And if it had gone on would Tony have sauntered home a different way, and the funeral and Gregory Hill's arrest and my mother hugging Mrs Silva would all have never happened?

Those questions meant a lot to me for about a year, conjured up repet-itive nightmares. Then the spectrum of tempting possibilities faded away and the past became dry and sepia-toned and varnished – what it was and what would never be changed and what we'd tell other people who hadn't been there.

Our damning secret was that we treasured the one meaningful event that had ever happened in our neighbourhood. This unspeakable admis-sion played like an anxious, unacknowledged pedal point for weeks, and when it was finally covered by the normal droning melodies of school and home, the single date of Tony's death was highlighted in thick red on our timeline of forever boredom: May 6, 1981. Life was always a little safer afterward. As if a powerful necromancer who had threatened all our futures had been vanquished. But we were at an age when we craved danger. The year crept slower towards graduation without his excitement.

Gregory Gill remembered most all of it. In the hospital emergency room, holding his hand over his ripped, bloodshot eye, he repeated over and over to the resident on duty that it was self-defence. It was his mother who must have gotten him the cardigan-sweatered lawyer from Manhattan with the long blonde hair tied in a ponytail. Who else would've called?

A few years later Gregory's sister Linda informed me in an adamant voice that the lawyer was just like Gregory, one of them, you understand. She flipped her wrist and batted her eyes to make sure we'd get her meaning. Like me, you mean, I said. She blinked her startled eyes and looked around for someone to nudge. That was how my youngest brother found out. My father had wanted him spared the burden till he was eighteen.

There Gregory was, sitting in the field behind the school, pencilling translations from his dictionary onto the margins of *L'Education Sentimentale*. He saw Tony from a long way off, fought his urge to stare. But the tugging pace of his heart pulled his eyes from his book. He said 'Hi' to fill in the castigating silence. Tony nodded towards him. Who you saying 'Hi' to? You, just to be friendly. Me? You want to be friendly to me? Gregory was saying that he'd just go back to reading and was that OK – *Ça va?* What did you say? Just was it OK. Yeah, it was fine, but if he really wanted to be friendly, something else might be better. Tony cupped his hand under his balls so that there'd be no doubt.

Mrs Gill had taken Linda shopping to Macy's at Roosevelt Field. Gregory's room was in what should have been a kitchen pantry. People said they could've added on another real room, that they had the money since Mr Gill's direct-mail business had taken off, but that they treated Gregory like a temporary visitor whom they didn't really want but had a religious obligation to accept. It had a small window that looked out on the side yard where Mr Gill had parked the old Rambler for the last time. For spare parts it was to be. After a while, when its wheels had been stripped and it had rusted beyond hope, it settled into its neighbourhood role as an urban sculpture.

The bedroom door was shut and locked. Mrs Gill had suggested the lock because she preferred not to accidentally find Gregory with something she shouldn't see.

Nobody in the neighbourhood said they heard a sound. But the window in Gregory's room had been shattered. Tony's hand, palmed over Gregory's face, had prevented him from screaming through the open frame. There were blue and yellow bruises on his cheeks for a week afterward. His collarbone and a rib were broken. The cornea on one of his eyes got torn pretty badly. Human tissues are surprisingly fragile when not made up for primetime television.

The knife was on top of a yellow plate next to the last slices of cake Mrs Gill had baked.

Afterward, Gregory would say he didn't know where he got it. Deflated, panicked, he sat at the edge of Tony's stain of blood, so silent that it was hard to tell what kind of voice might come out. His crusted fingers knotted together as if he was praying or locking inside his stomach the knowledge of whatever had happened. He never cried. Two big white medics, both with moustaches, walked him into the ambulance.

Mrs Silva was visited by the police. She said she knew it was terrible news. Tony had been conceived before her marriage and drew bad things to him. He wasn't ever gonna live a long life. Afterwards, on those muggy New York summer evenings when it seems our lives are endless, we sometimes saw her sitting on her porch. But she never talked to anyone except to her three youngest.

Though all the city tabloids called it a racial incident, she was all too aware of Gregory's reputation and formed her own scenario.

Mr Silva stopped drinking and managed to find his wife's image of God, coming to believe that Tony's death was a message from Him on the need to live a righteous life. He now does all the plumbing and some of the carpentry for the Our Lady of Grace church in Floral Park and only charges half for labour. Despite his wife's inattention and his own inclinations, he neither raises his voice nor lifts a hand against her. I guess you can change sometimes if it's a question of survival.

The Gill's house is still there, and Gregory's room is back to being a pantry for a Thai family from the Bronx. Pungent ginger and lemongrass smells come from there now, at all hours of the night and day. One morning when we walked by, we found that the Rambler sculpture was gone. In its place was this gawky plant with orange tubular flowers. Nobody knows where Mr and Mrs Gill went. My mother sees Linda now and then at the Pathmark supermarket, but doesn't talk to her.

I brought Gregory some French literary magazines which I found at an Italian bookstore on Fifth Avenue when he was out on bail and staying with his lawyer. He said *merci* but would only let me into the foyer. His attorney had said not to have guests. We stood talking in hushed, awkward voices for a few minutes. A black patch covered his right eye. He'd have an operation. It was feeling OK.

After I had a lover for the first time, we'd go to the old neighbourhood sometimes and I'd show him to the island playground. On nights when we'd secretly make love in my old bedroom under my childhood quilt, I'd daydream about those days and not be able to recognise the kid I was, as if that iron bind on my heart had never really been there because here I was in love now, lying with a lifelong friend, safe and secure. People forget how it was. It's like a kind of grace maybe that they do.

In front of the playground, in our car, I'd think of Tony and Gregory, what happened that day in the kitchen of the Gill's house. And the ripped body hugging the floor, covered with both their bloods mingling together and as mixed up as everything else except the local newspaper headlines. That ghostly scene infiltrated my mother's and father's thoughts, too, every time they looked at me from my darkened doorway. But parents are powerless after a certain point, and they never spoke about it.

My lover and I would invariably watch a game or two at the old island playground, and I'd remember Tony's loopy smile. It fled his face for a moment as he tugged his hands back through his hair, hesitating on the Gill's steps so he could look around for those watchful Portuguese eyes. Inside, behind the closed door, his walk was wild, confident, and he discovered his grin again, because letting go for the first time and playing for real was going to be a relief. Gregory's hands were dangling by his sides, and his beseeching, expectant expression was asking this basketball star for the secret, the password he had always wanted and never received. He closed and locked the door to the pantry. A blow hammered his back. He gripped the ground, turned. Tony was shouting that he was no faggot's friend, so he better suck it, choke on it now, and there was no getting away till he got what he wanted no matter how much it hurt and how much whimpered begging he heard. Gregory gave a dry shriek till Tony tossed him against the wall by the window. His collarbone and rib snapped under the force. His terrified glance caught a rivulet of blood snaking across his wrist. A hand palmed over his face cut his eye and held his screams, and a feverish voice was shouting for him to take it, take it, take it now, till the grip was loosened and a slap was stinging his cheek and Gregory was racing into the kitchen and holding the knife with both hands and thrusting it as hard as he could into Tony's chest when he leapt into the air after him.

It felt horribly right in the moment afterward, Gregory told me before he caressed the lawyer's door closed. Like a golden regret you'd polish forever because it meant you had a right to be alive.

About the Authors

Neil Bartlett is the former Artistic Director of the Lyric Theatre, Hammersmith (London) and has worked with the National Theatre, the Royal Shakespeare Company and various theatres in America as both dramatist and director. His books include *Who Was That Man? Ready to Catch Him Should He Fall*, *Mr Clive and Mr Page* and *Skin Lane*.

Sebastian Beaumont is the author of *On the Edge*, *Heroes Are Hard to Find*, *Two*, *The Cruelty of Silence*, *The Linguist* and *Thirteen*. He has contributed short stories to several anthologies.

David Patrick Beavers' novels include *Jackal in the Dark*, *The Jackal Awakens*, *Thresholds*, *The Colour of Green* and *Pathways*. He has contributed short stories to various anthologies.

Scott Brown has worked as travel correspondent for the Brighton-based *3Sixty* magazine and is currently the political and Middle Eastern correspondent for *Home Arena Asia*. 'A Casualty of War' was written while he was based in Baghdad working on a political media campaign in the Arab region. It is his fourth piece of published fiction.

Peter Burton has edited twelve books, six of them anthologies of gay fiction. His books include a biography of Rod Stewart, *Parallel Lives* and *Amongst the Aliens*.

Michael Davidson (1897-1975) was a distinguished foreign correspondent and the author of two autobiographical books, *The World, the Flesh and Myself* and *Some Boys*. 'Atti Innominabili' was his only published work of fiction.

Hugh Fleetwood is both a painter and a novelist. His books include *The Girl Who Passed for Normal*, *Foreign Affairs*, *The Past*, *The Witch*, *The Mercy Killers*, *Brothers* and *The Dark Paintings*. His sixth novel, *The Order of Death*, was made into a film starring Harvey Keitel and John Lydon (Johnny Rotten).

Stephen Gray is resident in Johannesburg, South Africa, where currently he is the local series editor of Penguin Modern Classics. His novels include *Time of Our Darkness* and *Born of Man*. Recently he has collected together his stories, published in several anthologies, and included them with a short novel in a volume called *My Serial Killer*.

John Haylock (1918-2006) was the author of a series of comic novels, mainly set outside England, including *See You Again*, *It's All Your Fault*, *One Hot Summer in Kyoto*, *A Touch of the Orient*, *Uneasy Relations*, *Loose Connections* and *Sex Gets in the Way*.

Desmond Hogan has published five novels, including *The Ikon Maker*, *The Leaves on Grey* and *A Curious Street*, and five collections of stories, including *Children of Lir*, *Lebanon Lodge* and *Larks' Eggs*. His awards include the Rooney Prize for Literature, the John Llewellyn Rhys Memorial Prize and a DAAD Fellowship in Berlin. Five of his recent stories have appeared in *The London Magazine*.

Alan James is a painter and writer. His short stories have appeared in the anthologies *Bend Sinister*, *Death Comes Easy* and *Serendipity*.

Cliff James is editor of the south-coast paper *one80news*. 'The Violence of the Gardener' is his first piece of published fiction.

José Luis de Juan was born in Palma in 1956. He is a lawyer and a journalist. He is the award-winning author of several novels, short stories and essays. He lives in Mallorca, and he writes for *El País*, *Revista de Libros* and *Clarín*.

Francis King is the author of almost fifty books, including the novels *An Air That Kills, A Domestic Animal, Act of Darkness, Voices in an Empty Room, Punishments, The Ant Colony, The One and Only, Dead Letters, Prodigies, The Nick of Time* and *With My Little Eye.*

Simon Lovat's short stories have been variously anthologised; his books include *Disorder and Chaos* and *Attrition.*

Patrick Roscoe is the author of seven books of fiction, including the novels *The Lost Oasis* and *God's Peculiar Care.* His next book, *The History of the Hopeful Heart*, is forthcoming from Southern Tier Editions (USA). For more information, visit www.patrickroscoe.com

Jeffrey Round is the author of *The P'Town Murders* and *A Cage of Bones.* Forthcoming books include *Death in Key West* and *The Honey Locust.* His short stories and poetry have been included in numerous journals and anthologies and his short film *My Heart Belongs to Daddy* recently won several awards, including Best Director. Visit his website: www.jeffreyround.com

Steven Saylor is the author of the popular and acclaimed historical mystery novels set in ancient Rome, the 'Roma Sub Rosa' series, featuring Gordianus the Finder. His most recent novel was *Roma* and the latest in the Gordanius series, *The Triumph of Caesar,* is forthcoming.

Michael Wilcox is a dramatist whose plays include *Rents, Lent, Green Fingers* and *Steinberg and the Byker Boy*; his books include *Outlaw in the Hills* and *Benjamin Britten.* He has contributed stories to several anthologies.

Ian Young lives in Toronto, Canada. His latest book is *Out in Paperback: A Visual History of Gay Pulps.* 'The Buggery Club' is from a work in progress, a group of interlinked short stories set in London in the 1980s.

Richard Zimler lives in Porto, Portugal with his partner, Alex. He is the author of several acclaimed historical novels, including *The Last Kabbalist of Lisbon.* His most recent novel, *The Seventh Gate*, was a number one bestseller in Portugal during 2007. His website is www.zimler.com. He welcomes comments from readers.